The ecclesiastic and the deputy dismounted and walked over to Wizenbeak. The monk smiled. "Am I addressing Doctor Wizenbeak?"

Wizenbeak stroked his troll-bat. "May I be of service?"

"Get on your mule, pappy," the deputy said. "Archdeacon Heiby was murdered night before last, and we know you an' him had a set-to a few days ago. So we want you to talk. Now c'mon!"

"How unfortunate. But I have work to do and can't waste time in your grungy dungeon," Wizenbeak said.

"This is resisting arrest!" the deputy growled.

Then Gruchka the troll-bat leaped from the wizard's shoulder to the deputy's and clasped the man's head in his hands. Wizenbeak grunted as Gruchka channeled the effort of the wizard's major back muscles through long fingers. The head twisted around and the neck broke.

"Yawp," Wizenbeak said in shock and amazement.

By Alexis A. Gilliland
*Published by Ballantine Books:*

WIZENBEAK

LONG SHOT FOR ROSINANTE
THE PIRATES OF ROSINANTE
THE REVOLUTION FROM ROSINANTE

THE END OF THE EMPIRE

# WIZENBEAK

## Alexis A. Gilliland

A Del Rey Book
BALLANTINE BOOKS · NEW YORK

A Del Rey Book
Published by Ballantine Books

ISBN 0-345-36116-4

Manufactured in the United States of America

First Ballantine Books Edition: September 1989

Cover art by Romas

# 1

# Slumming in Cymdulock

NIGHT, and the mists rising from the river, softened the aspect of the mean and tawdry streets huddled about the walls of Cymdulock, capital of Guhland. Lantern in hand, the tall clerisiarch walked past taverns and bathhouses, pawn shops and dance halls, barbershops and cheap lodgings. Finally he came to a battered green door next to a cobbler's shuttered workplace. Holding the lantern close to the door, he found a small wooden plaque, written on with a heated stylus: Madam Irenji, Fortunes Told, 2nd Floor.

The clerisiarch nodded and pulled at the bell rope, making a distant jangle. After a time a peephole opened, and he obligingly raised his lantern to his face. An old woman in a black shawl opened the door, and jerked her head for him to step inside the hallway, which was cleaner than might have been expected.

"Let me check your sword," she mumbled.

He rested his hand on the two swords thrust into his sash and withdrew the longer, which she took carefully in both hands, placing it in a rack at the back of the hallway. When she returned, she slowly preceded him up the stairs.

Madam Irenji's studio was cluttered with all sorts of magical paraphernalia of the grosser sort, props to impress the bulk of her trade. Lit only by the coals glowing in the fireplace and the tall man's lantern, it conveyed a sense of controlled power, of menace and hidden malice, together with a certain cheap theatricality. Madame Irenji pushed through the beaded curtain at the back of the room, and lit the candle on her desk. She had never been beautiful, but she had large, dark eyes painted to look larger and darker, and considerable presence.

"So, Heiby," she said, seating herself behind the cluttered desk, "What mischief do you bring me now?"

The clerisiarch produced a vial. "Nail clippings, some hair. From a Ghola, of all things." A Ghola was a dead man who walked and spoke and did the bidding of a living will.

"Heiby . . ." she said, "are you sure this is what you think it is?"

"Positive," he replied. "I, myself, obtained the hair, and the clippings came from a most reliable source."

Irenji took the vial and examined it. "From a Ghola? I doubt it, I really do."

So do I, thought Heiby, but Prince Kahun believes that the king is dead, a Ghola kept on the throne by the will of Queen Shaia, his stepmother. And Kahun wants his father to lie down and be . . . what did he say? "At rest." Like some fool courtier, I told him that would be an act of filial piety, and nothing would hold him after but trying some new spell to unknit the dead flesh from the living spirit that animated it. So here I am. If the king were dead, this would be high treason. If, on the other hand, he were *alive*, it would still be high treason . . . only a lawyer would believe that you could argue otherwise.

"You want . . . what?" she asked, at last.

"A doll to break the spell," said Heiby. "The dolls of Madame Irenji have attained something of a reputation among the cognoscenti."

"There is a counterspell," she conceded, "but I've never used it. Gholas are rarely around for long enough to be annoying." She grinned, showing her strong white teeth. "They often become useless after a few days."

"How much?" he asked. She named a figure.

"That's outrageous," said Heiby. "I might go a quarter of that sum."

The witch shook her head and pushed the vial back across her desk.

"A third, then. But no more."

"That's it. Take it or leave it. If you take it, come by and pick up the doll Volsday evening."

"That's high, damned high. Do you guarantee it will work?"

"No, Master Heiby, I do not. The doll should unmake a Ghola, but King Grathnys is not, in my opinion, a Ghola, and therefore the magic will not bite on him."

"Nobody spoke the name of Grathnys!"

"Wizards gossip as badly as women, Heiby, and your association with Prince Kahun is a matter of common knowledge . . . as is Kahun's belief in Gholas. I run a considerable risk making such a doll, but I need the money."

Heiby drew out his purse and counted out golden coins on the table. "Half now," he said flatly, "half when I get the doll."

The doll, when he picked it up on Volsday, proved to be a remarkable piece of work, unmistakably the old man, and with the intangible feel of live art. He paid the balance and headed for home.

As he crossed the street, heading for the bridge, a mercenary stepped out of the cobbler's doorway and followed him, iron-shod boots clattering on the pavement. A block later, two other mercenaries stepped out of an alley in front of him, one short and lean, the other tall and leaner. Heiby grinned and shifted the lantern to his left hand.

"That's the man," said the short mercenary, and the three of them drew their swords. Heiby drew his long sword with his right hand, and as the mercenaries came at him, he tossed the lantern at the tall mercenary, pivoting to the right as he took a step to the rear, bringing the sword around in a sweeping arc to cut the iron-shod mercenary across the chest, a hand's breadth under the heart, as the man came charging at him with sword upraised. Heiby continued turning, coming around to face the short mercenary, who had raised his sword for a two-handed stroke from the left side, as the iron-shod mercenary behind him stood contemplating the enormity of the disaster which had befallen him.

"Die, archdeacon!" shouted the short mercenary, as his tall companion came up a step behind him and on the right. The clerisiarch parried the two-handed downstroke, knocking his opponent's blade aside, and then reversed his own blade with a twist of the wrist to cut open his opponent's forehead with a short stroke aimed by wrist and forearm and powered by the torso turning left, the force of the stroke transmitted through the unmoving upper arm. As the short mercenary went down, the tall mercenary, relying on his superior reach, slashed at Heiby's head over the body of his comrade. Heiby ducked and cut at the extended arm, severing it above the wrist. The tall man gasped in shock, and ran away, clutching at his stump.

Behind Heiby there was a clatter, and the clerisiarch turned, coming to the guard position, but the iron-shod mercenary had dropped his sword before falling on his face.

Well, thought Heiby. Assassins. And one called me by my title. No doubt Kahun's pernicious younger brother, Prince Gatsack, set them upon me. He wiped his sword on the dead leader's cloak and returned it to his sheath as he considered the matter. Gatsack? *Someone* must have had me followed, thinking not unreasonably that I might be acting against their interest. He ran down the possibilities. Could it have been the Witch-Queen? Probably not. Her policy was to buy time, to keep old Grathnys alive until their little son, Prince Dervian, might be old enough to assume the throne. Besides, if he was on a fool's errand she'd know it and wouldn't bother him. No, it was probably Gatsack.

Unless of course Irenji's doll bites on the king. *Then* it might have been the Witch-Queen. Maybe. If the doll *doesn't* bite on the king, which it figures not to do for all the gold we laid out for it, it's got to be Gatsack.

He picked up the lantern, which was cracked but still lit, and walked over the bridge. So. In that case maybe we can still get some use out of the doll. Use it to incriminate, not Prince Gatsack himself but some creature of his. Someone, most likely a wizard, who might plausibly be involved with this sort of dirty work. Which someone? He shifted his grip on the lantern in the cold night air. Gatsack had gone to a lot of trouble recently to set up an audience with the king. For some backwoods wizard from up north. What was the fellow's name? Something strange. Wizenbeak, that was it. Heiby smiled grimly. He'd pay Gatsack back with interest!

# 2

# A Royal Audience

DR. W. W. WIZENBEAK, Water Wizard, looked around the brightly painted halls and corridors of the Royal Palace, ignored by the servants and petty functionaires bustling by him as he tried to retrace his steps.

"Ah, Gruchka," he said softly, "we should have paid closer attention when that imbecile chamberlain told us where to go." He petted the little animal in a vague and distracted fashion. "*This* looks like the door where we came in . . ." He tried the door that was locked. The wizard removed the troll-bat from his long, white beard, and lowered him down to the wrought iron lock. Gruchka looked into the keyhole, first one way and then the other, and finally inserted a long, webbed finger into the hole, carefully groping his way into the mechanism of the lock.

He chittered softly, and Wizenbeak felt the pull on his thumb muscles as the bolt was forced back, and the lock suddenly clicked open. As he stepped through the door, there was a flash of female flesh and screams! Guards swiftly laid hands on him, dragging him off as he protested that he had, in fact, an invitation, nay, a command to appear before King Grathnys on state business. On state business of high importance! Indeed, on state business of the *highest* importance! Gruchka, chittering, bounced off the walls and ceiling in high good humor, to the annoyance of his master who saw nothing humorous in the situation.

Eventually an officer read the parchment invitation bearing the royal seal, and after making inquiry, dispatched a fat chamberlain to lead him down corridors very similar to the ones he had been wandering, the wizard thought, to the place where he was supposed to be.

"This way," said the fat chamberlain, leading the water wizard into a small chamber beside one of the inner guard rooms. Dr. Wizenbeak looked around. It might have been a chapel once. Now it held a long wooden table and benches and various court functionaires were standing around killing time. There were noble-born guardsmen, wearing conical helmets under blue turbans and the standard army hauberk: a double layer of heavy canvas impregnated in a pattern of hexagons with a solution of mother-of-glass that was then steamed, resulting in stiff hexagons of black glass on a flexible tan field. There was an archdeacon in red and black, sporting a massive gold chain of office. And there was a court wizard, his green, yellow and lavender striped shirt professing his mastery of some arcane (since Wizenbeak didn't recognize it) and undoubtedly useless specialty.

"We have had threats and rumors of threats against the king's life," said the chamberlain blandly. "It was most kind of you to agree to change your wizard's garb before your audience."

"Of course," said Wizenbeak, putting a battered conical hat on the table and replacing it with the identical but impotent hat that had been laid out for him. His familiar, a troll-bat—a tiny creature with long webbed fingers that seemed inadequate to sustain any sort of flight and large ears framing a monkeylike face—leapt off one shoulder onto the table. Wizenbeak slid off the high collared black robe and stood in his long green and white striped shirt, which fell below knobby knees. He folded his somewhat lumpy robe and laid it on the table between the battered hat and troll-bat. As he reached for the robe that had been laid out for him, the archdeacon stood up, and clasping his hands behind his back, cleared his throat in a curiously peremptory manner.

"Excuse me, Doctor Wizenbeak, but I really must insist that you remove the shirt as well. If you would be so kind . . ."

Wizenbeak grinned behind his long white whiskers, and unfastened the three buttons at the collar. A shrug and a twitch, and suddenly he flourished the shirt like a cape, the substitute black wizard's hat still on his head. He stood there, a scrawny, hairy old man in long underwear and slippers.

"Check it out, deacon," he said. "I expect you'll find it harmless enough." The archdeacon handed the shirt over to the court wizard, who took it gingerly, as if he did not wish to be associated with such trash.

"*And* your glasses," said the archdeacon, plucking them off Wizenbeak's prominent nose. He raised them up over his head, holding them to the light—rectangular lenses, cut, apparently from emerald, in gold wire frames. He turned them slowly between the thumb and forefinger of his right hand. And dropped them. "Sorry, old fellow," he said.

The glasses never hit the floor. Diving from the table, the troll-bat snatched the glasses in midair, and returned them to Wizenbeak's hand.

"Ah, Gruchka," purred the wizard, cooing at his familiar. "Ya done good, little fella." He reached into his robe on the table and took out a dried avricod, which he gave to the troll-bat, who started eating it. Wizenbeak folded the emerald glasses in his hand and looked at the archdeacon. "You didn't finish examining my spectacles," he said grimly. "*Here.*" He offered the glasses to the clerisiarch. Gruchka put down his avricod. The archdeacon drew himself up to his full height, towering over the ridiculous figure in the useless wizard's hat. The guards suddenly clenched the hilts of their swords. Slowly, and with seeming reluctance to meet such an unlooked for challenge, the archdeacon reached for the emerald glasses.

Heiby is going to get himself killed, thought Dr. Rovira, the court wizard, and I am going to catch all sorts of hell if I let it happen. He tossed Wizenbeak's shirt on the table beside them and stepped forward.

"The shirt is harmless," said Dr. Rovira, placing himself beside but not between the combatants, and then, as the archdeacon took the emerald glasses in his hand, said, "Don't drop them, Heiby."

"Eh, what?" The clerisiarch gave a start.

"The glasses," said the court wizard, stepping between the two men. He plucked them from unresisting fingers and returned them to Wizenbeak. "You could get hurt if you dropped them." There was a palpable relaxation of tension as he turned to the guards. "See that nobody touches anything on the table here."

He gestured. "*This* table! Y'hear?" Wizenbeak donned his striped shirt and set the emerald glasses back on his nose.

"Well, well," he said. "Am I deemed safe enough to have my audience with His Majesty?" The guard captain looked at the court wizard who nodded, and at Archdeacon Heiby who merely looked sullen.

The captain shrugged. "That seems to be the case," he said. "You'll wait for Chamberlain Fudjak to lead you into the presence. What about the monkey?"

The water wizard petted his familiar and whispered in his ear. "Gruchka will stay right here, won't you, darling?" He looked up. "Gruchka will stay and help you keep an eye on my gear . . . a little troll-bat helping these brave soldiers." He slipped the sanitized and decontaminated robe over his long shirt. "A cat may look at a king, but not a troll-bat, eh? Poor little Gruchka." He pulled at his nose and stroked the troll-bat's long ears as the animal finished eating his avricod. Archdeacon Heiby simply folded his arms and sat down on one of the benches. Chamberlain Fudjak dithered around for a few minutes until finally he led the wizard down the hall, attending to the court's business with as much dignity as he could muster.

The audience room was smaller and less opulent than the throne room, which was intended to impress the diplomatic corps of the neighboring kingdoms, but it was still quite elegant in an outdated sort of way with its cloth-of-gold draperies and gilded mirrors. King Grathnys sat on a throne of ebony, crusted with gold and garnets, mounted on a small dais in the center of the room. An ancient little man with pale rheumy eyes and a white mustache attended by a score of courtiers. He looked old and frail, and he was, unarguably, old. He was also frail, but the memory of his past strength sat over that frailty like some magical cloak, causing his enemies to pause and wonder. Beside him sat Queen Shaia, much younger, a plain woman made radiantly beautiful by artful and extensive grooming.

"The water wizard, Doctor Wizenbeak," said the chamberlain, and Wizenbeak entered the throne room. So, thought Shaia, studying him. This is the fellow Rovira was so exercised about. He *appears* clean enough. If the book on him is right, he ought to *be* clean . . . still, it won't hurt to check him out. Absently she twisted the baroque pearl ring on her finger and watched as two guards behind the wizard rolled in a sand table, a rough, three-dimensional map of the sort used by the military in war games and strategic planning. Could it be that Prince Gatsack's interest is exactly what it seems on the surface? In that case the wizard is merely a distraction. On the other hand, maybe Rovira is anticipating three out of the next five disasters again. Her face relaxed into the faintest of smiles. Pay attention, she told herself. What does Gatsack *really* want?

Upon that sand table was molded the northern tier of counties, and the wastes of Semeryan on the high plateau, the altiplano, to the north and east of that region. A large part of Semeryan was marked with brown sand, showing half a million acres or more of potentially fertile lateritic soil. Lateritic soil had the striking characteristic of becoming impervious to water upon wetting, so that even a small rain would run off a slope. Prince Gatsack, the king's second son and Wizenbeak's master, felt that Semeryan offered an opportunity for colonization that should be exploited. King Grathnys, less interested in the future, nevertheless saw the possible colonization of Semeryan as a means of easing the present discontent of his landless nobility, and he was sympathetic to the project. If it could be done, he was inclined to do it. The recent invention of catch-basin farming—terracing the lateritic soil so that rain falling on two thirds of the land would run off onto the cultivated third—had aroused great interest.

"May it please Your Majesties," said Wizenbeak, bowing and scraping in his curiously limber fashion, "I have returned from Semeryan. I have, as my master demanded, made a survey of the groundwater available in that place. I am delighted to report that water is there, and that it is not terribly deep." He took a deep breath. "At Springhill, where there is a great conflux of aquifers, the waters gush from the side of the hill some five hundred feet below the crest to fall cascading down a mile or more to the River Linzauer. However, only fifty or sixty miles within the altiplano many of these same aquifers that feed the waters at Springhill sit only twenty or thirty feet beneath the surface." He picked up a handful of blue sand and carefully dribbled a line indicating where the waters might be found, making an irregularly shaped loop on the sand table. ''To the north—'' he gestured ''—the aquifers are not deep, but they are also not abundant. Within *this* area, however, there is water for wells to support many villages, water for drinking and washing and for watering livestock. It shows great promise, Your Majesty, the Semeryan . . . it is a prospectively fertile and prosperous province.''

''What about irrigation?'' asked the king.

''I fear not,'' replied the wizard. ''To raise cobgrain or legumes would drain in years as aquifer that would take decades, if not centuries, to recharge. Water is there. It is abundant, but not . . . not *copious*, Your Majesty. Also, it would not come gushing from the well; it would have to be drawn forth with much toil.''

''Let us have a closer look,'' said the king. He stood up, offering his arm to his queen, and the two of them stepped off the dais and walked over to inspect the sand table, the queen taking a position between the king and the wizard.

''Semeryan is a wasteland,'' said King Grathnys sadly. ''A province it is not. Besides, I have heard it said that there are dragons in that desolate place.''

''It has a certain rustic charm,'' said Wizenbeak, brushing blue sand off his hands, ''but in the years I was there, I must report, alas, that I found no dragons, nor, indeed, any *traces* of dragons. Only a rich and fertile—potentially—land.''

''You say all that it needs is water?'' said Queen Shaia, putting her hand lightly on the wizard's arm. ''That's all *hell* needs.''

''There are, I admit, some problems; otherwise it would have been settled long since.'' The wizard sighed. ''What I have seen, Your Majesty, convinces me that Semeryan could be colonized.''

''Could it, now?'' she asked gently. ''I mean, do you *really* think so?''

''Yes, Your Majesty.''

''What would be involved?'' asked the king.

''Contouring the land to capture and hold the rainfall, for one thing,'' replied Wizenbeak. ''But farming is not simple, and questions of what to plant and when to plant are best answered by experience. The nights, for example, are very cold, so that your succulent vegetables would have to be grown under glass, if at all." He removed his glasses and wiped them on the sleeve of his gown. "Small grains ought to do well, and pastureland, but cobgrains and legumes need too much water. The main thing is, the farmers must be strongly motivated. They need to . . . to *want* the crops to grow."

"What do you mean by that?" asked Queen Shaia, dropping her long-fingered hand from the wizard's arm.

"Why, that they must be freemen," said Wizenbeak. "The land of Semeryan is too harsh to be bound to. Serfs will not do what must be done . . . not on the altiplano."

"Do not presume to instruct the court on how to run the kingdom," said one of the courtiers a bit stiffly.

"God forbid," said Wizenbeak, with a smile under his white whiskers. "The kingdom of Guhland must surely require wiser counsel than I am able to give. The prospective Province of Semeryan, however, is another story, and perhaps a much simpler one. I concern myself only with how that high and desolate wasteland might be made fruitful in as short a time as possible."

"If you begin colonization with freemen, you will find the precedent quoted against you when you try to introduce serfdom," said the courtier, who wore a lawyer's gown, heavily decorated with bullion. "I say we should start with serfs, or, if you *must* have freeholders, give them revocable title. It will save trouble in the long run, mark my words!"

"Indeed," said Wizenbeak politely, "and how much revenue for the crown does Semeryan now generate? Nothing, right? What do you lose by going with freemen instead of serfs? At the most, some revenues you might in the future be able to capture will slip through your fingers. Send in serfs to colonize the land, you will wind up feeding them forever . . . or until you cut your losses and bring them home."

"We will consider these arguments," said the king. A failed colonization would be the devil to handle. At the very least it would start a season of rioting; at the worst—he shrugged. He was already too old. "There are any number of nobles who will be strongly in favor of the serfish solution, but when it comes to making the decision on the matter, it is we who have the final say. In your written report you set forth a hundred-year record of rainfall. How was that done in a wasteland where no such records were kept?''

"Your Majesty is most kind to ask," said the wizard. "In the three places I indicated I found deobab trees . . . stunted, it is true . . . but growing in natural basins. I took a core from each and measured the thickness of their growth rings, which I then compared with the thickness of the growth rings for which I had a rainfall measurement . . . not many, but enough."

"That hardly seems like proper wizardry," said a courtier in fur-edged cloak.

"I have agreed not to instruct *you* in matters of government," said Wizenbeak a bit stiffly. "Pray do not instruct *me* in my art."

"The wizard has a point, Lord Kunji," said the king. "Have we any further questions at this time?" When no one spoke he nodded to Wizenbeak. "You have done well, Doctor Wizenbeak, and we appreciate your labors on our behalf. If Semeryan does indeed become a jewel in the crown of Guhland, much of the credit will be rightfully yours." It was a dismissal. Wizenbeak bowed and backed out of the audience room, while servants removed the sand table. As he was leaving, Queen Shaia removed a baroque pearl ring from the forefinger of the hand she had rested on the wizard's arm, and placed it in a leather box tooled with the magically potent *tau* nabla, which she slipped into a pocket in her voluminous skirts.

# 3

# Authorization and Funding

RETURNING to the chamber where he had left his robe, hat, and familiar, Wizenbeak heard the sounds of tumult and the crash of furniture. He burst through the door, and Gruchka leaped into his beard, Archdeacon Heiby lunging after him. The wizard sidestepped the archdeacon's rush and kicked his leg out from underneath him, sending Heiby headlong against the door frame.

"Here, now," said Wizenbeak mildly, looking down at the prostrate clerisiarch. "What *is* all this?"

"His grace tried to look through the pockets of your robe," said one of the guardsmen, "and the monkey bit him."

"Ah, so," murmured Wizenbeak, disentangling the troll-bat from his beard and petting him. "Good Gruchka, you bit that nasty archdeacon, did you?" He automatically felt in his robe, but the garment he was wearing had neither dried fruit nor a pocket to hold it in. "Good little Gruchka." He reached into his robe on the table and took out a dried avricod. "This will take the bad taste out of your mouth." The troll-bat took the piece of fruit, sniffed it, and began nibbling. On the floor the archdeacon grunted and sat up, rubbing his head.

"Your pet demon attacked me," he growled. "I demand satisfaction."

"Accept my sincere apologies on Gruchka's behalf," said Wizenbeak politely. "I had no idea that *you* of all people would be rummaging through my pockets, or I would have told him: Nobody messes with my robe except good old Heiby, there."

13

He smiled under his whiskers. "I have nothing to hide. Would you care to look through my robe before I put it back on?"

"The little bastard drew blood!" said Heiby, raising his wounded finger. Climbing laboriously to his feet, he held that finger at the end of Wizenbeak's long nose. "I *demand* satisfaction!"

"Gruchka might have done much worse," replied the wizard mildly. "Are you sure that you don't wish to examine the contents of my pockets before I put the robe back on?"

"No!" snapped Heiby, "I am not *interested* in the contents of your grubby pockets! I want to avenge my injury!"

Gruchka chattered and pointed at the floor. There, where Archdeacon Heiby had fallen, was a little doll. Wizenbeak looked at it for a moment. It appeared to be a white-haired old man wearing a kingly crown.

"You dropped something," said Wizenbeak.

"What?" Heiby looked down, and his heart skipped a beat but he never paused. "Wizard's trash . . . none of mine." He crushed it under his heel, grinding it beyond recognition even as he regretted the extravagant price he had paid for the stupid thing. "I'll deal with the monkey later! And you, too, you long whiskered old fart!" He stormed out of the little room. Wizenbeak put on his many-pocketed black robe and conical hat.

"So," said Wizenbeak, touching the little pile of crumbled doll stuff with a slippered foot, "he wanted to put rather than to take, it being more blessed to give than to receive. Good old Heiby. . . ."

Returning to her quarters, the queen opened the box with the pearl ring and set it before a tiny censer, which she lit. Cupping her hands, she caught some of the fragrant smoke and carried it down to the ring in its case. This she did three times, reciting a mantra of great antiquity. After the third time, the blue smoke from the censer flowed downward voluntarily and swirled about the ring and case, in the lid of which was a tiny triangular mirror set with apex down—the basic nabla—which reflected the baroque pearl.

"The good Doctor Wizenbeak," she said softly, "today, this hour, in the minor audience chamber, did he speak the truth?"

The reflection of the pearl in the triangular mirror clouded over for a second and turned pink. She nodded. Yes, he spoke the truth, then. Two more questions. Best stick to the standards. "The good Doctor Wizenbeak," she continued, "today, this hour, in the minor audience chamber, did he seek to deceive?" The pearl in the triangular mirror turned blue. She nodded again; he was telling the truth and *not* trying to deceive. Could she trust him? It would waste a question to ask directly. He had been advocating a program . . . stick to what he said. "The good Doctor Wizenbeak, today, this hour, in the minor audience chamber, did he leave out anything important in his tale?" The reflected pearl turned pink, and then faded back to whiteness as the smoke from the censer ceased to curl about it. Queen Shaia sighed. Of course, she thought, he isn't trying to deceive—not by lying and not by omission—but the poor bastard is reporting on three or four years' work in half an hour. How could he not leave things out? In the event of royal interest—which he did his best to stir—he would presumably be more than willing to expound at whatever length was required. She nodded. Certainly he had made no effort to bespell the king as some had feared. No wizard was ever straight, but this Wizenbeak did not appear to be *malignly* crooked. Of course, he *was* the hireling of her stepson, Prince Gatsack. She smiled thinly. Perhaps Gatsack, too, would find that no wizard was ever straight. She extinguished the censer and put away the ring. The whole business had taken less than five minutes.

The winter home of Prince Gatsack was the Czajka Palace, one of the architectural ornaments of Cymdulock, an astonishing blend of styles wherein audacity existed in perpetual tension with bad taste. He disliked it because the grounds were too small for hunting or even the proper grazing of sheep. Wizenbeak walked past the fence of black iron spears to the great curlicued wrought iron gates, where one guard admitted him and a second walked him to the great front door. At the door, a butler in green livery escorted the wizard into the presence.

The reception room was ostentatiously large, paneled walls hung with tapestries to ease the chill, and a tastefully small suite of furniture set at one end of the room in front of a great marble manteled fireplace in which a meager fire was burning. Prince Gatsack stood before the fire warming his hands. Beside him was a foppishly dressed young man, who studied Wizenbeak with eyes the color of unpolished steel.

"You know each other, do you not?" said the prince. The wizard shook his head. "Wizard, this is Count Braley, my fencing instructor." Wizenbeak made an awkward bow and extended his hand. "Dr. Wizenbeak, who surveyed the Semeryan for us recently." Braley nodded, correct, reserved, ignoring the proffered hand.

I wonder if he wears eyeshadow? thought the wizard sourly, and rotating his wrist displayed a deck of cards which he fanned out before the fencing master. "Take a card, any card," he said smoothly, pleased at covering his embarrassment.

"Did you invite this 'gentleman' to entertain us, Your Majesty?" asked Braley with cool politeness. There was an awkward pause, broken by Gruchka the troll-bat who leapt from the wizard's beard.

"Get that monster off my shoulder!" yelled Prince Gatsack, spilling his glass of wine as the troll-bat lit on him.

"Here, Gruchka, come to papa," said Wizenbeak, gently lifting the troll-bat away from his royal patron. "*That's* a good boy." He picked up a grape from the cut crystal fruit bowl that graced the inlaid table and gave it to his familiar. "Is that what you wanted? Yes, yes . . . now stay right here." He patted his shoulder and the troll-bat settled down. Count Braley, seeing that the prince was in no danger, sheathed his short sword with an economy of movement that bespoke long practice.

"How can you put up with that beast?" growled Gatsack, brushing wine from his tunic. "One of these days he'll tear your arm off!"

"Not little Gruchka," replied the wizard. "He likes me, dotes upon me, even. Besides, if he wasn't so dangerous, he wouldn't be so useful."

"That's often the case," conceded the prince, "even with humans. Anyway, you saw my father at close range. Was there any sign that he was under magical control as Kahun is maintaining?"

"Not that I could see," replied Wizenbeak. "The king is

alive and well, but of course he is also old. I have no doubt that he relies on the queen for counsel and moral support.''

"If His Majesty had been so controlled," said Count Braley with exquisite diffidence, "would you have been able to tell?"

"Ah . . ." There was a moment's hesitation in the face of a direction question. "Yes, yes, I would. The raising of the dead into a crude semblance of life is not exactly what you would call subtle. Even to the layman." Wizenbeak returned the cards to his pocket. "Surely it is a curious complaint that Queen Shaia is *preserving* the king by means of the black arts."

"Kahun dislikes sorcery," Gatsack said, "and he dislikes my stepmother, so he accuses her of being a witch. But mainly, I think, my brother dislikes an old man sitting on the throne of Guhland beyond his allotted time." He limped over to the table and took a yellow plum from the bowl. "To a considerable extent my selection of policies depends on what my brother believes. It would help if I knew that he was mistaken. You understand?''

"Yes, yes, of course," said the wizard, pushing his emerald spectacles back up on his nose. "Kahun's argument is gross, if not downright crude. But the fact that it's untrue won't refute it because the charge has a certain vulgar plausibility. Is Shaia really a witch, for instance?"

"The suggestion has been repeated often enough," said Count Braley. "Probably she is. We've accepted the idea, though we haven't made any real effort to check it out."

"She's vulnerable to the charge," agreed Prince Gatsack. "Where there's smoke, there's fire seems to be the operational cliché here. Why do you ask?"

Here's your opportunity, thought the wizard. Change the subject and ask the man to his face. "One hears rumors, sir. Specifically, that you may be going to abandon the Semeryan project or give it over to the queen. I've put a lot of time into it, and I can't imagine why you'd give it up when it sits at the very brink of success."

"The short answer is that I can't afford it," said the prince.

"But *sir*!" The protest was automatic, a cry from the heart, and Wizenbeak felt foolish for having uttered it.

The prince smiled and spread his hands. "You want the long

answer? A prince, like a country, becomes a product of history." Gatsack walked over to the table and picked up a bunch of grapes. "The green grapes are the Crown, which sits in opposition to the black grapes, which are the Church, and also to the barons." He picked out some apples and peaches and ranged them in an arc between the two bunches of grapes. "Falenda, Bedirny, Viluji, Mihaly, Jamreaux—that lot. For realism, some of the apples should be rotten. Now pay particular attention."

Gatsack picked up the green grapes and split them into three bunches, one large, two small. "The big bunch is my father, King Grathnys. With him is my stepmother, Queen Shaia, and their two children, Prince Dervian and Princess Marjia. This bunch is Kahun, and this bunch is me. Now normally, we would sit around and wait for my father to die, at which point, the big bunch of grapes would become mine. I got my limp leading my father's army through the breach at Kalycas during the Lagualian War. He liked me better than Kahun, even though Kahun is the older." Grathnys had never named an heir apparent. If he died intestate, the crown would go to Kahun, the eldest.

Gatsack picked up his bunch and stripped off most of the grapes, and then he stripped most of the grapes off Kahun. "So. Queen Shaia has Prince Dervian, her darling little boy, whom she wishes to make king. Her policy to do this is to play off nasty Kahun against good old Gatsack, supporting first one and then the other." He removed a few grapes from the large bunch and distributed them between the two smaller bunches. "What is she doing? Playing for time until Dervian grows up."

He sighed and ate one of Kahun's grapes. "The only thing is, all this dynastic horsing around didn't stay in the family. Kahun became a lay preacher and went to the Syncretist Church for support . . ." He moved the loose green grapes from Kahun's pile over to the bunch of black grapes and returned a lone black grape to sit in front of Kahun. ". . . while I, perforce, sought the support of the nobility." He distributed his own loose grapes among the peaches and apples, finally holding up the stem of his bunch which now had two or three grapes still on it.

"Which is why I can't afford the Semeryan, Doctor Wizenbeak."

"Ah, yes. I see. Could you give me an example, sir, something a little more concrete than the transfer of grapes?"

"As you wish." Gatsack seemed in a mellow mood. "The Usury Riots in Rosano, for example. You'll remember them, I expect. We tried to take over the city from the local clerisy, who were supported by Kahun. Duke Jamreaux came out ahead, and the Church came out ahead, but the Crown was a net loser in terms of blood and treasure."

"Kahun had a hand in Rosano, sir? I wouldn't have believed it," said Wizenbeak. "What plans have you for the Semeryan, then?"

"Count Braley?"

"We all felt it best to cut our losses," said the count. "However, the idea is promising, so we gave you a chance to make a presentation to the court. If Her Majesty is interested, we shall assign you to her as a preferred agent."

"A what?" asked the wizard.

"A preferred agent. A mark of esteem, actually," said Braley, smiling. "You remain oathbound to Gatsack, while on assignment to Her Majesty. When the job ends, you return here. If, God forbid, he dies before then, your oath transfers automatically to the queen, who is then obligated to keep you on the payroll."

What's going on here? thought the wizard. They could get rid of me a lot easier, a whole lot easier if that's what they wanted. "Why, thank you, Count. I'm much obliged, actually . . ."

Braley laughed. "It was nothing, just a bargaining device to impress Her Majesty with what a great deal we're offering her. If we offered you for free, she'd turn you down!"

"I understand," said the wizard. "But why do you assume that the queen is the one taking an active interest?"

Count Braley arched one beautiful eyebrow and plucked a single green grape from the big bunch and set it in front of Gatsack's. "Her Majesty is looking for our continued support against the noble Kahun," he said mildly.

"At my presentation the king seemed alert and interested. Why would you assume that Shaia is the prime mover?"

"You mean rather than the king?" asked Gatsack. "Her Majesty has taken over much of the routine business in the last few years. Old age is taking its toll on my father.''

"King Grathnys isn't so very old," said Wizenbeak, standing a bit straighter. "He could have many years left him, even now. What is he, seventy?''

"Seventy-two," said the prince. "He is also infirm, which gives an added point to this pushing and shoving between Kahun and myself.''

"Things have been notably tense recently," added Count Braley, his right hand resting lightly on the hilt of his sword.

"At least the rumors have been interesting," said the prince, eating another grape. "Now that we mention it, perhaps you've heard something?''

"I seem not to be connected with the appropriate grapevine," replied the wizard. "But there *was* a most curious incident. . . ."

"Pray continue," Gatsack murmured.

Wizenbeak stroked the ears of his familiar. "After my presentation to the king and queen . . ." he began softly, and proceeded to relate the story of the doll which might or might not have been Archdeacon Heiby's. "After pondering the matter," he concluded, "I don't believe that I was the target. More likely someone was striking at me to discredit your own most noble and worthy self. I *assume* that the doll had some validity. . . ."

"Ye-es? You can get an awful burn playing that game," said Gatsack at last. "The king is well protected against threats sorcerous, but to be caught *holding* such a threat . . ." He hesitated for a moment. "Did you see what it was for? I mean, specifically?''

The wizard shook his head. "No, sir. I had only the briefest of glimpses before Heiby crushed it under his heel.''

"We understand," said Gatsack, putting the fruit back into the bowl. "I'm glad you brought the matter to my attention. The clerisy really ought to be a little more responsible about that sort of thing. Archdeacon Heiby, eh?" He nodded to himself. "Heiby has been a real pain for a long time. I'm glad you brought the matter to our attention.''

"Well, now," said Wizenbeak, "they act from the most noble motives, which only happen to coincide with their perceived interests. What could be more responsible than *that*?''

There was a polite knock on the door, and a footman entered, bearing a silver salver. On the salver was a three-by-five inch plaque of wood, split down the middle and tied together with a red ribbon. Gatsack picked up the message and untied the ribbon.

"Well," he said, glancing at his wizard, "*we* have been invited to dinner at the Royal Palace."

"We?" asked Wizenbeak.

"The queen asks for you specifically," replied Gatsack. "She is interested, can you imagine, in the wastes of Semeryan." He looked at the wizard and then at the message. "Tomorrow at seven. I'll see you then."

After Wizenbeak had gone, Count Braley took a sip of wine. "So," he said softly. "Heiby is in it up to his ears, if we can believe that wizard of yours. Where did you get him?"

"From Rosano . . ." said Gatsack after a moment. "When our people were trying to loosen the dead hand of the Church, about seven or eight years ago . . ."

"The Usury Riots?"

"Yes. He was managing a glass factory for one of my supporters, and carried messages back and forth for us." A shrug. "When the mob burned the factory out, I took him in service."

"Right." Braley rested a long, graceful forefinger against his lips. "Shall I take out Heiby?"

"He's very strong," said Prince Gatsack turning away from his fencing master.

"I understand. I'll take my time and do it right."

Gatsack caught Count Braley's eye in the mirror and gave the slightest of nods. The fencing master raised his glass in a formal toast. "To Heiby," he said softly.

The dining hall in the Royal Palace could seat two hundred if pressed to do so. Tonight, however, the company was hardly two score. Wizenbeak decided that on the whole, they dressed better than they talked. Certainly they drank better than they ate. The trouble with gold service was that the food got cold, but the royal cellars were undeniably impressive.

After dinner, as the Guhlish nobility meandered into the conservatory to hear a chamber orchestra perform some classical masterpiece, Chamberlain Fudjak came up to Wizenbeak and tapped him with his fan.

"You," he said, "Master Wizenbeak . . . Her Majesty has directed me to bring you to her." Clearly he disapproved of Her Majesty's choice of company, but if dead cats were what was required, dead cats he would produce. The chamberlain led Wizenbeak to a small alcove where the queen was waiting with a sleek and portly nobleman whom the wizard didn't recognize. Servants and guardsmen stood about, discreetly unobtrusive.

At the threshold of the room, Chamberlain Fudjak paused, and with a ruffle of lace and a flourish of his silk-lined cape announced, "The most learned and eminent Doctor W. W. Wizenbeak, master of arts necromantical, thaumaturgical, and sorcerous."

"That's very impressive," Queen Shaia murmured. "Please come in, Doctor Wizenbeak." And as the wizard came over to make an awkward bow, she smiled and introduced him to the Master of the Royal Exchequer, the Duke Falenda.

"How d'ye do?" said Falenda gruffly, attempting to be civil to an obvious social inferior because the queen wished it so.

"Very well, thank you," replied Wizenbeak, deciding that Falenda was pompous and possibly a buffoon.

"The chamberlain announced you as 'W. and W.' " said Shaia. "What names go with those initials?"

"William Weird, may it please Your Majesty," replied the wizard, regretting his youthful choice of a middle name. To conceal his nervousness, his hands took a pack of cards from his pocket and shuffled them in flashy display of manual dexterity. He sighed as he realized he'd committed a social blunder.

"Do we *really* need to see this mountebank?" asked Falenda brusquely.

"At court," said the queen, "he advocated colonizing the wastes of Semeryan. A bold proposal. An *audacious* proposal."

"A stupid proposal," said Falenda, "if Your Majesty will forgive my saying so. A . . . a *ludicrous* proposal." Wizenbeak put the cards back in his pocket. "The Semeryan is useless desert."

"We believe that it might be colonized," said the queen. "You were asked here to establish what the start-up costs would be. The wizard will answer your questions." She smiled and would have been charming had not the gesture been so slickly rehearsed. "Not so, Doctor Wizenbeak?"

"It will be my pleasure, Your Majesty," replied Wizenbeak. "At Prince Gatsack's request I have made a most thorough study of that region."

"The royal interest in worthless real estate is utterly amazing," growled Falenda, wiping his forehead. "Well, then. Having been there, doctor, how would you proceed?"

"Deliberately, Your Grace," said the wizard. Ask for more then you expect to get, yes. "At least two fortified settlements or maybe three. Support them and let them learn the way the land needs to be farmed in that part of the world. Freeholders would have more incentive to work than serfs, and in this case might be more economical to use."

"You are opposed to serfdom?" asked the duke blandly.

"It is the law of the land," said Wizenbeak. "How should I presume to oppose it?"

"Our social order is founded on serfdom," said Falenda. "I could not approve establishing a province of freeholders."

"Freeholders would be a lot cheaper, Your Grace," said the wizard incautiously. The back of his neck was getting warm.

"I fear Your Majesty has been misled," Falenda said gravely. "There is nothing useful to be done in the Semeryan."

"Hey! Two villages, *one* village, a few hundred people to lay out the foundations for agriculture in that place! You offer them land that costs you nothing! What have you got to lose?"

"The wizard is right, Falenda," said Shaia. "You're worried about something that will only happen if the project succeeds."

"Could you proceed with serfs, Doctor Wizenbeak?"

The wizard gentled a bellicose no to probably not, and recited the mantra for serenity, annoyed that Falenda should have provoked him. "If you could farm with serfs, I expect there'd already be serfs up there." He pulled at his whiskers. "Are you willing to risk future problems for the promise of future wealth?"

"Not if it isn't going to be my wealth, doctor."

Definitely a buffoon, decided the wizard. But in a duke, one puts up with a lot. He pushed his glasses back on his nose. "Ah," he heard himself saying, "the good of the kingdom doesn't concern you, then?" Oh shit, thought Wizenbeak, what's the mantra to keep my foot out of my mouth?

Falenda laid one hand on the short companion sword which was worn at all times by those who were permitted to wear the two swords. His sleek face wore a bemused expression, but his eyes were like chips of flint. Wizenbeak felt a surge of adrenaline surging through his system, and Gruchka popped out from under his beard to see what was going on.

"Apologize, you mangy son of a bitch!" said Falenda softly.

"Doctor Wizenbeak is our guest," said the queen with icy formality. "We will not be pleased if you draw steel in our presence!" Falenda sighed and eased the sword back into its scabbard.

"I apologize for doubting that the good of the kingdom might not concern you," said the wizard. "I should have known . . . ." There was the briefest of pauses as ego and superego coerced the id into adding ". . . better."

"I regret calling you 'mangy,' " replied Falenda, enjoying no such inhibitions. "A less hasty choice of words was clearly indicated."

"Now that we're all on good terms again," said Shaia, "what do you think of a pair of villages?"

"One village," said Falenda.

"A village and a fort," said the queen firmly. "Put in, oh, say one hundred mercenaries and set them to growing food along with the villagers. The treasury can afford it, I think."

"Fifty should be entirely adequate," said the duke. "Who is to lead them?"

"Doctor Wizenbeak, of course," she replied. "Prince Gatsack has very kindly offered us his services."

"I shall, of course, go as my master sends me, Your Majesty," said Wizenbeak with a bow, "but I am a wizard, no leader of men. Surely there are others better suited to the task."

"Then you must go down to the Chateau Militaire and hire one," said Shaia pleasantly. "He will be your lieutenant and arrange for those details that you find yourself unfamiliar with.

The duke will see that you have a letter of authorization tomorrow, won't you, Your Grace?"

"For a company of fifty men," said Falenda, making a note in his diptych, "Yes, Your Majesty."

"What about the village?"

"You will be given authority to grant title to a certain amount of land," said the queen. From the conservatory came the sound of stringed instruments as the evening's concert began. "Excuse us, doctor, we must take our place in the royal box." Falenda extended his arm, and she took it, sweeping out of the alcove with a flourish of royal skirts.

# The Show Gets on the Road

EVENTS moved after that. Not with great speed, but in their own deliberate course. The authorization to hire a company of soldiers came the next week rather than the next day, while the authority to grant land for which there were no formal maps took rather longer. Wizenbeak went out and began the work of interviewing an assortment of prospective lieutenants. Peace was oppressive in the land, and there was a lot of military talent unemployed.

Outside the city wall, across the moat from Northgate, Chateau Militaire, otherwise known as the Mercenaries Hall, was a large stone barn with a slate roof. To the north, an archery range and an exercise field. To the south a bathhouse and a field kitchen. East and west were twenty-seat pit latrines, draining into the moat. As an institution, the chateau was an expedient designed to keep unemployed warriors from becoming brigands. At the Mercenaries Hall they had a place to sleep, a place to exercise, and food for ten days. Then they went to the next hall down the road, going around the circuit until they found mercenary employment or dropped out of soldiering to take a job. From a theoretical point of view, it kept unemployed warriors on the move and under a measure of control. Practically, it cost less than suppressing brigands after demobilization. In time the wizard hired a strongly built man in his late forties, one Lasco Genzari, and very shortly afterwards, he found himself ready to march north.

The morning that Wizenbeak and company marched off to

Semeryan, Archdeacon Heiby was found floating facedown in the moat.

Following the river north, Wizenbeak's troop had stopped for lunch in a copse of birch and alder trees, when two officers of the law rode up. One was an ecclesiastic, a representative of the Holy Inquisition. With him was a deputy sheriff, representing the secular authorities. They dismounted and walked over to Wizenbeak.

"I am Brother Rhimkas," said the monk, a lean, dark man with a sallow complexion, "and this is my esteemed colleague, Inspector Eaklor, of the Cymdulock Sheriff's Office. Have I the honor of arresting—" He smiled. " 'Scusi. *Addressing*. Have I the honor of addressing Doctor William W. Wizenbeak?"

Wizenbeak stroked the ears of his troll-bat. "Not exactly," he said. "I am, as you may have heard, the acting governor of a prospective province, a title which might possibly supersede a mere 'doctor.' May I be of any service?"

"Get on your mule an' let's hit back for town," said Eaklor. "We want to talk to you, pappy." He was tall and muscular under an overlay of fat, and wore the standard black and tan hauberk under a dark blue cloak. He carried a jitte—a truncheon cased in steel with a steel hook—thrust in his belt, and a black lacquered inspector's hat. "Seems as how your good buddy, the right reverend Archdeacon Heiby, was murdered the night before last . . . an' we know you an' him had a set-to a few days ago . . . so we want to talk. We want *you* to talk. Now c'mon."

"How unfortunate," said Wizenbeak, "and here am I, bound on a mission for their majesties. I would be *delighted* to sit down and talk with you, but I am not at liberty to do so. Why don't you ride with me and we will discuss the matter?"

"That won't do, pappy," said Eaklor. "Ah been told to bring you back for questioning."

"Perhaps Brother Rhimkas would agree to ride along with us," suggested Wizenbeak.

"I'm sorry, doctor . . . we have a report that you and Heiby came to blows," said the monk. "Heiby filed a complaint against you before his untimely demise, and I'm afraid you're going to have to come back to Cymdulock." Lasco Genzari, Wizenbeak's able lieutenant, quietly motioned his men to spread out and surround the three.

"I'll answer any questions you may have," said the wizard, "but I have work to do, and I can't be running back and forth and freezing my ass in your grungy dungeons while you puzzle out if I'm telling the truth or not." He petted his familiar with one gnarled finger, and Eaklor laid a heavy hand on his shoulder.

"This is resisting arrest!" he growled. Wizenbeak sighed and turned to the monk.

"Brother Rhimkas—" he began, when Gruchka the troll-bat leaped from the wizard's shoulder to the deputy's. The deputy raised his left hand from under his cloak, striking at the troll-bat with a small dagger. Gruchka slid past the thrust, and Genzari drew his sword in a single sweeping motion. As Deputy Eaklor recovered to strike again, the troll-bat clasped the man's head in his hands, and Wizenbeak grunted involuntarily, as the troll-bat channeled the effort of Wizenbeak's major back muscles through long, webbed fingers. The wizard staggered backwards.

Eaklor looked mildly startled as his head was twisted around to break his neck. As he fell onto the ground, Gruchka leaped nimbly from the falling body into his master's beard. Wizenbeak sat down on the grass.

"Yawp," he said in shock and amazement.

Genzari smiled faintly. Well, Brother Rhimkas, he thought, the question now is what are we going to do with *you*? Two dead law officers would be infinitely less trouble than only one. The monk's sallow face went pale as the thought came to him, and he suddenly darted for his horse. The mercenary cut him in the side as he passed, and Rhimkas took three or four halting steps before he stumbled and fell into the tall grass. Genzari wiped his sword and returned it to his scabbard and then went over to help Wizenbeak to his feet.

"Wah," said the whey-faced wizard. "What did you do *that* for?"

"It seemed like what you would have wanted done if you had thought the matter through, sir," said Genzari politely. The soldiers, buzzing with conversation, had just started to walk over to examine the dead men. Wizenbeak looked utterly appalled.

"How could you know what I'd want done?"

"The situation is a familiar one," Genzari said. "After your troll-bat killed the big fellow—"

"Ahr," growled the wizard. "Bad Gruchka!" He snatched at his familiar, who easily eluded his uncertain grasp. "Bad, *bad*, Gruchka!"

"Beg pardon, sir. The little monster did the right thing." Genzari knelt beside Eaklor's body and pushed back the grass to show the knife clutched in the dead hand. "You see? When you refused to come with him, he would have killed you."

"He struck at Gruchka in self-defense."

Genzari looked pained and shook his head. "No, sir," he said patiently. "The knife was in his hand when Gruchka jumped at him. It was you he was after."

"In front of fifty men? That's ridiculous!"

"No, sir. Fifty mercenaries. They'd defend you as long as you drew breath, but avenging you isn't part of their contract. When he couldn't arrest you, he resolved to kill you."

Wizenbeak looked down at the knife clutched in the dead man's hand and shook his head. "Maybe Gruchka did right," he conceded, "but you didn't have to kill the little monk, did you?"

"Yes, sir," said Genzari. "It would have been difficult to justify not killing him."

"My God," protested the wizard, "you cut him down without a word. How could you *know*?"

Genzari fingered his closely clipped mustache for a moment, his dark eyes hooded. "I knew," he said at last. "Think about it, sir."

"I will," said the wizard after a pause. "Now what?"

"Bury the dead, sir," Genzari said. "I'll see to it." He gave orders, and men fell to digging.

Presently he walked over to the edge of the freshly dug grave and looked down. "That should do." He nodded. Then, as Wizenbeak came up, he added, "Don't you think, sir?" The wizard seemed far more composed.

"That's fine, Mr. Genzari," he said calmly. "A good piece of work. Did you check their saddlebags?"

"Yes, sir," was the reply. "A little food, a little money, and this." He handed the wizard a cylindrical scroll case of worn black leather that had been sealed with wax. Wizenbeak opened the case and examined the scroll, which was an order to arrest and detain a certain Dr. William W. Wizenbeak for interrogation in connection with the recent death of Archdeacon Heiby. All perfectly legal and in proper order.

Wizenbeak tossed the order into the open grave and examined the case, first one way, then another. At last he pried off the end cap, revealing that the wall of the case was, in fact, double. Between the inner and outer walls of the case was a second document, a blank, legal-sized parchment, embossed with the royal seal and signed with a flourish by Prince Kahun.

The wizard whistled softly. "Now, *this*," he said, "is strong magic. Doubtless Brother Rhimkas would have filled it out appropriate to any occasion whatsoever." He tossed the case into the grave but hesitated a minute with the carte blanche. Then he shook his head and discarded that also.

"A powerful magic you said?"

"Yes, Mr. Genzari. But far too dangerous to use."

"Very good, sir." Then the grave was filled in and the carefully cut turf tamped down on top of it.

Wizenbeak mounted his mule and Genzari his horse, and the men formed up in a column of twos, their spears shining in the afternoon sunlight.

"We have dispatches," said Kahun softly. "Wizenbeak is making thirty to thirty-one miles a day on his advertised route. Nothing has been seen of Eaklor and Rhimkas since the second day. They seem to have fallen off the face of the earth."

"You think something happened to them?"

"Of course, you old fool! They're dead. Buried in some unmarked grave, most likely. What are you going to do about it? Pray for their souls?"

"Now, now, Brother Kahun," protested the clerisiarch. "I loved Brother Rhimkas like he was my own son, but we should not have tried to avenge Heiby's death by killing the wizard. I see no point in pursuing the matter further."

"We should not try to avenge Heiby's death?" sneered Kahun, his dark eyes blazing.

"No, Brother Kahun!" said Nasar-Namatu with unexpected force. "The late Archdeacon Heiby involved himself far too much in secular politics, and . . . you are not the only one to receive information on dark matters; his death may be waylaid at the door of Prince Gatsack, your own brother." The old man smiled, showing worn yellow teeth. "There is a rumor of a little doll that wore a kingly crown. The rumor says that Heiby tried to plant it in one of Wizenbeak's pockets, and further, that when he *failed*, the little doll fell on the floor, where he quickly stepped on it."

"Rumors," sneered Kahun.

"Rumors are also facts," replied Nasar-Namatu, "just like a fart in the congregation. There is no attribution of origin, and nobody sees it, but it is there. No doubt the queen will perceive it in her magic mirror . . ."

"Anybody who spends as much time on her face as *she* does hears all the gossip in the world from her cosmeticians and hair-dressers," said the prince. "Magic mirror *indeed*! Bullshit disbursed by my gimp brother is all, pure bullshit!"

"You protest too much, I think," said the old man softly. "Now when I heard that story—which has been closely held, I might add—I thought that perhaps it was a reflection on Heiby's well-known interest in the black arts. An attempt to denigrate his memory. But Heiby is dead. And the story is consistent in its details with the report which Heiby filed, charging Wizenbeak with simple assault. So I considered the story as it came to me and asked myself: Who would benefit? If Heiby had done this thing, who would benefit?"

"And your conclusion?" asked Prince Kahun.

"Who would benefit?" repeated the old man. "Why you, of course. If Heiby had succeeded, Wizenbeak would die, to nobody's great distress except perhaps his own, while his master, Prince Gatsack, would have fallen under a cloud . . . so that the beneficiary of the risk Heiby was taking would be you!"

"So?"

"You are mixing politics and religion, Brother Kahun! In the crudest, grossest sort of way! Two of the clerisy have died in a vain attempt to advance your secular ambitions!"

"Listen to him," said Kahun. "Who was it who said: 'Politics without religion becomes vile; religion without politics becomes sterile'?"

"You quote out of context, as usual," said Nasar-Namatu. "The Church has no business involving itself in the struggle for succession!"

"Heiby would have disagreed," Kahun remarked mildly, "and in fact, he took risks on our behalf. Besides, the Church is *already* involved in the struggle for succession. In *our* behalf. To disengage—if you wished to disengage—would involve serious risks for you, personally."

"Indeed?" said the old man, pouring himself a glass of water from the cut glass decanter sitting on the table. "I have taken risks before now, and was not always the worse for it."

Kahun sat and looked around the study, with its racks of horizontal cases holding precious scrolls. He smiled thinly and stood up, removing the simple black robe.

"I am not only Brother Kahun," he said softly, "I am Prince Kahun, and I shall become Kahun III, King of Guhland, and when I do, I shall reunite church and state becoming both king and patriarch." He dropped the robe on the floor, never doubting that it would be in his wardrobe when he required it. "The tolerance extended to witches and wizards is coming to an end. They will burn as they deserve, and their flames will kindle the fires for the heretics and unbelievers that infest Guhland!"

"When you are king," replied the clerisiarch. "You are not even heir apparent."

"Do you doubt that I shall be king?"

Nasar-Namatu took a sip of water. "Do you think that you are *already* king, Brother Kahun?"

"No," said Kahun, scowling darkly.

"Keep it in mind, then," said Nasar-Namatu, "and for my part, I will believe in your future kingship. I do not believe that we ought to waste any more time or treasure on this Wizenbeak."

"What about Rhimkas and Eaklor?"

"Write them off as unlucky, Brother Kahun."

"And Heiby?"

"You have a score to settle with Prince Gatsack, do you not?" Kahun nodded silently. "Well, then, add Heiby to that score.

And for God's sake, learn to be patient!'' Almost, he added, The king will not live forever! but decided that any further rattling of Kahun's chain would be unwise.

# 5

# A Witch is Rescued . . .

As Wizenbeak's little troop marched into the northern piedmont, the hills became steeper and the road became rougher and more winding. Once they crossed a ravine on a rope suspension bridge because the stone bridge had fallen into the little river underneath, and once they had to go out of their line of march to find a fording place because a bridge had fallen and not been repaired. The forests, also, began to change, slowly shifting from the deciduous trees of the lowlands to the conifers that flourished in the higher altitudes.

"This is where I came from," said Genzari as they rode along at the head of the column. "That's Cunhavi across the valley over there. We'll bivouac outside Huitmire tonight. I was born on a farm near there . . . used to think it was the big city." He laughed. "I went for a soldier as soon as I could persuade the recruiter I was seventeen."

"Did you ever go back?" asked the wizard.

"A few times. It's a wretched, mean place . . . but I had some friends there. Comrades who went back to farming. I was even a godfather to somebody's son. By now he's probably enlisted himself."

The bivouac near Huitmire was a hayfield with a small stream running from the side of a rocky hill to the ditch beside the road and through a culvert to join the river on the other side. The hay had been cut and laid out in sweet-smelling rows to cure before being piled in haystacks or barns. The sun was three or four hours past noon when Genzari gave the order to make camp, and the men unfolded their shields to pitch their shelter for the night.

The shield of the Guhlish infantry is composed of a single piece of canvas, rather lighter than the canvas used in the hauberk, reinforced with glass, in which seams of unimpregnated canvas have been left between the armored panels. The shield, which is a rectangle four feet long and a little less than two feet wide, unfolds at the bottom and on each side to form a one-man shelter. There is a flap of canvas impregnated with glass in a hexagonal pattern on each end, and this serves to close the shelter once the sides have been pegged down.

Wizenbeak, in contrast, had an officer's pavilion, a kind of folding beach umbrella with a span of twelve feet and a telescoping center pole nine feet high. The wall of the pavilion was a long strip of cloth with through-battens, which were set into the ground around the perimeter of the roof and laced to the roof with attached strips of cloth. Four men could set it up in half an hour, and the gonfalon was set before it, a pale blue banner, suspended from a crossbar upon which was set a small crown of Guhland, surmounting a shield bearing the green and white stripes of a water wizard.

After camp had been set up, with a few hours to kill before supper, Wizenbeak and Genzari walked around the area to see what might be going on.

"Feh," growled Genzari. "You can hear the mice under the hayrows. Do you want to walk into town and check it out before we give any of the men a pass for the evening?"

"Why not?" said Wizenbeak. "Riding all day, my legs could use a little stretching." He looked up at Gruchka climbing around in the ribs supporting the tent roof. "Stay, put, baby . . . don't let anybody mess with my gear."

He put his conical wizard's hat aside and picked up a farmer's hat he had bought—black felt with a low, round crown and a wide, stiff brim. It gave him a totally altered aspect, and when Wizenbeak folded down his tall collar, he could, at a sufficient distance, pass for a farmer. When he stepped into the late afternoon sunlight, Lasco Genzari was waiting for him with two mercenaries: Sejenics, a lean, tough fellow in his thirties who would have been an officer if he had not been totally devoted to the mastery of his sword, and Kulyk, a youngster not yet twenty, who was a fast runner over any distance. Genzari and Sejenics wore black and tan hauberks and carried the long sword and the companion sword thrust into the sash. Kulyk simply wore a brown tunic and the companion sword. In case of trouble he was to run for reinforcements.

They walked down the dusty road four abreast until they came to the gateposts, a pair of carved stone pillars that said HUIT on one side and MIRE on the other. The pillars had been topped with some sort of decoration, which had been broken off. Tall, bristly hedgerows forming a sort of city wall came up to the pillars where they were neatly trimmed for a yard or two on each side. There was no gate, but there was a gate house with no one in it just behind the MIRE side pillar.

They paused for a moment and went on into Huitmire, past wattle and daub houses with thatched roofs, which stood wall to wall, until they came to a circular water fountain marking the apex of a triangular plaza. On the left was the tithe barn and the deacon's residence freshly painted, the courthouse with barred windows, a carefully tended cemetery, and the Syncretist church. On the right were shops, and at the far end of the plaza, the jail house, with the sheriff's office in front. The wide end of the plaza was set with more shops and a public house. The road they were following was paved on the left side, made a turn to the right at the end of the plaza, and a turn to the left to leave town. In that little plaza, a triangle bounded by the fountain, the church, and the jail, were a gallows, a stocks, and a whipping post. And a stake with a pile of faggots beside it. On the stake was a neatly cut piece of birchbark proclaiming that one Eilena Jankura would be burned as a witch and a sorceress on Grasday the 12th—tomorrow—at the second hour after noon. The plaza was deserted except for a few old men who were sitting in the shade of the ancient beodar trees in front of the courthouse. Kulyk remarked that the houses seemed to have wooden chimneys and wasn't that dangerous? Genzari told him that the flue from the stove was made to run under the floor to give the house a little extra heat, so that the wooden chimneys never caught fire. Across the plaza, the old men sitting in the shade in front of the courthouse ignored them.

"Now what, sir?" asked Sejenics, studying the plaza as if it were a field of battle.

"Well, Nick, I suppose we check out the situation and the terrain," replied Wizenbeak thoughtfully. "See what, if anything, is going on. And that, of course, means talking with the local folks . . . the good old boys sitting in the shade over there." He twisted a strand of beard around his forefinger. "For openers—what was the name of your godson, Mr. Genzari? Do you remember?"

"He was 'Guldy' Gudajati's boy," was the reply. "His given name was . . . was Ison. He'd be nineteen, now."

Wizenbeak nodded and tipped his black farmer's hat at a rakish angle. "Wait here," he told his three men. "No sense in scaring anybody by walking up in a bunch." He strolled leisurely across the plaza to where the old men were sitting and approached one of them, a flabby old man with mottled hands.

"Good afternoon, sir," he began. "My name is Wizenbeak, and I'm looking for a certain Mr. Ison Guldajati. Do you know him?"

"I don't remember, mister . . . ah, mister whatever your name is."

"Of course," said the wizard. "The drought and the heat of the afternoon will make the memory grow faint every time. Do you suppose it would help your memory revive if I were to buy it a drink over at the public house?"

"The Golden Horseshoe is closed," said the old man, squinting at the sun. "Won't open for more'n two hours."

"We're travellers," said Wizenbeak. "We've been on the march the whole day. They'd serve us if we asked, I'm sure."

The old man licked his lips. "You aren't from around here," he conceded, and he began to think about his thirst. "Tell you what, Mr. Wizenbee . . . if you buy me a pint of ale, I'll drink it with you. Call me Josut."

"Good enough," said the wizard, and they walked across the dusty square to where his men were waiting. He introduced them to the old man, and the five of them went down the street to the Golden Horseshoe. As Josut started down the cellar stairs, Wizenbeak paused and looked at his three men, young Kulyk, the

runner, Nick Sejenics, the master swordsman, Genzari, his lieutenant and strategist.

"I'll stand you a drink," he said, "but you're still on duty.
You let me do the talking. I don't care what you know, I want
to know what *he* knows. Or doesn't know. And I don't want
anybody interrupting us. You understand?" Below, Josut was
ringing a bell and pounding on the door. Someone opened it on
a chain bolt.

"Come on, Josut," he said, "we're closed. Come back in a
couple hours when it's opening time."

"Hey, Tom," Josut protested. "These here are travellers . . .
they told me they've been marching all day. It's legal for them
to drink, right?"

Wizenbeak stepped down the stairs. "Good afternoon, sir,"
he said. "May I and my companions come in for a pint of ale?"

"I suppose," conceded Tom, unbolting the door. "But four
ales, only, for four travellers." Josut looked distressed, but Sejenics nodded.

"That's all right," he said to the wizard, "I don't drink. Give
him mine and I'll keep watch outside the door."

"That should do," said Wizenbeak. "Come on in so you get
served."

Inside, the Golden Horseshoe was pleasantly cool and dimly
lit through the small curtained windows at street level. The floor
was beaten earth with straw spread over it, and there were
benches set around the walls. At the end of the room opposite
the door was an unlit fireplace, and to the left of the fireplace
was a dark wood bar behind which Tom was drawing four pints
of ale. Wizenbeak paid him; Nick Sejenics slid his stein over to
Josut and went back outside. One of the men who had been
sitting in front of the courthouse had evidently waited until they
went into the public house, because he was now shuffling rather
hurriedly down the street toward the jail. Sejenics raised an eyebrow and squatted down on his heels, his back against the wall.
Promising, he thought. We might see a little action yet.

"Well, now, Mr. Wizenbee," said Josut after he had taken a
first pull at his ale, "who was it you were asking about?"

"A young fellow named Ison Guldajati," replied the wizard.
"He'd be nineteen."

"Ah," said the old man sadly. "Young Guldy. He's dead. Dead and buried. Four or three days ago." Wizenbeak leaned on the bar, his own glass of ale at his elbow, and looked interested. Josut took another swig of ale and wiped his mouth on the back of his mottled hand. "They hanged him. On the gallows out on the plaza."

"What for?" prompted Wizenbeak. "Poaching? Did he steal a sheep?" Josut shook his head.

"Don't raise sheep around these parts, mister. No, he tried to kill someone." There was a long silence.

"I'll need to know the details," said the wizard quietly.

Josut said nothing, regretting that the offer of a free drink out of hours had led him to come here. Belatedly he was beginning to wonder who this stranger was and what he wanted. And how he could get out of the Golden Horseshoe without saying anything else. He felt trapped and vaguely threatened. Even in the coolness of the basement, he was beginning to feel uncomfortably warm.

"I'll need to know the details," repeated the wizard with an intensity that confirmed the flabby old man's worst fears.

"He punched out the witchfinder, Young Guldy did," said Tom, the pub keeper, responding to the urgency in Wizenbeak's voice without feeling any of Josut's apprehension. "So they hung the poor bastard."

"Indeed?" murmured Wizenbeak, taking a sip of ale. Sour, he decided, and flat and too warm. With musty flavor highlights—probably the malt had been made with moldy barley.

"See, the reason he hit the witchfinder—" began the pub keeper.

"Mr. Wizenbee ain't interested, Tom!"

"Now, Josut," said the wizard gently, "if Tom's tale is as good as his ale, I'll have no complaints."

"Thank you, sir. What happened was that Young Guldy came back from being a soldier, because he had a tiny little cottage from his ma, and he courted this orphan girl what had a little piece of land for her dowry."

"Weren't so little," said Josut sourly, "twelve acres . . . more'n what he had."

"Right." Tom nodded, wiping the top of the bar with a damp

cloth. "Well, the Church was holding her land—her dowry, I mean—and the deacon, bless him, said that it belonged to the Church, because everybody knew she was going to be a nun, she being all of twenty-two with no prospects and all—"

"Why not?" asked the wizard. "By rights she should have been wedded, bedded, and bred five or six years ago."

"Well, sir . . ." Tom wiped the top of the bar with a damp cloth. "Eilena was kind of plain, in a manner of speaking, and she was a bit of a scold. A man don't need that. At least most men don't. Young Guldy . . if he didn't marry that twelve acres, he was going to starve. Wizenbeak nodded. "Well, the deacon said he wasn't going to give up her dowry, that she should become a nun like they had agreed she ought to. Well, of course, she said she wasn't going to be a nun, and she was, by God, going to get married, and there wasn't nothing in writing where she had even said she was thinking about becoming a nun. But the deacon wouldn't budge. Said it was too bad. Her husband could sue the Church, if he was fool enough to marry her. Well, Young Guldy said he was going to marry the wench, and of course don't you know, he went and had them put up the banns. And two or three days after the banns went up, someone wrote her name an' her sin on a little piece of wood and dropped it into the mouth of the stone lion in front of the courthouse."

"Anonymously, of course," said Wizenbeak.

"Of course," said Josut. "If witches could find out who was denouncing them, they'd take terrible vengeance, right?" The wizard nodded and took another sip of ale.

"Anyway, when the witchfinder came around on his circuit, he took a look at the denunciation, and called Eilena in, and decided she might be in league with the Devil. Well, sir, she stayed in the jail for two days and a night, and the witchfinder came out and said that yes, she was indeed a creature of darkness, and her only hope was to accept God and join a nunnery." Tom took another swipe at the bar with his damp cloth. "Well, Young Guldy lost his temper an' went for the witchfinder's throat. It took the sheriff, and the deputy, and the deacon, and old Josut here to pull him off. Well, that was attempted murder, no doubt about it, an' so they hung him."

"We gave him a fair trial," said Josut.

"We?" asked Wizenbeak.

"Josut here was on the jury," said the bartender.

"Well, and I'm sure he did a good job, then," said the wizard.

"Thank you, sir," said Josut glumly.

"This witchfinder," said Wizenbeak, "where might such a paragon of holiness and virtue be found?"

"He travels a lot, sir . . ." replied the flabby old man, his sentence hanging in the air. The wizard took out a small silver coin and laid it on the bar before him.

"I'll bet you don't know," he said.

"You'd lose," said Tom, picking up the coin. "Everyone in town knows that Brakle the witchfinder is here to watch the burning tomorrow."

"A good thing he found her out," said Josut.

"Eilena Jankura? Is that Young Guldy's Eilena?" Josut nodded. "Ah, Huitmire is a fortunate town." Wizenbeak sighed. "To have young people to burn. Will the deacon make a last attempt to save her soul, poor child?"

"After sundown . . ." said the bartender at last. "This will be the third night." A pause. "I wish they'd burn her and be done with it."

"Her soul is immortal," mumbled Josut. "Her body, she's through with it, Tom. But to save her soul from damnation . . . it's the best that can be done for her."

"Absolutely," said Wizenbeak. "*Much* better than giving her twelve acres for a dowry and letting her marry a man to farm it and father her kids. No doubt the Church needed the land more than she did, and I'm sure that Witchfinder Brakle and the deacon will make better neighbors. Keep the neighborhood free from witches . . . or at least old women who mumble. Right, Josut?"

"Yes, sir," the old man said. He finished his ale, and then looked at Wizenbeak. Nothing the wizard had said was wrong, but there was a nasty edge to his voice. "Excuse me, please, I got to be going. Thanks for th' drink." He scuttled off, stumbling up the stairs as he hurried out of the bar.

"Anything else, sir?" asked Tom.

"The deacon," said Wizenbeak, "tell me about him."

"Deacon Menjiver?" Tom looked uneasy. "He's one of the big men in town, sir. He's also the judge over at the courthouse when somebody has a case coming up." He wiped the immaculately clean bar in front of him. "I don't really know anything about the deacon, sir."

"I understand," said the wizard, and when Kulyk and Genzari had finished their drinks, the three of them left, the pub keeper bolting the door behind them.

"A bit of action while you were in there," said Sejenics, standing up and stretching. "When I came out to watch, I spotted one of the old gaffers on the park bench scuttling into the sheriff's office, and just now old Josut went off to the deacon's house in a tearing hobble."

"Thank you, Nick," said Wizenbeak. "Our next move looks like a stroll over to the jail."

"In a bunch?" asked Kulyk. "We don't want to panic anyone, now, do we?"

"In a bunch," said the wizard. "We don't care if they panic."

The jail was a round stone tower with slit windows and a conical slate roof, the residue of some ancient fortress, while the sheriff's office was a later addition built on the front, a kind of enclosed porch built of whitewashed brick with barred gratings set in front of the windows, and a roof of thatch, which made a graceful curve as it swept around the line where the roof intersected the tower. The wizard knocked on the door and pulled the latchstring. The door opened and the four of them stepped inside. The sheriff, a large man in his late forties, looked up from the boot he was polishing, and nodded to Genzari.

"Hello, Genzi," he said. "I heard you were in town. What brought you back after all this time?"

"I did," said the wizard. "I am Inspector-General Wizenbeak, and Mr. Genzari is on my staff, as is Mr. Sejenics, here—" the lean warrior bowed "—and Mr. Kulyk. Who are you?"

The sheriff put aside his boot and looked the wizard over for a moment. "Sheriff Rulka," he said. "Genzi knows. What are you here for?"

"I'm investigating the hanging of Ison Guldajati," said Wizenbeak sternly. "Simple assault is not a hanging offense."

"It is when you assault a law officer in the performance of his duty," said the sheriff.

"Witchfinder Brakle is a law officer? Did you deputize him as such?"

The sheriff shook his head. "Makes no difference," he said. "Young Guldy is going to stay hung, you know."

"He was my godson," said Genzari softly.

"I'm sorry, Genzi . . . I just carried out the sentence of the court."

"His betrothed is still alive," said Wizenbeak. "Eilena Jank-ura." He pulled his long nose between thumb and forefinger. "What offenses was she guilty of before being proclaimed a witch?"

"Looked that up for Judge Menjiver," said Sheriff Rulka. "She'd been in a couple of fights . . . nothing serious. She was kind of tall, and kind of plain, and too smart for her own good, if you know what I mean—she scared away her would-be suit-ors—but she hadn't got into any real trouble."

"She had a temper?"

"You know it, Inspector Wizenbeak, and a tongue like a rasp."

"Why wouldn't Deacon Menjiver give her that twelve acre dowry he was holding for her?"

"You'd have to ask *him*. I expect she made him real mad at her." The sheriff produced a flint and steel and struck a fire for the tall candle on the table. The sky was still light, but the office was getting dark. "The deacon, he was the judge, too, you know, both at her trial and at Young Guldy's. She told him, you have a conflict of interest, and he said that was the silliest thing he'd ever heard. She tried to defend herself, but he ruled against her every time. Same thing with Guldy. It was the judge that said Witchfinder Brakle was an officer of the court, and it was the deacon that told the jury to bring in a verdict of not guilty at the risk of their immortal souls."

"Josut looked like he'd be easily swayed," said the wizard. "I suppose the others were pretty much the same?"

Sheriff Rulka nodded.

"I see. And of course it was Deacon Menjiver who pro-nounced the sentence of death . . . he being the judge." Wizenbeak sat back and pulled at a strand of whisker, twisting it around his finger. "I'd like to talk to Eilena Jankura," he said at last. The sheriff took a ring of keys from a peg on the wall.

"You'll have to go to her," he said. "I've been ordered not to open her cell except in the presence of the deacon or Witch-finder Brakle." He picked up the candle from the table, slid the glass chimney up over the flame, and opened the door leading through the three-foot wall of the tower.

Wizenbeak turned to Sejenics. "Wait here," he said. The lean man adjusted the swords in his sash and nodded.

"It's all right," said the sheriff. "I have the keys." He held them up and jingled them.

"Now it will be even better," replied the wizard. They stepped onto the landing which led into a room beyond and a spiral staircase going upwards and downwards. The sheriff led them downwards, into the cool, damp dungeon. He opened a second door, and Wizenbeak posted Kulyk to see that it stayed open. Inside was a chamber with various instruments of torture, and tiny cells, in which one could neither sit, stand, or lie. The sheriff went to the end of the row and kneeled down.

"There she is, inspector," he said, "sleeping like a baby and dreaming she's rescued."

"How can you tell what she's dreaming?" asked Genzari.

"She's smiling," replied the sheriff. "What else could she have to smile about?"

Wizenbeak walked over, the straw rustling under his slippers, and looked down through the cell door. The woman curled up on her side wore a piece of dirty burlap stuff pulled over her head and tied at the waist. She looked like she might be a bit taller than he was, and her head had been shaved, even the eyebrows. The effect was, as it was intended to be, dehuman-izing. He knelt beside the sheriff.

"Wake up, Eilena," said the wizard. She opened her eyes and pushed herself up on one elbow, disoriented. The wizard in her dreams was no longer wearing crimson and gold robes, he was shorter and scruffier, but he was undoubtedly here, in the reality of the dungeon.

"Is it time?" she asked, blinking at the light. Maybe I conjured him, she thought, as hope suddenly flared up in her heart. "Who are you?"

"My name is Wizenbeak," said the wizard, making a hand signal. If she saw it, she ignored it. "I have a few questions I'd like to ask you. First, how did Mr. Brakle prove that you were a witch?"

"He told me to admit it," she said. "He shouted and ranted and bullied, and I told him it was bullshit. Which it was. Then he had me arrested, and they stripped me naked and stood me in the stocks—not the public stocks, the ones over there—while his oafish assistants sat around watching for the Devil to come suck at the witch teat. One of them finally fell asleep on the job, and they said: 'Aha! The devil made him do it! And that *proves* she has a witch teat.' Then they took me out of the stocks and put these chains on my wrists—" she held out her hands, manacled in cold iron and held with about a foot of heavy iron chain "—and on my ankles. So I couldn't fly away, I suppose."

"Go on," said the wizard quietly.

"Then they stretched me out on that table, with the old woman holding my arms, and one of his louts holding each leg, and he took a needle in a fancy brass handle and began probing for the witch spot. I couldn't see what he was doing, but it wasn't really bad, just a prick here, a prick there. A witch teat—you can't see it, and when you prick it, you can't feel it and it doesn't bleed. After maybe a half hour he got bored pawing over my naked body and he said: 'Aha! I've found the witch teat!'" And he stick the needle into my left nipple a few times, and I didn't feel a thing, and it didn't bleed, and that was it."

"The needle," said the wizard, "did he name it?"

"Yes." She frowned, trying to remember. "He called it . . . he called it Mambrino's Needle. He held it up and said it would prove my guilt. Maybe they're going to burn me, but they haven't proven a goddamned thing."

"Mambrino's Needle?" said the wizard. "That hasn't been used for nearly two hundred years! That's all the proof he gave?"

"That's right."

"You weren't charged with any specific acts?"

"Trying to get my own back from the Deacon Menjiver,"

she said. "They're going to burn me because they want my land."

"Blasphemy," said the sheriff, making a *pro forma* protest.

"I expect she's right," Wizenbeak said. "Did they charge her with any specific supernatural acts?"

"No," said Sheriff Rulka, "the deacon just condemned her to burn on the strength of the witchfinder's finding her a witch."

Wizenbeak reached into his robe and pulled out a small pocket knife, one blade of which was an awl for punching holes in leather. He opened the awl blade and tested it on his finger.

"Sharp enough," he said. "Not a needle, maybe, but it will do. Let's see your left nipple, young lady."

"What are you going to do?"

"The reason you are a witch is because your left nipple, so the witchfinder says, is the witch teat. He proved it with his little needle. I wish to see whether this is, in fact, the case," said Wizenbeak, holding up the awl. "I'm going to jab you and see if you bleed."

"All right," she said, "suppose I do? What then?"

"I'll let you out of here," said the sheriff, grimly.

"Let's give it a try, then," said Eilena, untying the laces at each side of her waist. She then pulled the sacking over her head and piled it in her lap, and leaned up against the bars of her cell, cupping her left breast in her manacled hands. Her back was crisscrossed with welts and whip marks, some of which were crusted over with blood. Wizenbeak knelt down, poised his knife, and made a quick, precise thrust and withdrawal. She flinched but said nothing, and a moment later, blood began to flow from the wounded nipple. She's too thin, thought the wizard, flat chested, and plain. No wonder she never married.

"Put your clothes back on," said Sheriff Rulka, sorting through his keys. "I think we're going to have a little talk with a certain witchfinder." He opened the cell door, and Eilena Jankura crawled out.

"Am I going to be free?"

"Probably," said the sheriff, taking a hammer and cold chisel from beside the tiny forge where irons were heated. He set her manacles on the anvil where they had been put on her, and cut the rivet holding each shackle in place. Then he took the chains,

which were, after all, part of his inventory, and hung them on
the wall with all the rest.

"Probably not," Wizenbeak said, "but you'll be out of *here*
at least." She followed him out of the dungeon, Kulyk bringing
up the rear, and as they went up the spiral staircase, they heard
someone above shouting angrily. When they reached the gate
where Sejenics had been posted, they found him standing out in
the sheriff's office, his back to the entrance, the short companion
sword in hand, a leather-clad body, holding an ax in one lifeless
hand, lying at his feet.

"Arrest this man, sheriff!" shouted a large, portly man in a
black cape and black hat, clutching a silver-headed walking stick
in one black gloved hand.

"Damnation! The witch is out of her cell!" exclaimed a
smaller, leaner man, also in black, who wore a golden nabla on
a massive golden chain over a plain white shirt. Before them
stood an old crone, holding a stick of firewood she'd picked up,
and a clubfooted man in leather, holding a long, carefully honed
knife, the witchfinder's two servants. The sheriff faltered for a
second, facing men he had customarily deferred to, for the man
with the cane was Witchfinder Brakle, his smaller companion,
Judge-Deacon Menjiver.

"Permit me to introduce myself," said the wizard, stepping
forward. "I am Doctor Wizenbeak, Inspector-General of the
Courts of Guhland." Which is a flat-out lie, he thought com-
placently. If I'd kept that damned carte blanche I could have
backed it up . . . assuming I had the nerve to use it. "Which of
you is Judge Menjiver?"

"I am the Deacon Menjiver," said the smaller man with an
attempt at dignity, "but I also serve, your honor, as the judge—
magistrate, actually—in this small and rustic courthouse."

"Where you dispense the high justice with a rather lavish
hand, by all accounts," said Wizenbeak with icy formality. Let
the good deacon chew *that* for a while, he thought, worry is
good for the soul. "Is that Brakle the witchfinder standing beside
you?"

He swept into the room without waiting for an answer. Genzari followed him, and Eilena, with Kulyk bringing up the rear.
Sejenics, seeing that reinforcements had arrived, wiped his sword

on a piece of cloth and replaced it in his sheath. The crone threw down the stick of firewood she was holding, and the clubfooted man put away his knife. The wizard walked over to the big man in black and looked up at him. "Brakle, the so-called witchfinder?"

"I am the witchfinder, old man," proclaimed Brakle in a resonant baritone, lifting his silver-headed cane. "I protect the seven counties of the piedmont from the forces of hell and damnation—"

"With Mambrino's Needle, you faker!" shouted Wizenbeak, with such fury that the big man recoiled. "Give it to me!"

When the witchfinder made no move to obey, the wizard turned to Genzari. "This man is responsible for the death of your godson. If he does not give me Mambrino's Needle *at once*, you may, if it pleases you—"

The witchfinder hastily removed a beautifully wrought case from his purse and handed it to the wizard, who snapped it open. Inside, nestled on red velvet, was a needle about two inches long, extending from an elaborately carved handle of gilded bronze. Wizenbeak took the device, turned it around in his fingers a few times, and found the hidden latch he was looking for. He held the needle point downwards and pressed his forefinger against the point. The needle slid back into the handle until the forefinger rested on the handle's end. He removed his finger and the needle descended without a sound. He removed his thumb from the operating catch and dropped the needle into the wooden table, where it stood quivering. *The son of a bitch used that toy to kill people for fun and profit,* thought the wizard grimly.

"I fear, Judge Menjiver," said Wizenbeak, "that this foul villain has deceived you with his mask of seeming piety and has caused you to unwittingly commit judicial murder. With that needle I could find a witch teat on the end of your nose—or on *anybody's nose.*"

"Eilena, here, isn't a witch," said the sheriff, supporting the self-proclaimed inspector-general. "Brakle found the witch mark—the witch teat—on her left breast. I was there when he did it. It doesn't bleed when you prick it, he said. So we tried it out. Prick her and she bleeds."

"You are being deceived by the Devil himself," said the

witchfinder with great sincerity, clutching his silver-headed cane in both hands. "Oh, my brothers—"

"Enough!" snapped the furious Wizenbeak. When Brakle continued to plead his case, the wizard gestured to Genzari who hit Brakle across the mouth with the back of his hand, knocking his black hat across the room. I'm going to kill him, thought the wizard gleefully, as part of him recoiled in shock and horror.

"Judge," said the wizard, pointing at the smaller man, "either you are a dupe or you are an accomplice. If you are a dupe, an innocent victim as it were, you will hang this man Brakle for murder, attempted murder, and whatever other charges strike your fancy. Hold the trial tonight and hang him in the morning. If you let him go, you are an accomplice, and I shall see that you *both* hang."

"Try me and be damned," said Brakle, licking his lips. "At the trial I'll tell them what I know about *you*, and by God, we'll hang together!" Judge-Deacon Menjiver wiped his forehead with a white handkerchief. Wizenbeak caught Genzari's eye. This is how a man dies? he thought, but he felt himself utterly calm, utterly rational, utterly strange. One can act rightly without interminable debate, he decided . . . and when his lieutenant put his hand on the hilt of his long sword, the wizard nodded. The old strategist drew his sword and cut Brakle under the heart in one smooth motion. Witchfinder Brakle looked distressed. The silver head of his cane fell off and rolled on the floor. Gaping at it, he opened his mouth to speak, then blood gushed from his wound and he fell down dead.

"Tried to escape," said Genzari pleasantly, wiping his blade and returning it to its sheath in a single precise gesture.

"Th—that's wh-what it l-looked like to me . . ." stammered Judge-Deacon Menjiver.

It's irrevocably done, thought Wizenbeak, suddenly prey to a swirling host of doubts, aware that he couldn't afford the luxury of entertaining them. What would a real inspector-general be doing? "You have the young lady's clothes?" he asked the sheriff.

"They're gone, sir. We gave them away after the trial."

"It's all right. We'll find her other garb. Now, as for you, most honorable Judge-Deacon Menjiver, there is the matter of a dowry of twelve acres.''

"It isn't hers . . .''

"Of course not,'' agreed the wizard, stroking his whiskers. "It goes to her husband . . . whom you wrongfully hanged.''

"It wouldn't have been *his*, either—''

"Quite possibly, but you should *not* have sat on a case in which you were, in effect, one of the parties. You are getting off lightly, Menjiver—*very* lightly—and I think that giving Miss Jankura her twelve acres is an opportunity you should jump at.'' The wizard pulled at his nose. "I strongly urge you to settle.''

"I can't do it,'' said the judge-deacon blotting his forehead. "Title has already been transferred to the Church, and it can't be revoked—''

"We understand,'' said Wizenbeak, "but you have done her great and grave harm, not maliciously, I hope . . . and the proof that it was not malicious would be to make restitution to her. If not the land, then some equivalent value.'' He touched the golden nabla that the judge-deacon wore on a massive golden chain. "How many acres would *this* little trinket be worth, I wonder?'' Genzari stood quietly, his hand resting on his long sword, looking rather bored with the whole business.

"About forty . . .'' said Menjiver, as cold perspiration bespangled his brow. "Look, Miss Jankura . . . take it as reparation for the harm I was tricked into doing you!'' He handed the nabla and chain to Eilena. "Please. Take this and go.''

"Take it,'' said Wizenbeak. "The land is gone.''

"If I do, I can't stay here,'' she said. "Where would I go?''

"Come with me,'' said the wizard. "Take it, and let's leave this unhappy place.''

"Hey, wait!'' protested the sheriff. "What about *these*?'' He indicated the two corpses.

"Burn them,'' said the wizard. "You already have the makings of a bonfire out on the plaza. You can do it tonight.''

"And these two?''

Wizenbeak looked at the crone and the clubfoot. I should show them mercy, he thought, but he desperately wanted to be out of there. "Accessories before, after, and during the fact, I imagine," he said coolly. "Don't ask *me*; Judge Menjiver here can make the determination."

"Lock them up," said Menjiver, wiping off his forehead. "We'll try them after burning the witchfinder. Tonight." The clubfooted man slid his sheathed knife off his belt and put it on the table in a gesture of resignation. Sheriff Rulka led them one at a time to their cells.

"A pleasure doing business with you, judge," said the wizard, extending his hand. Menjiver looked at it for a moment and then shook it. Reluctantly. "I'll see you tomorrow morning. The loose ends . . . clean them up and everything will be copacetic." At the doorway he paused and picked up the head of the witchfinder's cane, a smoothly worn skull. "That way we *both* look good, right, judge?" He tossed the silver skull in the air, caught it, and put it in his pocket.

As they moved down the street, Kulyk in the lead, Nick Sejenics bringing up the rear, Genzari and Wizenbeak walking on either side of Eilena, Genzari looked up at the still-bright sky. "We just might make it back to camp in time for supper," he said cheerfully. Wizenbeak, looking very pale, nodded, and a short distance beyond the village gates he suddenly stopped.

"Hold up, there," said Genzari softly. The wizard stood at the edge of the road, resting his hands on his knees, panting through his mouth. Then he bent over and threw up.

"Was that the first man you killed?" asked Sejenics.

Wizenbeak nodded in mute distress.

"You did real well, sir," Sejenics said. He offered his bota, and after a moment the wizard played an unsteady stream of water into his mouth and spat it out.

"Thanks." He sighed, handing the bota back. "I'm all right now." Genzari nodded, and they resumed the march.

As they approached the bivouac area, Genzari cleared his throat politely. "What are you going to do with the girl, sir?"

"Good question," said the wizard. "I'll change her into a boy, temporarily, and use her as my orderly. When we find a place to put her down, I'll change her back. Satisfactory, Mr. Genzari?"

"An excellent solution, sir. May I ask, also, why you went so lightly on Judge-Deacon Menjiver? Most probably it was *he* that wrote the denunciation, using the witchfinder as a tool to get him out of an awkward situation.''

"You think so, Mr. Genzari?"

"Yes, sir. Menjiver had let Miss Jankura's twelve acres slip out of his custody and couldn't give them back . . . and when she demanded them, he also couldn't *not* give them back. So he called in the witchfinder. You blamed the witchfinder for everything and let Menjiver go his merry way. Why?''

"We-ell," said Wizenbeak. "I am not, as you know, any sort of an Inspector-General. I had no legal standing whatsoever.''

"That didn't stop you from having me cut down the witchfinder," Genzari replied. "Why not Menjiver, too?''

"Because I'm already in trouble over the late Archdeacon Heiby," the wizard said. "The Church thinks I did it—they aren't sure, but that's what they think, I think—and I just *couldn't* wipe out Deacon Menjiver on the way through town, no matter *how* gross he was. This way, *he* gets the credit for taking out the witchfinder, and I'm off the hook.''

"If it would get you in trouble, why did you do it?'' Eilena asked. They rounded a bend in the road and paused in sight of the bivouac, barely visible in the soft light from the summer sky. Wizenbeak pulled at his nose.

"Injustice," he said at last. "Injustice makes me itchy. Come along and have some supper . . . you ought to be starving.''

After the evening meal, he took her into his tent and lit the glass-enclosed candle. Gruchka looked up and scolded his wandering master, and the wizard picked the little troll-bat up and petted him, talking softly into his ear. Eilena Jankura sat down on the edge of the canvas cot, knees pressed together, hands clenched.

"Are you really going to turn me into a boy?'' she asked.

"Hell no," said the wizard, opening his trunk and rummaging through it. "That would be too much like work." He pulled out a clean set of long underwear and an extra pair of sandals which he set aside. "As long as the men *think* I turned you into a boy, and you *look* like a boy, that's all we need. You understand?'' He took out the hauberk that had been packed for him and held it up. "You can wear this," he said. "It'll probably fit you better than it does me." He put the hauberk with the underwear and sandals and went back to his trunk.

"Doctor Wizenbeak," said Eilena timidly. He looked up. "I owe you a lot . . ." She paused and unwrapped the golden nabla on the golden chain. "Anything I got, you can have." She held the chain out to him. "Right about now, if you hadn't come along, that witchfinder's clubfooted toady would be twisting me apart like a boiled chicken." She shivered. "Here. I don't need a dowry."

"Hang on to it anyway," said the wizard.

She shook her head. "Where could I put it? I'd be afraid to lose it."

"Do you want me to keep it for you? I could put it in the trunk."

"Please," she said.

He pulled out a jar of wound salve. "Aha," he said. "I knew I had some. Here." He handed the jar over to her. "That's good stuff. Take a sniff."

She opened the jar and wrinkled her nose. "That's awful!" Eilena said, handing it back.

"I wouldn't like it spread on flatbread," agreed the wizard, "but for your back, it's the best there is. Take off your clothes."

"Yes, doctor," said Eilena meekly. When she had disrobed she lay belly down on the cot, pushing herself up on her forearms, and Wizenbeak began to apply the ointment, sparingly on the welts and bruises, more lavishly on the cuts.

"When did they do this?" he asked.

"After they shaved my head. The bruises from the pinchers were the first night, the whip marks were the second. Trying to 'save' my so-called soul—ow!"

"Sorry. When that soaks in, we'll do the other side. And when we've finished with your front, we'll see about altering your appearance."

She lay on the cot, watching Gruchka climbing slowly around the shadows in the tent roof, patrolling the little gaps between the wall and the ceiling, which were covered by the crenelated flap outside.

"I used to dream of being rescued by a brave knight," she said. "All girls do, I suppose . . . someone young and strong and handsome. But I never thought about what kind of trouble I'd have to get into to be rescued out of.''

"Right," agreed Wizenbeak, scooping up more of the foul-smelling wound salve. "Dream about the good parts."

"I never thought I'd be rescued by somebody weird looking."

"Weird is my middle name," said the wizard. "Doctor William Weird Wizenbeak, at your service." He picked up her burlap shift and smelled it. "Wash this if you want it, otherwise burn the damn thing." The golden chain he wrapped in a piece of clean cloth and put in the trunk.

"And I never thought I'd be rescued by somebody *old*."

"This is the youngest age I have left, young lady." He sat back, twisting a strand of whisker around one finger. "We can't call you Eilena anymore . . . Eilebert, perhaps?"

"No. There's an Eilebert in the village . . . a real dolt."

"Right," said the wizard. "Roll over." She did so, covering herself with her hands. He almost smiled. "Put your hands on top of your totally bald head," he said. "Your gesture toward modesty is appreciated." And, of course, your gesture to weird, old, funny looking Doctor Wizenbeak, covering up as if he were a possible lover.

She obeyed, and he applied the wound salve to the front. "What about Janko?" she asked. "In the village they used to talk about my father as Young Janko."

"Fine and dandy," said Wizenbeak. "Janko it is, then." He took more salve and smeared it on. 'Janko' Jankura giggled. "Are you ticklish?"

"No," she said, "I was just thinking of something."

"Right," agreed Wizenbeak. "You should feel better in the morning." He put the lid back on the jar. "Probably you'll be entirely healed in a day or two. None of your wounds is serious by itself . . . but you have a lot of them."

Jankura sat up and examined herself. "The bruises will be gone in a day or two?" The pinchers had left unlovely plum-colored marks over her arms and lower body.

"Your wounds will be healed," corrected the wizard. "You'll be able to move around without hurting. The bruises—they'll turn all colors of the rainbow and spread out before they're gone—in a week or more. The whip welts should be the same thing. The whip cuts . . ." He shrugged. "There is good news and bad news. The bad news is that you'll have scars. The good news is that you'll have a back to wear them on."

"Couldn't you say a spell to get rid of them?"

"The scars? Not really. I'd have to have . . . never mind." The wizard sighed and sat back in his camp chair. "Saying a spell isn't free. It's like promising to pay for something. You only have so much credit you can draw on, and you don't use it unless you have to." He handed her his long underwear. "Here, put this on."

She took the underwear, but remained seated. "Do you like me?" asked Janko.

"Yes, actually," Wizenbeak said. "You could have behaved a lot worse than you did."

"That's not what I meant."

"Right. If you could see yourself in a mirror, you wouldn't ask. Put on that underwear, young trooper."

She giggled again, and struggled into the underwear.

"Not a bad fit," said Wizenbeak, pulling at his nose, as she buttoned up. "You should have a tunic to go under the hauberk, but that can come later." He picked up the hauberk with its pattern of black hexagons and held it over her head. Janko raised her hands and slid into it, standing up to push her arms into the sleeves.

"You fit the shoulders better than I did," said the wizard, looking her over. He handed her a padded cap, the helmet liner. "Put this on." Janko did so, and Wizenbeak studied the effect for a moment. Then he went back into his trunk. After a moment he came up with a little paintbox.

"What's that for?" asked Janko.

"You look funny without eyebrows, young trooper, so I'm going to paint some on." He opened the box and removed a tiny, pointed brush.

"Will it come off?"

"Not easily," said the wizard. "Rain and sweat won't touch it. Now hold still." He painted the eyebrows, carefully following the natural browline where they had been. Then he added a wispy mustache. "That's it," he said. "Today you are a man."

"I am?"

"For all practical purposes," said Wizenbeak, "you are now Janko Jankura, my new orderly. You sleep in my tent and use the officer's latrine out back. And do what I tell you? You'd damn well better!"

"I will," said Janko, "but shouldn't you swear me in or something?"

"Hunh . . . Mr. Genzari can administer the mercenaries oath in the morning if you want. You don't have to take it, and probably you shouldn't."

She looked forlorn. "I wanted to take service with *you*," she said.

Ritual, thought Wizenbeak. She wants to belong to someone . . . an oath customarily binding both giver and the receiver. It was something to consider. He reached into his pocket and took out the smoothly polished silver skull that had headed the witch-finder's cane. It still had a short stem of dark wood protruding from its base. The wizard tossed it in the air, caught it in his hand, made a fist, and displayed his empty palm. Then with his other hand he pulled it out of her ear.

"The witchfinder's head," Wizenbeak said softly. "That's what you'd be swearing on. The oath is simply to obey me unconditionally, until death or I release you." She swallowed. "You understand?"

"I do," she said in a small voice.

"Fine. Think about it. Sleep on it. When you're ready, let me know." He tossed the silver skull in the air and slipped it in his pocket.

"All right," she said, sitting up. "What sort of work do you need done?"

"You've had a busy day, Jankura," said the wizard. "Go to sleep. We'll talk about it in the morning."

"Where?" she asked. "This is *your* bed, isn't it?"

"Yes," agreed Wizenbeak, unfolding the extra blanket, "but I won't be using it tonight. I have to write a report of today's events before I forget what happened."

"But that shouldn't take long," said Janko.

"I want to set out what happened so my enemies can't use it against my master," said the wizard, "or against me. It might just take a while.'' He covered her with the blanket. "Now go to sleep."

He opened his traveling desk and screwed down the candle-holder to give him the best light. From the other side of the tent, Jankura giggled.

"What's funny?" he asked.

"I was just thinking of something . . . sir? Doctor? What should I call you?"

"Call me master, or Master Wizenbeak, as befits your lowly station," he replied. "What were you giggling about?"

"I was just thinking about Witchmaster Brakle's face when the head of his cane fell off," she said.

On the third night after, Janko found the wizard at his field desk, playing solitaire by candlelight.

"Master Wizenbeak," she said softly, and when he looked up she smiled nervously. "I've been thinking about what you told me," she continued, "and I've decided I want to take your oath."

The wizard shuffled the red-backed cards together, squared the edges of the deck, and gave them one last riffle. "Your bruises haven't faded; your hair hasn't grown back yet. Hunh . . . you don't even have your own eyebrows . . . and you want to take the oath?" He grasped the deck of cards in both hands and turned to face her.

She nodded.

"The thing is," Wizenbeak went on, "that isn't something you use to bind a chambermaid to the household. I gave you the gist of the oath that binds the apprentice to the master. Do you want to study magic?" He pulled at his whiskers.

"Well, yes, actually . . ." said Jankura uneasily. "Have you ever had an apprentice before?"

"What do you think turned my hair white?"

She giggled. "No, really . . . did you ever have an apprentice?"

Wizenbeak sighed. "Yes. A likely lad, back in Resano. About five years into his course of study I got involved with politics . . . well, my *employer* was involved, so I did what I could to help him along. Generally I liked what he was on about, you understand—social justice, institutional reform, all that sweet smelling garbage.'' He shifted his grip on the cards and began to shuffle them.

''Go on.''

''I helped the old fool, never mind why, but what he was doing was conspiring against the City of Resano. Throw out the clerisy, put in a count who was loyal to Prince Gatsack, that sort of thing. He was, as it happened, heavily in debt. To the clerisy, of course.'' A pause. ''Ah, well . . .'' He shuffled the cards. ''There was a big fuss, riots, rape, arson, anything you could think of. A mob burned down the glass factory I was running . . . you don't need magic to make mother-of-glass, but it helps.'' He shuffled the cards again. ''Dalmaji and his son wound up with their heads on pikes. My apprentice . . .'' He shook his head.

''Put up those cards and tell me what happened to him!''

''He died.'' Wizenbeak slipped the pack of cards into his pocket. ''And I'm still up to my ass in politics.'' He sat back in the camp chair and crossed his legs. ''And *you* want me to take you on as a 'prentice?''

''If you hadn't come along, I'd be just as dead as your old apprentice by now,'' she said. ''And, yes, I want to—to—''

''To what?'' he asked. ''It makes a difference, you know.''

''I want to belong to you, and I want to learn magic, and I want to go on like this,'' she blurted.

''Well,'' said the wizard. ''Well, I guess that's clear enough.'' He reached into his beard and rousted out his familiar. ''Ah, Gruchka,'' he murmured, ''wake up. You can be the witness.''

He opened one of the drawers in his desk and took out the witchfinder's silver cane head. ''So you want to swear?'' Jankura licked her lips and nodded. Wizenbeak pushed back the black sleeve of his robe, and Gruchka walked slowly down his forearm, putting one forepaw on the back of the hand that held the silver skull. ''Go on,'' he said softly, ''put your hand on the witchfinder's head.''

''That's all?'' Jankura seemed dubious. ''Shouldn't I take my clothes off or something?''

Wizenbeak covered his mouth with his other hand to hide a smile. ''You've been listening to too many granny tales,'' he said at last. "Do you *want* to strip and have me stick this icy cold lump of silver up your ass to swear you in?" She shook her head and put her hand on the silver skull. Gruchka shifted on the wizard's forearm to spread his webbed fingers over both their hands; Jankura felt a slight tickling where cold silver touched her skin.

"Well, then," he said gravely. "Do you, 'Janko' Jankura choose to become apprentice to the wizard, Doctor William Weird Wizenbeak, which is myself?"

"I do," she said, and gasped as blue flame sparkled from the silver skull, running between her fingers.

"Will you obey my commands, lawful and unlawful, from this time hence, until death or I release you?"

"I will," she said, and again blue flame ran crackling over her hand and wrist.

"Let the Names of Power, which I know and you must learn, bear witness to your oath." A cold wind blew out the candle, and Jankura gave an involuntary cry as the blue flames burned her fingers. Wizenbeak set the silver skull on his desk, where it glowed fitfully in the darkened tent, and fumbled around for a dried avricod to feed Gruchka.

"That's it," he said.

# 6

# With Unexpected Results

THE morning after killing the witchfinder, Wizenbeak heard the black cock of night, and at the second cock crow he reluctantly came awake. Outside he could hear bustle and stirring in the bivouac, and had to face the prospect of another day on the march. Wearily, the wizard sat up on his ground sheet feeling hundreds of years old. Why am I sleeping on the cold, hard ground, he wondered, when I have a nice soft bed? Then he remembered. Yesterday he had rescued a maiden. Last night, actually. She'd been in bad shape, and he'd let her use his cot. Running his fingers through his beard, he found his familiar, curled up and blissfully asleep. He picked up the troll-bat and fondled his familiar until it showed signs of life.

"Time to earn your keep, you little monster," he mumbled. "Daddy needs a massage. A massage, you understand?" Gruchka tilted his little head and nodded, and the wizard laid himself facedown on the ground. Gruchka, moving with great care, laid his long webbed fingers on Wizenbeak's scalp, and drawing on the force from the large muscles of the wizard's legs and back, he began to stroke and manipulate the accumulated aches and tensions away, moving slowly down through the neck and shoulders, up and down the length of the spine, then the backside and the legs, and finally the feet. The troll-bat tapped his master to roll over, but Wizenbeak shook his head and sat up. There wouldn't be time.

"Ah, Gruchka," said the wizard, "that was very good. Thank you, little fella." He stood up and slipped on his robe—a wizard's robe being altogether too lumpy to sleep in—and gave his familiar a slice of dried ground-peach. Then he went to shake Jankura awake. The cot was empty, the blanket neatly folded at the foot with the pillow sitting on top of it.

"Janko?" he said. "Where did the young fool go?"

"Here, master," said Jankura, pushing through the canvas tent flap. "I brought your breakfast." She handed him a glazed wooden bowl of boiled grain with a fried egg on top.

"An egg?" Wizenbeak raised his long eyebrows. "We don't have eggs. Where did you get it?"

"I talked to the local chickens," she said. "Fifty eggs is ridiculous, but one or two . . . *that* they can arrange." The wizard ate his breakfast in silence. She had a bedroll slung over one shoulder, and a grub sack, and a camp axe thrust into her belt. No sword, no shield, no helmet. She couldn't use them, so why should she carry them? He finished and handed her the bowl and fork.

"Here," he said. "Wash 'em up good. And let me see 'em before you pack them away." Dysentery I can do without, he thought.

Jankura grinned. "Yes, Master Wizenbeak," she said. When she brought them back he took them and examined them closely in the early morning light. They looked clean. He checked with one finger. They felt clean. He shrugged and gave them to her to put away. Outside, he stood with his hands in his pockets, his familiar perched on his shoulder, and watched as they struck camp. Genzari was telling Jankura what to do, and she was doing it. And doing it right the first time, more often than not.

The morning mist hung heavy over the fields alongside the river, giving the landscape a pearly gray luminescence. The day, however, promised to be clear, and the sun would soon burn off any fog. At the gates of Huitmire there were still wisps of mist across the road, and as Wizenbeak and Genzari rode up at the head of their column, a small boy, no more than ten or eleven, ran out of the gate house and scampered down the road into the village.

They met the village reaction force just before the plaza fountain, a dozen men, two or three with swords, the rest with spears or pole arms. Deacon Menjiver was fully prepared to deal with the four visitors of the previous evening. As the village militia saw the line of soldiers materialize behind the two mounted leaders, they simply stood aside without argument. As Wizenbeak looked down from his mule, he saw old Josut standing with a spear. The wizard smiled and tipped his hat. Josut just stood there, looking sour. It occurred to Wizenbeak that perhaps Josut had approved of what Witchfinder Brakle had been doing. Well, that figures, he thought. Brakle needed the tacit approval of a lot of people, or he'd have been stopped long since.

As the column marched into the plaza, he looked over at the stake and the gallows. The pile of faggots had gone, and the stake was charred but no longer smoking. From the gallows hung the old crone and the man with a clubfoot. The third member of the witchfinder's entourage, the axeman Sejenics had killed in the sheriff's office, hung by his heels between them. Posted on the gallows was a neatly lettered square of birchbark, proclaiming their crimes to the village at large.

"They didn't waste any time, did they?" said Genzari.

"No . . . no, they didn't," agreed Wizenbeak. "From the look of it, they burned the witchfinder's dishonored carcass last night and hung his familiars this morning." He reached up and rubbed Gruchka's long ears. "Did I say 'familiars'? I must have meant 'henchmen' or maybe 'running dogs.' " He flicked the mule's reins and rode over to read the notice on the gallows. Genzari made a hand signal and halted the column. After a moment, the wizard returned.

"Good, good . . ." said Wizenbeak, pushing his broadbrimmed black hat back on his forehead. "Nothing but a barebones list of the witchfinder's misdeeds, with special emphasis being placed on Mambrino's Needle."

"We aren't mentioned?" asked the old strategist.

"No. Not at all."

"Right. You *have* written a report of your own?"

"Yes, Mr. Genzari," replied the wizard, "I wrote it out last night."

"Very good, sir," said Genzari, signalling the column to move on. "There's a post station at Sifoty about fifteen miles up the road. We'll send it on from there."

"You are one of those who believe that the pen is mightier than the sword?" asked Wizenbeak.

"No," replied the old strategist, "if you want a copybook motto, it would be 'Pen and sword, in accord.' You use the one to secure the gains you make with the other."

Queen Shaia sat at ease as her hairdresser stroked her long dark tresses with an ivory-handled brush, and a pedicurist groomed her small lovely feet with meticulous care. Dr. Odilao Rovira, the court wizard, sat by her left hand discussing the formulations of facial creams, and which might be best for her skin in which season. A courier came in with a satchel of dispatches—stacks of three-by-five inch wooden chips, neatly tied together with red ribbon and sealed with various colors of wax. She went through them, breaking the seals and reading. Some she handed to the wizard to retie, some she dropped into a brazier where they burned with a fragrant white smoke.

The last in the lot was from the piedmont. Her water wizard, Dr. William Weird Wizenbeak, described simply and in detail what had happened at Huitmire, placing special emphasis on the death of the witchfinder. *May it please Your Majesty, I do not believe that such an evil man could enjoy the success that Brakle enjoyed without a strong measure of popular support. Killing him did not end that popular support which is, I fear, likely to prove troublesome in the future. At the very least, it is a potent weapon in the hands of your enemies, whether they use it to raise up another witchfinder or divert it to other uses.* The queen handed the last chip of wood to Dr. Rovira.

"What do you think?" she asked.

"That may well be true in the hinterlands, Your Majesty," was the deferential reply, "but here in the Cymdulock the people are highly sophisticated. I think you really have very little to fear."

Archdeacon Gorabani was urbane and polished, cynical and, a weakness of character he at times regretted, witty. He was bound to Prince Kahun by ties of blood, their being cousins, and by ties of personal history, having gone together to the Royal Fencing School, and finally by ties of mutual interest, the greater part of Gorabani's income deriving from Kahun's favor. When the Congregation of Clerisiarchs adjourned for lunch, he joined his master for a frugal repast of flatbread, cheese, and clean pure water in the refectory.

"They turned down Rhimskaia," said Prince Kahun, draped in the black cloak of a lay preacher. "How could they?"

"By a vote of fifty-four to thirty-nine," replied Gorabani pleasantly. "You had a majority, but it fell seven votes short of the two-thirds needed to place a man on the steering committee. Would you like some of Nasar-Namatu's nectar in that cut crystal goblet?"

Kahun leaned back against the stone wall and held out his earthenware cup, which Gorabani filled with water. "Rhimskaia was the only one they had who could replace Heiby on the steering committee," he said. "No one else is competent."

"Darussis is all right."

"Darussis is an ass." The prince shook his head. "I won't have him."

"Nasar-Namatu won't have Rhimskaia," said Gorabani, leaning on the wooden board, "which means that we won't have an adept on the steering committee." Prince Kahun scowled and ate a piece of flatbread, chewing slowly. "Which means that you are going to have to stop playing games with the Witch-Queen. Unless, of course, you want to use your own people outside the magic circle of the Church."

"That would be treason," said Kahun at last. "I myself could not do it."

"Of course," agreed Gorabani pleasantly. "And Archdeacon Nasar-Namatu is no longer willing that the Church should do it for you."

"He supported Heiby."

"Heiby, as I need hardly remind you, is dead. He *was* a bold and skillful man, but his murder is a reminder that he—and you, my prince—were pursuing a policy that bordered on the reckless." Gorabani cut several pieces of semisoft cheese with his knife and ate them one at a time. "The fact that Heiby's murder took place at all suggests to some people—such as the astute Nasar-Namatu, and, I must admit, to me—that your policy was on the other side of the border."

"Risk nothing, win nothing," said Kahun.

"When you risk and lose," replied Gorabani pleasantly, "it is unwise to play the exact same game a second time. The good Rhimskaia may be more cautious than Heiby, but he is also weaker. Push him for the post again and he will lose by a wider margin."

"Which of our people are defecting?" A touch of anger.

"Gorabani, for one," was the cool reply. "Give up on this stupidity, Prince Kahun! You are attempting to strike at the Witch-Queen where she is strongest." The archdeacon took a sip of water to wash down the flatbread. "There is more than one way to pursue your goal."

"What did the archdeacon have in mind?" asked the prince coldly.

Gorabani laughed, showing his white even teeth. "Forgive me, Your Majesty. I didn't mean to tick you off. Figure that we aren't going to put an adept on the steering committee. It isn't going to happen, you understand?" He took a carefully folded piece of parchment out of his tall red hat and laid it on the table. "I have here a petition from the village of Huitmire asking that we replace the local witchfinder. A check with the local tax rolls shows that *everybody* in the village signed the petition." He replaced the parchment in his hat, which he put back on his head. "It wouldn't be hard to get up more petitions if we wanted."

"Witchfinder?" Kahun looked interested. "Aren't they pretty much self-appointed crackpots?"

"Self-appointed crackpots doing the Lord's work," replied Archdeacon Gorabani, "and, of course, they don't *have* to be self-appointed. The Church simply hasn't appointed any *recently*."

"Hmm . . ." mused Prince Kahun. "A witchfinder for the Witch-Queen. That's a lot more dangerous than mucking around with magic."

"Risk nothing, win nothing, I believe you said?" was the cool reply.

"Ye-es, but this is direct bald-faced confrontation." Kahun shook his head. "Old Nasar-Namatu would never put up with it."

"Of course not. That's why we want to put someone on the steering committee who will. There must be at least half a dozen Mambrinistas in the congregation, of whom you could surely select one." When Prince Kahun sat silent, the archdeacon refilled his cup with water. "Or perhaps you have changed your mind about your father?"

"No. My father—the king—is dead. He is a zombie, a Ghola, kept animated by the will of the Witch-Queen." Unspoken was the thought that the Witch-Queen was thus usurping the place of the rightful heir.

"The King is dead, long live the King," said Gorabani softly. "What are you going to do about it?" Kahun's dark eyes suddenly flashed fire, but he said nothing. "Putting the Mambrinista of your choice on the steering committee would be very easy," Gorabani continued, "and we can arrange matters so that you can appear to be opposed to what you are in fact promoting. And certainly no *official* witchfinder would ever be appointed against your wishes. Or before the time Your Majesty sets for him."

Prince Kahun finished the bread and cheese on his plate and washed them down with a swallow of water.

"Whom did you have in mind?" he said.

# 7

# Into the Wastes
# of Semeryan

THREE day's march east of Springhill is the Merida Gap, and at the foot of the Merida Gap is the village of Autmerida. The gap is not a metalled highway into the altiplano, but it is an easy path, and the sheep herders of the high piedmont drive their flocks onto the altiplano for summer pasturage, so that the dirt trails are well marked and broad.

"Well," said Master Perjics, the mayor of Autmerida, doubtfully, "I suppose that opening the altiplano to colonization would be a good thing. On the whole. But why *here*? Why not at Springhill?"

He was standing on the fighting platform of the watchtower, sixty-four feet above the meadow below. Above them was the observation deck, protected from sun and rain by a canvas canopy, and above the observation deck rose a twenty-foot flagpole. Standing beside him, as they inspected the watchtower for workmanship and conformance to plan, were Wizenbeak and Genzari. The air was warm in the late afternoon sunlight and redolent with the aroma of fresh cut wood. They stood together, leaning on the battlements, which had been faced with carefully fitted tiles of fire-resistant carbonized wood, and looked out over the open vista toward Merida Gap, ten miles distant across the gently rolling countryside.

Mostly it was meadowland, but here and there on the steeper slopes were copses of trees cut for timber and firewood, and now and then a stand of small grain. Few houses and barns were visible, and those close in. In the winter, a cold wind blew down

from the altiplano, and the barns were built into the south sides
of hills, seeking warmth from the sun and shelter from the wind,
while the houses huddled in the bottom of the valleys, where
the wind blew less fiercely. Often the houses were surrounded
by hedgerows or clumps of trees planted as windbreaks. The
ridges were bare, sometimes even of grass, mute testimony to
the ferocity of winter.

"Why not at Springhill?" repeated Wizenbeak, stroking
Gruchka's long ears. "There is no road into the altiplano there,
only a tiny goat track on which two men could not walk abreast.
Here we can move heavy wagons."

"There is no water up there," protested the mayor, "only the
little springs that dry up at the end of summer."

"I have surveyed the area *personally*," said the wizard, "and
I assure you that there is water. I am a water wizard and I ought
to know. That is another reason why we are starting from here."

"The mayor may be concerned about the corvée," said Genzari politely. "To send hundreds or thousands of his people into
the altiplano to build our fort at the end of summer when the
springs are drying up, and especially when your promised well
has yet to be dug—his concern is prudent."

"Thank you, Mr. Genzari," said the mayor. "I would feel
much better about sending my people sixty miles into the wastes
of Semeryan if there was a well where they were going."

"As you see, Doctor Wizenbeak," said Genzari, "the problem is really very simple. First dig the well, then build the fort."
He smiled. "I, myself, have no doubt that you will find water
without difficulty. The mayor must worry about his people dying
of thirst. It is, after all, his duty."

"Well—" the wizard pulled at his long white mustache "—I
had thought that the corvée would dig the well and also raise the
fort."

"Digging the well is a much smaller effort," said the old
strategist, folding his hands on top of the battlement. "You
surveyed the area. How deep would we have to dig for water?"

"There is an underground river," replied Wizenbeak, "and
you could dig twenty or twenty-two feet to reach damp sand if
you knew where it was. Ten steps to the side, you could dig a
lot deeper and find less." He twisted his white whiskers reflec-

tively around his forefinger. "You should dig another four or five feet into the aquifer to ensure a good flow of water."

"So you have a twenty-seven-foot well," said Genzari. "Besides the digging it will need the earth removed, and the sides of the well must be shored up." He scratched his head. "Maybe eighteen men, in three teams of six; they ought to be able to do it in about a week. Maybe less, if we push them."

"We can get more men," said the wizard. "Couldn't you do it faster?"

"Your limit is the well size," was the reply. "More men will dig a *bigger* hole, but not a deeper one. And the three teams spell each other, so you dig and rest, and move dirt and rest, and put up the shoring and rest. Besides, what's your hurry?"

"I want the fort in place!"

"I'll see that you get it, Doctor Wizenbeak. But you have to consider the logistics. You are moving men and animals through an arid land—I'd call it a desert if you hadn't explained that it wasn't—and it will be much easier if we don't *also* have to carry our water with us."

"What do you mean 'also'?"

"This tower," said the mayor, slapping one of the supporting timbers for emphasis. "We built this tower for you, so that it could be disassembled and carried to the site of your fort, where you could put it back together again. Also, the fence and the bridge have been done for you, but we are still at work cutting wood for a barracks and a barn. These labors are being performed in lieu of taxes due the king for this year and next. All of this lumber has to be moved on wagons drawn by horses or mules through the Merida Gap and into the altiplano. You look at the models on the table and say, 'Fine, fine, do it at once!' I tell you that it is very hard to do at all, and that we must plan very carefully to do this thing. Your Mr. Genzari understands this. You should listen to him!"

"Perhaps so," agreed the wizard, stroking the troll-bat sitting on his shoulder. "This may well be a time when one must make haste slowly. How would you suggest that we proceed, Mr. Genzari?"

"Set up a bivouac at the top of Merida Gap," said the strategist. "That will give the men a chance to get used to the thinner air on the altiplano, and it will give the mayor a place to deliver and store the timbers that are being cut for us. Then you and I and the digging crew will go to the site you have selected and dig the well. It will be within the fort, of course?"

"Of course," agreed Wizenbeak and the mayor together.

"Right. Then in addition to the barn and barracks, we will also need a well house to go into the motte."

"Motte?" asked the wizard. He had attended the planning sessions but had sometimes been inattentive.

"The mound of dirt all those hundreds of workers are going to pile up," said Genzari. "It will be about thirty feet high and seventy feet across the top, and it is called a motte. If you had something more substantial than this watchtower and board fence, it would be a motte and bailey. A bailey," he added, seeing the wizard's blank look, "is a masonry building designed to withstand a siege. Which brings us back to the motte, which will wind up on top of our well, unless we build a well house."

"Well house?" asked the mayor, unhappy at a new and unlooked for imposition.

"Well house," repeated Genzari. "Thirty feet tall, eight by eight feet on the inside . . ." The mayor took out a wax tablet and began making notes with a stylus. "You have that? And three floors. We don't need stairways, just access ladders, and we don't need good wood, particularly. The whole thing is going to be covered by the motte."

"We have lots of scrap wood," agreed the mayor, making a note.

"That should do." The strategist nodded. "Now as I was saying, what we'll do is make bivouac at the top of Merida Gap tomorrow, and you can move the lumber up as you get it cut."

"And the well-digging party?" asked Wizenbeak.

"Patience," said Genzari. "We'll move out from the bivouac. It has to be established, and although the bivouac will maintain itself once it's set up, I can't go off well digging until it is."

"We're losing time," complained the wizard.

"Not really, sir. I expect that the corvée will be ready to move out a few days after the wheat harvest is in."

"But that's six weeks off!"

"Yes, sir. Everybody will be much happier and more cooperative if you wait until after the harvest, which means that we have lots of time to get set up and lots of time to dig the well."

*"But I promised the queen!"* He hadn't actually, he only felt the urgency to make haste.

"You're doing your best," said Genzari soothingly. "I'm sure that she'll understand."

"I hope so," said Wizenbeak at last. "When will you strike the tower here?"

"As soon as possible," replied the mayor. "The day after you get set up at the head of Merida Gap we'll move it up there for you."

Two weeks later, in the middle of the morning Wizenbeak dismounted, and Genzari signalled the column to halt. A dust devil went dancing past, a khaki swirl against an otherwise blue and cloudless sky. The wizard walked over to a little pile of rocks and turned the bottom one over. On the underside of the rock was scratched a crude *WW*.

Genzari handed the reins of his horse to Janko, who was holding Wizenbeak's mule and walked over to his master.

"This is the place?" he asked.

"Ye-es," said the wizard, "but there ought to be *two* piles of rock. To mark the edges of the underground river. That strip of grassland over there meanders parallel to it around here, but I can't tell if we want to dig on the grass side or the anti-grass side of the one marker pile."

"How long would it take you to find out?" asked Genzari. "I would prefer not digging a dry hole, if I had the choice."

"An hour, maybe," said Wizenbeak. "The water is truly there—I can feel it in my feet—but to pinpoint the place to dig, I'll have to work on it."

"Fine," said his strategist. "You do that, and I'll set up camp. You think we're within a few hundred yards of where the well is going to be?"

"Less. Twenty yards at the most." Wizenbeak pulled at his long beard and began to walk around, shuffling forwards and backwards over the place where the rocks had been piled. On his shoulder Gruchka spread his long, slender fingers and made very, very slow flying motions. Gradually, the shuffling became a little faster, and the wizard began to pick up his feet between steps, and now and again as Gruchka's wings beat harder, he would leap into the air, as if the troll-bat were seeking to fly away with his master.

Camp was set up in twenty minutes; and Genzari, Jankura, and Sejenics stood at a respectful distance with the well-digging crew and watched Wizenbeak dance. He danced and pranced, spinning and whirling, mumbling and singing a few words now and then as he found the breath. At last he stopped and sat down upon the dusty earth. Jankura ran over to him.

"Are you all right, master?" she asked.

"Heh . . . out of breath . . . a little . . . is all," was the slow reply. "The water . . . I'm sitting over it. The underground river . . . runs north by northwest—" he pointed "—and it's twenty-one feet to damp sand." He started to rise, and she gave him her hand, which he took. "If I wanted to show off, I'd say twenty-one feet and three inches." He reached into his pocket and found a piece of dried fruit for his familiar. "Good Gruchka . . . good little fella."

Jankura picked up a sharp-edged stone from the ground and scratched a big triangle where he had been sitting. The triangle was about fifteen yards closer to the grass than the stone marker had been.

"Hey-yah!" she yelled. "This is where we're digging!"

The next day, shortly after the noon meal, the digging crew found damp sand at twenty-one feet and three inches. The workers carefully rounded out the bottom of the well shaft and lined it with vitrifying plaster to a height of eight feet, forming a reservoir. Then they sent down a little portable boiler and played a jet of steam over the dry plaster until it turned from a flat white to a semigloss white, showing that it was not impervious to water.

The well-digging crew took turns steaming the wall and inhaling the intoxicating vapors which the heated plaster gave off as it vitrified. The following morning, sober and hung over, they went down into the well, which now had two or three inches of water over the wet sand, and dug down into the aquifer with picks and shovels and buckets to remove the wet dirt, and finally to bail out the incoming water. At last Doctor Wizenbeak came down to watch them, getting in their way and insisting that they go down deeper and deeper, until finally they reached five feet on the measuring pole he was using. When they had finished he stayed behind, watching the ground water flow into the reservoir, and climbing slowly up the ladder as the water lapped at his feet. The reservoir crested at five feet, exactly as he had calculated.

Wizenbeak clambered out of the well late in the afternoon, laughing and scratching, and pronounced the work well done.

"Very good, sir," said Genzari. "I have allowed a week or ten days to dig a well, and we seem to have done it in three. If this is to be the well for the fort, why don't we also dig a well for the village?"

"Right," said the water wizard. "Where should we put it?"

The old strategist stroked his closely clipped mustache and smiled. "The village will be established just outside the fort, here." He gestured at the desolate plain. "Within a bowshot from the fence that we shall erect on top of the edge of the motte."

"I remember," said Wizenbeak. "The motte is the big pile of dirt. Yes. And how far does a bow shoot?"

"Figure two or three hundred yards," replied Genzari. "The thing to do is mark the site for a second well. Say two hundred and fifty yards downstream from the well we've just dug. Can you do that for us?"

"Easily." The wizard smiled. "I have a firm fix on the underground waters here. I have sniffed them out and clocked their rise. Two hundred and fifty yards, you said?" He took a little string of beads out of his pocket and slid them between his fingers a few times. Then he walked over to the well and paced off the distance, counting the paces on his beads. He followed the center line of the unseen underground river, which was not exactly straight. "Two hundred and fifty," he called. "Is this good enough?"

"Perfect," said Genzari. "We'll dig a couple of feet to mark the place and finish it tomorrow."

"Wait," said Wizenbeak, "before you get started, let me explain to the digging crew why we're doing all this."

"You already have," Genzari replied, "and a couple of them are thinking about trying to settle out here."

After digging the second well, they returned to the bivouac, where they found the timbers cut and ready, with wagons for their transport standing by. Teams of horses and mules were available in the countryside around Autmerida, but the corvée order did not cover drovers, and none would volunteer except for outrageous prices. Genzari hired one man to serve as head drover and told him to use his warriors. To complaints that this was not warrior's work, Genzari explained patiently that they were building a field fortification, than which nothing could be more warlike, and which was unquestionably work. There were grumbles, but the warriors moved the timbers and put up the watchtower and the well house at the site.

Moving back and forth, they also established way stations at intervals. These were simply haystacks and barrels of water partially buried in the hay to protect them from the sun. They served to water and feed the draft animals and to reassure their drivers that they were following a trafficked route. Hay moved north from the bivouac, and water moved south from the wells, and Genzari saw to it that water and feed were both maintained.

"Harvest," said Wizenbeak. "When is the harvest going to be over?" He sat on a large rock looking over Autmerida at the top of Merida Gap.

"The haying's done," said Jankura, holding Gruchka against her breast and stroking the troll-bat's long ears. "And the grain is cut and in the barns. Now is threshing and winnowing and bagging the grain."

"Will it be done soon?"

"Yes. Yes, of course," she said. "Nice little Gruchka. Does that feel good, baby?"

"What's the problem?" asked Genzari.

"I'm bothered about the corvée," replied the wizard. "I'm worried that fat little mayor isn't going to send it out for us."

"Nobody likes to march sixty or seventy miles on forced labor," agreed Genzari. "That's why we have the hay wagons so they can ride part of the way. And the beer. It took a little doing, but we put the harvest festival on the road. It'll be one big picnic, then dig like hell to pay off your obligation to the king, and another big picnic on the way back.''

"Amazing," said the wizard, twisting a strand of whisker around his finger. "That's wonderful! I'd never have thought of it."

"It was Janko's suggestion," Genzari replied. "I would have gone down to the mayor and told him we needed a road as well. And threatened to ask for it if he didn't turn out the corvée in a timely fashion."

"Who pays for the food?"

"People bring their own," said Jankura. "We paid for the beer. That is, we paid for some of the beer. There is a certain amount of volunteer brew coming along for the ride.'' She smiled and ran her fingers through her short black hair which had started to grow back again. "Also, I've been talking up the idea of getting a freeholding out by the fort. A lot of them are interested in taking a look at the place.''

"Go on," said Wizenbeak. "What do you know about freeholding in the Semeryan?"

"Quite a lot," she replied, rubbing Gruchka's nose with the tip of her finger. "You talk about it all the time, and I listen, and I know about catch-basin farming and lateritic soil, and the crops that you'd grow up there, and all that stuff.''

"Go on again," the wizard said. "Even *I* don't know what crops to grow."

"The local people do," Jankura said. "I asked them, and they told me. Not firm, 'This is what you grow!' but reasonable guesses. They wanted to know why you went so far into the desert.''

"It is not a desert," exclaimed Wizenbeak, sliding off his rock. "We went as far as we did to reach water.''

"Don't the underground rivers run any closer?"

"No, Janko . . . well, they do, in fact, run closer, bending over toward Springhill, but they *also* get deeper and deeper underground. Thirty miles from here, over in *that* general direction—" he pointed "—lies the very same aquifer we tapped into for the two wells we dug. Maybe three hundred feet down, instead of twenty. At Springhill, you can see the falls gushing out of the rocky cliff face, starting maybe *five* hundred feet below the top of the cliff. Of course, the cliff face rises about a mile over the high piedmont at that point.''

"Some of the springs gush out much lower than that,'' remarked Genzari.

"It's true,'' agreed Wizenbeak, twisting his whiskers. "Some day I'd like to go into that hill and sort them all out.''

The corvée began the Grasday after the threshing was done. The peasants and their families gathered at the foot of the Merida Gap, with their little carts and their provisions, and the mayor checked them off on the tax list, and when a group of them got together, they went up the gap to the bivouac area.

There they waited as more and more groups came up, and at midmorning the next day, they set off on a festive migration into the Semeryan. At night, when they made camp, Wizenbeak explained to them how catch-basin farming worked and what crops he thought (Jankura having told him what she had found out) might grow there. The peasants nodded and agreed that that sounded like it might do very nicely. Afterwards a keg of beer was opened and there was a little singing.

The corvée and their escort walked and rode the whole of the next day and arrived at the site of the tower and the two wells the next afternoon. Genzari marked out the lines where they were to dig, and where they were to dump, and they fell to work with the understanding that they could party when the job was done.

The motte went up very quickly, and when the top of the motte was level with the top of the well house, and seventy paces from shoulder to shoulder, Genzari announced that they were finished digging, and a great cheer went up. Then he announced that there was going to be a bridge building and a barn raising, and everyone booed. However, building the bridge across the ditch around the motte (which was not a moat, since it had no water in it) to the top of the motte right at the foot of the tower, turned out to be perfectly straightforward. And the barn timbers were put in place by sundown.

That night whole oxen were roasted, kegs of beer were drained, and there was singing and dancing around the fire until the sky grew light. The next morning—late the next morning— they raised the barn.

After lunch, Doctor Wizenbeak took a number of possible colonists on a walking tour around the area.

"That there's a nice bit of grassland," said one of them, looking at the meandering ribbon of grass, turned brown and sere in the late summer. "Wonder why the sheep didn't graze it?"

"No water," said another. "Besides, this here's a pretty far piece into the desert."

"This is *not* a desert," insisted Wizenbeak, "and with a very little trouble, you could make that strip of pasture three or four times as wide. And grow small grains as well as hay."

"Temmil, perhaps," said one of the older men. "I doubt you could do much with amarynt'."

"You're crazy with all that digging, Dom," said another. "Amarynt' ought to do better than temmil. Hey, you might even be able to grow barley!"

"The only way to find out is to try it," said Wizenbeak pleasantly. "I will convey title to a sixty-four acre lot to each of the first two hundred families that come here to colonize this place."

"You won't get no two hundred," said Dom. "Fifty might be more like it. Maybe, just maybe, you'd break a hundred."

"We'll see," said Wizenbeak. "It's a long time till spring."

# 8

# A Masked Ball in Cymdulock

On the winter solstice Prince Gatsack held a masquerade ball at the Czajka Palace, to which flocked the nobility of Cymdulock with great eagerness, it being the social event of the season. It might be overstating the matter to say that all the men were handsome and dashing and that all the women were beautiful and flirtatious, but they at least dressed the part. The best chefs toiled to serve up the costliest victuals, and the best musicians worked in shifts to play the most popular music.

"Nice party," said Queen Shaia, pushing the black velvet mask up on her forehead.

She stood in a little room off the peach-colored marble landing where the two curving staircases swept together to form a grand descent into the majestic central ballroom. Duke Falenda stood at her side, wearing an absurdly long nose which somehow imparted character to his otherwise bland countenance. The room was lit by a few dozen votive candles, set before a niche containing a marble bust of the last queen of Guhland, Prince Gatsack's deceased mother.

"Good evening, Mother," said Prince Gatsack, kissing her hand. "I'd like you to meet Archdeacon Gorabani, a friend of my brother's." Gorabani, wearing the robes of a lawyer and the cap and bells of a court jester, bowed, jingling slightly as he did so. "You said you wished to see me on some matter of consequence?"

"What were we talking about, Guillard?" she asked.

Taken aback, Duke Falenda removed his long nose and looked from her to her stepson.

"Why, ah, ah . . . we had been wondering about the enormous quantity of mother-of-glass that your man Wizenbeak is using up in the Semeryan," he said. "We do not understand the justification. What, pray tell, is a Trombe wall and why do they need it?"

"Simple, really," said Gatsack, walking over to the linen-covered sideboard and pouring himself a glass of nonalcoholic punch. "It's a stone or brick or adobe wall set behind a south-facing window so that it can soak up the heat from the sun during the day and release it at night. Keeps you warm and comfortable in the bitter cold of winter, but it's got to be a glass window, of course."

"Well, yes," said the duke, fiddling with his nose, "I mean, I could see it for the barracks—got to keep the troops happy, after all—but for the *peasants*? Wouldn't it be cheaper to burn wood?"

"Not when you have to haul it seventy or eighty miles," replied the prince. "The Semeryan doesn't have any wood to speak of."

"Then how will they cook?" asked the queen, interested in spite of herself.

"They'll burn dried cow patties," said Gatsack. "They'll have enough to cook with, but not enough for heating the house. This is surely not the business that brought you here."

Shaia looked around. "Where is Prince Kahun?"

"The prince is otherwise engaged," said Gorabani urbanely, "fasting and praying, as is his wont at this season. He asked me to come in his place." He picked up a tiny cake soaked in avricod liqueur and ate it.

"No doubt," she said. "Well, then." She took a breath. "Prince Kahun asked that he be named crown prince, that he be officially proclaimed the heir apparent."

"It is his right," said Gatsack mildly. "He is, after all, the firstborn son." He took a sip of punch. "It's something he's wanted for years."

"Yes, but he demands it under threat!"

"No threat," said Gorabani. "He wants to help you."

"Threat," said Duke Falenda, picking up a handful of shelled nuts. "Prince Kahun has threatened to reinstitute the office of witchfinder unless he is named crown prince."

"Oh, surely not," replied the archdeacon. "Prince Kahun is opposed to reviving that office for many reasons. But he will have great difficulty preventing it unless he is proclaimed heir apparent. The Congregation of Clerisiarchs—" he picked up another tiny cake "—*they* are the ones that want it." He ate the cake. "Perhaps in reaction to Your Majesty's own reputation." A slight inclination of his head set the bells jingling.

"Prince Gatsack," said Queen Shaia, "help me rein in your brother. This witchfinder business is nothing but a trick to reach him the crown."

"Where is my father?" asked the prince. "I would think this matter touches his interest as well as your own."

"Sleeping," the queen replied. "He did not wish to come to the party."

"He sleeps a lot, these days, King Grathnys," Gorabani observed mildly.

"He is not a young man!"

"Yes, Mother," agreed Gatsack. "But it is only proper that he should name the crown prince." He finished his glass and refilled it from the punchbowl. "He has, after all, two choices."

"I need your help."

"Of course you do, Mother. But what do you offer me? Only the pleasure of sticking it to my brother."

"What do you want, Gatsack?"

"What my brother wants; to be proclaimed heir apparent. I am even willing to abide by my father's free choice, if you will permit him to make it."

"Naming Prince Gatsack would be a direct repudiation of Prince Kahun," said Archdeacon Gorabani, "and it would effectively end his influence on the Congregation of Clerisiarchs. It would, I expect, ensure that a witchfinder will be appointed, and sooner rather than later."

"I'll protect you, Mother," said Prince Gatsack.

"It would hardly be in your own self-interest," she replied coldly, "and you have *never* been noted for your altruism."

"Well said, Your Majesty," Archdeacon Gorabani told her,

miming applause. "It is in the interest of Guhland that the succession to the throne be announced, and it is in your own interest that it should fall to Prince Kahun."

"I need time," she protested.

"Your Majesty has ample time," said Gorabani, smiling. "A week, perhaps ten days. A fortnight could be arranged. Think things over. Discuss it with King Grathnys, by all means." He tossed his head and his bells jingled.

"You do *not* have time for your children to grow up," Gatsack observed politely.

"Prince Dervian has as much right to the throne as you do!" she snapped. "Or Prince Kahun, for that matter!"

"Ah, Your Majesty," murmured Duke Falenda, "Prince Dervian is a lovely child, but he *is* a child. Even *I* could not support a regency."

"I never intended such a thing," said Queen Shaia, "but King Grathnys will refuse to name an heir apparent, as he has done in the past. Of that I am sure!" She stood up and pulled the mask down over her face. "And Grathnys is still king! Come, Guillard, I wish to return home."

After they left, the prince turned to the archdeacon.

"And once my brother is crown prince, why should he *not* see that a witchfinder is in his own interest?"

"Many reasons," said Gorabani, eating the last tiny cake. "A witchfinder, once raised, would be the very devil to put down."

"No doubt," said Gatsack, "but my brother might find such a creature useful if not amusing."

"You miss the point, Your Majesty. The clerisy is totally inflexible in some directions, but in others it bends very easily." The bells jingled softly as the archdeacon shook his head. "I had expected *far* more resistance to the reintroduction of Mambrino's ideas than we actually got . . . were able to muster, I mean."

Prince Gatsack hid his smile behind his hand. "Kahun was surprised at how popular his proposed witchfinder turned out to be?"

"We do not admit 'proposing' anything." There was a long pause. "But, yet, Prince Kahun was surprised."

* * *

In the foyer of the Czajka Palace, as Queen Shaia and Duke Falenda waited for their coach to be brought around, the duke fretted.

"You really should consult King Grathnys on the matter of the succession, Your Majesty."

"It's useless, Guillard. He would simply ask what I thought best. On this matter, at least, he holds no opinion."

"Ye-es . . . ?"

"Yes. And you can ask yourself if we would be better off with or without Kahun as crown prince."

"That is no longer the whole question, Your Majesty. Would you be better off with Kahun as crown prince and no witchfinder, or with a witchfinder and no line of succession?"

"I don't know," she admitted. "Kahun as crown prince . . . that's bad. It has been our firm policy to prevent it. The other . . . it *looks* bad, but it is far from clear how it would come out in the actual event."

"Far from clear?!" protested Falenda, distressed. "It's a prescription for civil war!"

"Well I *said* it looked bad," replied the queen. But we could win a civil war, she thought, and if that is what it takes to put Prince Dervian on the throne of Guhland, then that is what we shall do. She smiled sweetly and took the duke's arm as their carriage rolled up. "Let's go," she said.

# 9

# Castle Wizenbeak

"WE really ought to give this place a proper name," said Wizenbeak, gazing down from the fighting deck of the lookout tower. Below, the adobe houses of the village ranged themselves in huddled rows, facing south to soak up the meager warmth of the winter sun in their glass-faced Trombe walls.

"What have you been calling it in your reports?" asked Genzari, a wax-faced board and a stylus held under his arm.

"The Semeryan Colonization Project," replied the wizard. "SCP for short, as in Fort SCP and SCP village."

"That really won't do," said his strategist. "The men had been calling the place 'Fort Wizenbeak' until I pointed out that it wasn't strong enough to be a fort. So they changed it to 'Castle Wizenbeak' as a kind of joke."

"That may be funny," agreed Wizenbeak, "but if I put it in writing, the queen is going to think I've gone funny in the head."

"So stick to Fort SCP. The villagers started out calling this place 'Wizenberg,' and then 'Izenberg,' but lately I've heard 'Zenberg' quite a bit."

"Zenberg? That might be possible," said Wizenbeak. "Especially if the name was self-selected."

"I'm glad to hear it," replied Genzari. "I told the village headman that you'd probably approve, and he's all set for the naming at tonight's solstice festival. Have you decided what you want to do about glazing the platform here?"

The wizard sighed. The choice was to use the available

mother-of-glass to put windows all around the fighting platform—which would greatly improve its livability in the
winter—or to use the glass for several new houses in the
village.

"We *are* a colonization project," he said at last.

"Yes, sir," agreed his strategist. "And glass windows would
be pretty useless up here. On the fighting platform, I mean."

"They'd get broken in a fight, wouldn't they, Lasco?"

"Yes, sir."

Wizenbeak sighed again. He had seriously been thinking of
fixing up the fighting platform as his personal apartment.

"We-ell, Lasco," he said at last, "I guess the thing to do is
to use the glass to build housing for the peasants."

"Very good, sir," said Genzari. "Including Kulyk?" Kulyk
had requested permission to resign from the company to homestead a farm in the village. If he got it, somebody's sister had
agreed to marry him.

"Including Kulyk," agreed Wizenbeak, leaning on the
wooden parapet. "He'll get his sixty-four acres like everybody
else."

"Yes, sir. And the other seven?" Including Kulyk, eight of
the fifty mercenaries had applied for a homestead, but Kulyk
had been the first.

Wizenbeak felt around inside of his beard and stroked Gruchka's curled-up back. The weather was already a good bit colder
than the troll-bat liked.

"They can wait till spring," he said. "They'll *have* to
wait till spring. We'll build what we can, but there's no
point in letting them go off before they have a place to live.
Right?"

"Yes, sir," agreed Genzari. "However, most of them have
wives in the village, and the others are expecting them to arrive
in the near future."

"They married villagers?"

"No, sir. They were married already. Some of them have
small children."

Wizenbeak shook his head. "Why did they come here?"

"They had no place else to go," said Genzari quietly.

"What would you suggest that we do, Lasco?"

"Set aside one end of the barracks as married quarters," replied the strategist. "The women will keep each other company, and as long as they understand that it's temporary, there should be no trouble." He fingered his closely clipped mustache. "It might be best if you were to deed the men their sixty-four acres and give them a definite release date. Contingent, perhaps, on good behavior."

"You could be right," said Wizenbeak, pulling at his long nose. "Perhaps the thing to do is dig a new well and install our seven married men as the cadre of a second village. In the spring. First, of course, we have to dig the well."

Twelve miles northeast of Castle Wizenbeak, Eilena Jankura signalled for a halt.

"This is the place," she said, "I think."

"That's nice," replied the wizard unhelpfully. Gruchka, peering out of the wizard's whiskers, gazed mournfully at the girl and did not stir. Jankura rode over beside the wizard's mule and dismounted, handing him the reins. The digging crew, four peasants and four of the married soldiers, watched impassively from the hay wagon they were riding as she reached up and lifted Gruchka gently from the wizard's beard. The troll-bat wore a tiny yellow sweater she had knitted for him, and his breath made puffs of vapor in the chilly air.

"Ah, Gruchka, baby," she murmured softly, "are you going to dance me? Are you going to climb on my shoulder and help me dance?" The troll-bat sat in her arms for a moment, but eventually he climbed to her shoulder, huddling into himself for warmth, as she tossed her loosely woven wool scarf over him. Then she began, walking slowly away from the wizard who sat holding her mount. "Ah, ah, ah," she crooned, "good little Gruchka, *lovely* little Gruchka. Good baby . . ."

And she started to dance, very slowly at first, moving in a stately pavane, arms extended, stepping ever so smoothly, as she turned first to the left and then to the right. Gruchka stopped shivering, and then he unfolded himself and began to beat his tiny wings in time to some unheard music. At first the troll-bat followed the beat Jankura set for him, but then Gruchka began to lead, quickening the tempo, and perforce she had to follow him, leaping and turning, as they followed the sinuous path of some unseen river.

She leaped in the air, and her hat blew off, sailing through the chilly air and rolling on the ground until one of the soldiers picked it up. She ended several hundred yards from where she had begun, panting and puffing, blowing great clouds of steam into the chill morning air. Gruchka she carefully slipped inside her tunic so that he wouldn't catch a chill.

"Here," she called, "over here."

Wizenbeak rode over and returned her black felt hat. "*What's* over here?" he asked. "Or what do you *think* is over here?"

She put the derby hat on over her short dark hair, as Gruchka remained in the warmth of her bosom. "Water," she replied. "About four feet down. In sandstone." She grinned. "I felt it in my feet, and like you told me, once you feel it, you know what it is."

"Dig here," said the wizard.

"Aren't you going to check my work?"

"Certainly," he replied. "If we find water four feet down, I'll know you found it. I'd sooner weary the digging crew than little Gruchka." He dismounted and they stood holding the reins of their mounts as they watched the peasants digging where Janko Jankura, apprentice water wizard, had said they would find water. At the four-foot level they found hard rock, the tip of a mighty boulder of grayish-white fused ignimbrite, hard, touch, impervious to water. There was no visible dampness in the soil. Wizenbeak knelt and ran the loose dirt through his fingers. Bone dry. He studied the rock itself. It looked totally unpromising as an aquifer.

"You felt sandstone and water?" he said. Jankura nodded. He reached into her tunic and gently removed the napping troll-bat. The smooth skin of her breasts brushed warmly against his hand, reminding him of something he had known when he had been an apprentice. He cradled Gruchka in his arms and eased himself down into the hole, where he stood, turning first left, then right, then left, and left again.

"You could be right," he said at last. "Break out the picks, you men. I want at least six inches penetration into the rock formation.'' There was a little grumbling, but the soldiers came back with picks and began chipping away at the hard gray stone. After they had gone into it about three inches, the gray color turned to reddish brown, and then wet sandstone. Encouraged, they dug deeper, and abruptly water gushed into the hole, rising to the surface and flowing over the edges, turning the loose dirt into mud.

"Well," said the wizard. "You called it right on the money, Janko. It looks like we have a well, and an artesian well at that.'' He knelt and tasted the water in his cupped hands. Gruchka, nestled in the wizard's beard, began to whine. "Ah, ah," said Wizenbeak, wiping his hands on his robe. "I didn't mean to spill that cold water on a poor little troll-bat, Gruchka, no indeed!''

But when he went to caress his familiar, he found that Gruchka was not wet at all.

"How was the water?'' asked one of the soldiers, who might be settling here in the spring.

"Pretty good," said Wizenbeak. "Moderately hard, but no sulfur and no iron.'' Gruchka, his ears being stroked very gently, whined again.

"How can you tell there's no iron?'' asked Jankura, taking a mouthful of water and spitting it out.

"You learn the taste," replied the wizard. "The well in the village has just the barest touch of it.''

"We can plant a grove of trees," said one of the diggers.

"This is really great," said another, "a spring in the middle of the desert.''

Gruchka pushed his face next to his master's ear and began to whine very softly.

"Time to head back for Zenberg," said Wizenbeak, mounting his mule. Gruchka burrowed deep into his master's beard and clung to him. Curious, thought the wizard, I'd swear he isn't sick, but little Gruchka is *definitely* unhappy about something.

"All right, you men," he said, "this here is hostile country, and I want you all keeping a sharp lookout for any trouble.''

They were in sight of Castle Wizenbeak when Jankura turned

to the west to admire the spectacular reds, golds, and purples of the Semeryan sunset.

"Look," she said.

High in the western sky was a golden dragon, its serpentine form supported by three pairs of tiny green wings.

# 10

# The Witchfinder of Cymdulock

THE streets of Cymdulock were covered with dirty snow as the procession investing Dr. Fadel approached St. Mambro's Church. The official reason was that St. Mambro was the namesake of the theologian Mambrino, whose doctrines Dr. Fadel would be enforcing as witchfinder. An unspoken but equally important reason was that the people in the local parish were fearful of witches and consequently sympathetic to the witchfinder. Kahun was planting his seed in fertile soil.

"I don't like this at all," said Archdeacon Gorabani, as he trudged in the snow behind the chair bearing the illustrious Dr. Fadel. "You *know* that Fadel believes all that metaphysical horseshit, don't you?"

"As long as he forks it in the right direction I don't care," replied Kahun, "but he does seem sincere."

"He is so sincere it hurts," said the archdeacon. "How can you deal with someone who is a total fanatic?"

"You point him in the direction you want him to go and give him a good rousing cheer," said the prince. "And when he gets killed, you replace him."

"How do you call him off?"

"You don't."

Gorabani looked distressed. "Then when he goes after Her Majesty . . . ?"

"The queen had a chance to step aside," said Kuhun. "The Witch-Queen is going to burn."

"That means civil war, Prince Kahun," said the archdeacon, as they climbed the granite steps into the church.

At the door, Kahun paused for a heeltap. "We'll win," he said.

The official witchfinder was a tall slender man with a high voice and a high forehead. At a distance he looked totally ineffectual, but his pale blue eyes, when they showed any expression at all, burned with passionate belief. Today, he concentrated on the mechanics of his investiture and did not deviate from the script which Nasar-Namatu had prepared for him. After the investment ceremony, the assembled clerisy went downstairs to a small reception provided by Prince Kahun.

"This is rather lavish," said Archdeacon Nasar-Namatu disapprovingly.

"You sound as if you think I was trying to buy votes with a few deviled eggs and sausages," replied Kahun. "If that's all it takes—" he poured himself a glass of red wine "—I have been sadly misled."

"*You* are hopeless," said the old man, "but I had hoped that you would spare the clerisy the temptations of the flesh."

Archdeacon Gorabani came over with his arm about the new witchfinder's narrow shoulders.

"Prince, permit me to present Doctor Fadell."

"Doctor Fadel," corrected that worthy in a scratchy tenor.

"I beg your pardon. Doctor Fadel, this is Prince Kahun." The tall man started to make an awkward obeisance, but Kahun stopped him.

"It is I who am honored to meet you on this occasion," he said smoothly. "As a representative of the secular as well as the clerisy, what aid can I extend you?"

Abruptly the pale blue eyes glittered.

"There are witches and warlocks in high places," said Fadel. "All over the city. Back me and I shall destroy them."

"I have backed you, and I shall continue to do so," replied Kahun, "but perhaps you should start slowly at first."

"Whatever for?"

"To educate the people in what you are doing, Doctor Fadel. How many souls have been steeped in lore as yours has been?" asked the prince, taking a sip of wine. "Very few, I'll wager.

Go slowly, bring the people along with you, and you will become the Scourge of God.''

"And a comfort to the righteous," added Nasar-Namatu.

"You speak wisdom, truly . . ." said the witchfinder, nodding his agreement. "We shall undertake this great task slowly and with the greatest precaution, but in the end we shall bring justice to the Witch-Queen herself!''

"Be careful!" snapped Archdeacon Nasar-Namatu. "What you are saying borders on treason!''

"Ye-es," agreed Kahun, grinning, "but treason, as you know, is a matter of dates. Right, doctor?''

Ten days later the first witch burning took place in the plaza in front of Saint Mambro's Church.

Queen Shaia was pacing back and forth before the fireplace in her audience chambers. Dr. Rovira wrung his hands together and watched his mistress with a kind of deferential agitation. Across the room, Duke Falenda stood at the tall Palladian windows and stared out into the snow-covered courtyard. Beyond the wall the pearl gray winter sky was smudged by a distant plume of greasy black smoke.

"So what if Fadel *does* burn a few crazy old women?" asked the queen. "The mob will tire of his game soon enough!''

"It's you he's after," replied Falenda. "He's moving on the Royal Palace.''

"Truth, Your Majesty," said the court wizard. "He abused me by name only yesterday.''

"What do you want me to do?''

"Rouse the king to take an active part in putting a stop to this treason," said Falenda. "It isn't enough that he should be seen walking around at dinner time and chatting. He has damned well got to start holding court again and put a stop to this business!''

"It might kill him," objected Shaia. "He is an old man and frail.''

"Grathnys was always a tough old bastard," Duke Falenda replied. "Do you have a better suggestion?''

"Break a few heads in the streets," said Odilao Rovira. "Fadel has all sorts of toadies and henchmen . . . catch one and hang him!''

"You'll make martyrs hand over foot," said Falenda. "Put the king in charge, for God's sake!"

"No." Queen Shaia shook her head.

"Your Majesty . . ." the duke took a deep breath. "He will not live long without your ministrations in any event, why not at least use him to crush your enemies?"

"We can't," said the wizard.

"What?"

"Waking four hours and sleeping twenty is a strenuous regimen," said the queen. "I've long since pushed him beyond the limit of his strength. Grathnys should have been dead years ago."

The duke wiped his face with a lace handkerchief.

"What does Your Majesty suggest, then?"

"Fight a mob with a mob. If they yell 'Death to the Witch-Queen,' yell 'Death to Traitors' back at them. As the wizard said, break a few heads."

"Your Majesty is out of her royal gourd," said Falenda. "Do you openly solicit riots, disorders, and civil war?"

"If the alternative is to burn at the stake, why yes, Guillard, that is exactly what I—to use your lawyerly turn of phrase— 'solicit,' " she said grimly.

"I'll hire more mercenaries, then," said the duke. "Although most of the good ones have been skimmed off already." He stood watching the evening sky darken for a time. "What about Prince Gatsack?"

"No help," Shaia said. "We've played him off against Kahun for too long."

"He doesn't *like* Kahun, of course," added Dr. Rovira, "but he won't lift a finger to help us."

"Then why not make him a present?" asked Duke Falenda. "Have King Grathnys proclaim Gatsack as crown prince."

"I will *not* yield Prince Dervian's claim to the throne!"

Duke Falenda sighed and turned back to the window, pushing back the green velvet drape with one hand.

"Your Majesty," said the court wizard softly, "if you press your son's claim to the throne, he may never grow old enough to seize it."

"Think about it," said the duke.

"Whatever the hell for?"

"At the very least it would give Prince Kahun a powerful incentive to rein in the witchfinder. Why should he set his brother on the throne of Guhland?"

"No," said Queen Shaia. Then she hesitated. "If we were in as much trouble as you say, why are you still here with me, Guillard? I know you for an opportunist that turns his face to every wind that blows."

"Your Majesty gives me too much credit," Falenda replied, wiping his sleek face again. "Where could I now go?"

"And what would making Prince Gatsack heir apparent do for us, Guillard?"

Falenda shrugged. "It would annoy Prince Kahun, who is our enemy. What else do you want?"

"I want to hold what is mine," said the queen.

"Then get a handle on the witchfinder," said Dr. Odilao Rovira, who had a powerful interest in achieving that precise end. "He turns his victims over to the secular arm of the state for burning . . . for the execution of his judgment. Why not take a case and appeal it?"

"Why not?" Shaia smiled thinly and nodded. "It might at least put Doctor Fadel off his stride."

A few days later the Widow Oshlo, who lived with a dozen or so cats in a ramshackle house outside the city wall, was accused, interrogated, and convicted by Dr. Fadel's Office of the Holy Inquisition. She was subsequently delivered to the central jail for burning.

At that point, a lawyer filed an appeal before the King's Bench claiming that the Widow Oshlo had been denied due process, and that in fact no proof existed that she was indeed a witch. A hearing was set for ten o'clock the following Marday.

Lieutenant Zeldones, Deputy Commander of the Third Precinct, marched his forty men down the alley separating the courthouse and the central jail. The plaza was already full, not with a normal crowd—a mixture of men and women, young and old—but with young men, mostly under twenty-five. Here and there, scattered through the crowd, he could see a gray beard, usually under the cap of a lay preacher. Around the plaza the

shops remained closed and shuttered, and at the center of the
plaza was a tall wooden stake, with bundles of faggots piled
around it to a height of about six feet. Beside the stake and above
the faggots was a movable platform which the executioner and
the deacon and the witch would mount. The witch would be
bound to the stake, the platform would be moved away for reuse,
and the faggots would be fired.

"What do you think?" asked his sergeant.

The lieutenant glanced at the overcast sky. "It might snow,"
he said. The appeal meant that the witch wouldn't be burned
today, and this crowd wasn't going to put up with it.

"You know what I mean."

"I think we're looking at a riot waiting to happen," said
Zeldones, shifting his dark blue cape over his patterned hauberk.
He was tall, nearly six feet nine inches, with broad shoulders
and a broad, good-natured face.

Normally he would have put one squad on each side of the
square, the men posted as individuals, the squad leaders patrolling, while he and his sergeant, with one man from each squad,
would have formed the strategic reserve.

Now Lieutenant Zeldones posted squads on three sides of the
square, pulling the squad that would have gone on the side opposite the courthouse and jail into the alley under his direct
command. The men were not posted; they patrolled in pairs,
and the pairs stayed in sight of each other.

Widow Oshlo's lawyer appeared with several bodyguards,
walking toward the courthouse steps. One of the older men ran
up onto the platform beside the stake in the center of the plaza,
where he waved his cap and shouted "Death to Witches!" The
several lay preachers scattered through the crowd picked it up,
and the crowd, nothing loathe, began to chant. The lawyer and
his bodyguards were having difficulty making their way through
the press of bodies, but no one had yet raised a hand against
them.

Then the preacher standing on the platform shouted "Death
to the *Defenders* of Witches!" The crowd took up the chant and
closed in on the three men struggling toward the courthouse.

"Disperse!" shouted Zeldones. "Disperse, you sons of
bitches!" He drove his reserve squad like a wedge along the

edge of the crowd, and when he had collected a second squad, he made a right angle turn, trying to reach Widow Oshlo's lawyer. Looking around, he saw one squad assembling in front of the stone lions that flanked the entrance to the jail. The fourth squad, split up in ones and twos, was no longer a unit.

Jittes held low, thrusting at belly and groin, the police at first encountered little opposition from the mob except a few snowballs. Then a dock worker jumped on the point man, and the police wedge became a tangled clot of men edging slowly forward, Lieutenant Zeldones walking immediately behind the point with his hooked truncheon thrust into his belt.

The police wedge had bulled their way to within a few paces of the lawyer and his two remaining bodyguards when a cobblestone hit Zeldones on the left shoulder. As he recovered, he saw a youth with beautiful eyes strike at the lawyer with a filleting knife. The lawyer parried with his leather scroll case, and the youth slid past him and grabbed him by the hair with his left hand.

The lieutenant drew his jitte and, reaching over the shoulder of the officer on his right, clubbed a turbaned head with the butt and on the recoil brought his truncheon down on the skull of the civilian grappling with his man on his left. Reversing his grip so that the hook of the jitte covered his knuckles and the steel-sheathed truncheon rested along the inside of his forearm, Zeldones pushed between his two officers. When a man wearing a butcher's apron kneed him on the hip bone, Zeldones hit him on the angle of the jaw with a right cross, the hook serving as a steel knuckle. Unable to fall, the fellow slid backwards into a kind of sitting position, and Zeldones stepped over him as the youth pivoted so that his knife hand could reach the ''Defender of Witches.''

Lieutenant Zeldones had to take one step more to reach his man, one step too many. He saw the youth with beautiful eyes laughing as his filleting knife cut the lawyer's throat. Then he slipped out of reach into the crowd. The lawyer dropped his scroll case and tried to staunch the flow of blood with his fingers.

A second cobblestone glanced off the lieutenant's padded helmet, sending a spray of fireworks before his eyes, and a porter with a long black mustache grabbed him by one leg. The crowd was chanting, "Death to! Death to! Death to! Death to!" Struggling to break free, Zeldones smashed the butt of his jitte against the porter's temple, crumpling him to the pavement.

The remaining bodyguards helped the dying lawyer to the little cluster of police that had followed Zeldones, and they pushed their way back toward the courthouse under a pelting hail of snowballs and cobblestones.

Inside the marble foyer of the Cymdulock Municipal Criminal Court, Lieutenant Zeldones was counting his officers—of the twenty he had started with, fourteen were still with him—when a bailiff came up.

"The Widow Oshlo's appeal is being heard in courtroom two," he said. "Please follow me."

The Marquis Gelenian, otherwise "Big Bill," sat quietly on his big black horse as the Cymdulock police fell out. His sergeants could do the yelling for him, he thought. He would just sit there as the point for everybody to form up on. He'd give them another ten minutes. The turnout was already pretty good, actually—maybe half the force was standing in place, jittes in hand and ready to go—easily enough to disperse the sectarian mob at the courthouse.

A messenger wearing the livery of the Palace Guard came galloping up to him.

"What is it?" asked Gelenian.

"Orders from the king," said Count Rigano, reining up, "the army, under General Eaklor, is to disperse the mob. He orders the police to stand fast!"

"Hey," Gelenian said, "I have orders from the queen to disperse the goddamned riot! What happened?"

Rigano took off his scarlet plumed helmet and wiped his forehead with his sleeve, leaving a streak of dirt. "The king woke up before his appointed time. Maybe the noise of the riot—you could barely hear it at the palace, but it's an ugly, ugly sound—I couldn't sleep through something like that." His bay gelding danced around, and the count brought it under control using his legs and the reins. "His Majesty anyway came shuffling into the council chamber in his old blue robe and mangy slippers, to take charge. He asked the queen how she planned to disperse

the rabble, and she said she'd ordered the police to do it."
Rigano put his helmet back on, adjusting the chin strap.

"Well so she had," observed Gelenian mildly. "As you see,
we're forming up now."

"That started the most awful fight. It wasn't the police or the
army they were fighting about, it was who was running things."
Rigano shook his head. "He gave me a direct order while the
queen was distracted with that wizard of hers, and here I am."

"Who told General Eaklor to move the army out?"

"King Grathnys himself. Eaklor was there."

Gelenian rubbed his chin. Finally he summoned one of his
senior captains to stand in his place. "I've got to go to the palace
to get my orders straight," he growled. "Wait for me, y'understand?" The officer saluted, and Gelenian and Rigano galloped
off.

The lawyer clutched Zeldones' arm with bloody fingers, and
mouthed "Help me," but no sound came out. Willy-nilly, the
lieutenant and one of the bodyguards helped him down the hall
to courtroom two. Outside, the chant, "Burn Witch Oshlo!"
was clearly audible, and the first stroke of the clock in the courthouse tower striking ten.

The judge didn't look up from his bench.

"Since counsel for defendant is not present—" he began.

"Here is counsel for defendant," said the bodyguard. The
judge put his hand over his eyes, as if this were the last straw,
and the lawyer, his face a ghastly white, the front of his brown
robe soaked with his blood, let go of his bodyguard's arm and
took a shaky and hesitant step toward the bench.

"Counsel requests a continuation of the case," said the bodyguard, as the lawyer sank to his knees and fell forward.

"Drunk again," muttered the judge. "Request denied."

Lieutenant Zeldones turned on his heel and walked out of the
courtroom. The next thing that would happen was the storming
of the jail and the lynching of the defendant. He assembled his
remaining force and took them up the marble stairs to the second
floor where there was an enclosed bridge connecting courthouse
and jail. There was a gate at each end of the bridge and a guard,
but they recognized him and let him and his officers pass through.

The jail was built of gray granite, close-grained and hard. The corridor walls were polished somewhat by the constant touching of groping hands, and the floors were worn by the passage of slippered feet. Zeldones found the Widow Oshlo's cell and posted officers Kjely and Luetge to guard it.

"*Nobody* and I mean NO body is to take her out of there without my permission," he said. "Your ass depends on it!"

Then he and the sergeant and the remaining twelve men went downstairs to the jail door. Eight of the ten officers that had assembled by the stone lions in front were there. The corporal was lying unconscious on a wooden bench, half his face reddish purple and swollen. Someone had put a blanket on him. Outside, the crowd had stopped chanting and was listening to some lay preacher orating on the steps in front of the courthouse.

"Lieutenant . . . lieutenant!" It was one of the men he had posted in front of Widow Oshlo's cell. "The judge and a bailiff come to get her!"

"Hold the damn door, sergeant!" said Zeldones. "Miznik and Scupji follow me! You too, Kjely." The four of them dashed up the stairs and raced down the corridor to where Officer Luetge was telling the judge from courtroom two and the bailiff and a large man in a black hood that he had his orders.

"Ah," said the judge. "There you are Lieutenant . . . Zeldones, is it? Tell your officer to permit the bailiff to release the prisoner into my custody." Zeldones looked at the judge and then at the executioner standing behind him. They're going to take her out to that stake in the square and burn her, he thought. How many men have I lost for nothing?

"What will you do with her?" he asked.

"That's none of your concern," replied the judge. There was brandy on his breath. It had been a bad day for him also.

"You're drunk," said Zeldones. "You are, by God, a disgrace to the bench! *Bailiff!* Lock the son of a bitch UP!" There was an empty cell two doors to the left. *"There!"*

"I can't lock up the judge," protested the bailiff.

Lieutenant Zeldones laid his jitte across the man's throat in a stranglehold without applying pressure.

"This is insubordination and mutiny and treason!" shouted the judge, "Lock me up and you'll hang for it, lieutenant!"

Zeldones applied pressure on the bailiff's throat, and the man selected a key, and when he was released, opened the cell door. Zeldones gestured, and the judge walked in with as much dignity as he could muster. After a while the executioner and the bailiff excused themselves and went away, and Zeldones stood in front of the Widow Oshlo's cell and let the crazy old woman talk about her cats.

An hour or more later Captain Senzik, Commander of the Third Precinct, and Zeldones' superior officer came up. Zeldones saluted, and Senzik returned the salute.

"You've had a busy day, lieutenant," said Senzik mildly. "You are relieved of your command as of right now."

"Yes, sir," Zeldones replied.

"Return to quarters. I'll deal with you later."

"Lock him up!" yelled the judge, "I'm going to hang the bastard!"

"You sound drunk to *me*," said Senzik. He turned to Miznik and Kjely. "Was the judge drunk when the lieutenant locked him up?"

"Yes, sir," said Kjely. Officer Miznik nodded in agreement.

Then Lieutenant Zeldones was led away, and the bailiff released the judge, and they took Widow Oshlo out into the square and burned her.


Queen Shaia put a wet cloth on her forehead, but it didn't help. It had been a bad day, everything had gone wrong, and she had made some serious mistakes.

The mantras didn't help either. This was going to be one of *those* headaches. She sighed and lay back on her ornately decorated chaise longue, wishing for once that it was a little less pretty and a little more comfortable.

I should have let the old fool send in the army, she thought. The dithering at the top had left them without an adequate response to the riot. Grathnys was becoming harder to control, but she could have let him send in the army . . . she *should* have let him send in the army. She pressed her fingertips against her temples and tried the mantras again.

No use. Grathnys might be old, but he was tough and smart. She ought to make use of those qualities instead of routinely opposing every initiative he made. Well, he *had* been tough and smart. Mentally he was still as tough as they came . . . as long as he could stay awake. And he was as smart as ever but lacked the patient attention to detail that assured true mastery. She sighed. Too often he made a hard decision from memory.

A riot was a riot. His instinct was to stamp it flat. Which is what the police would have done, too. Silly to argue, but she had argued. This was one of those cases where quick and dirty was best. Grathnys just wanted to deal with the situation.

The thought stirred a ripple of dissent. Just wanted to deal with the situation, did he? *What* situation? Maybe he wanted to put her in her place. *That* situation. Maybe he wanted to do both. Probably he wanted to do both . . . but in what ratio? A really futile line of thought. She sighed. She wanted what was best for him; she was trying to keep him alive as long as possible. Why did he fight her? She turned the cloth over to press the cool side against her head. Grathnys fought her because she had usurped his throne. He didn't want to live forever, he wanted to be the king.

The mantras didn't help. How much detail did you need to truly master a riot? The army or the police, either one would do if they moved in a timely fashion. The police would have been better, but not if they came late. As they had done. She had won her argument with Grathnys and lost her argument with the rioters. She couldn't afford to lose to either of them, but her hold on Grathnys was secure.

She lay quietly for a time watching the colored pinwheels behind her eyelids. Her hold on Grathnys wasn't secure. She was keeping him alive . . . but he could slip away. And he wanted to be king, so he was struggling in her grasp. Did I ever love the old fool? she wondered. So well did I pretend to love him that I fooled myself, the better to convince him. Now all I want to do is keep him alive until Prince Dervian can take the throne. She shook her head and almost cried out.

The rioters were something else, a pack of dogs urged on by her loving stepson. They weren't dangerous, but Kahun was. All unwanted a thought bubbled up. You aren't going to make it, little girl.

She might have slept briefly; the pain had lessened. When she tried the mantra, it bit. Several repetitions eased the pain to manageable levels. Maybe I won't make it, she thought grimly, but I'll die trying. Cautiously she sat up and then stood up. Moving very slowly she walked to the door and opened it. In the antechamber Dr. Rovira was sitting with her little black dog, whose secret name was Grathnys, sleeping beside him on the sofa.

"Feeling better?" he asked. The room was hung with soft, heavy green drapes, stiff with gold bullion, which retained the faint pungency of recently burned incense. The marble floor was pleasantly cool.

"Relatively," said Shaia, pulling her dressing gown tighter. "What's new?"

"Quite a bit—" he gestured at a couple of long boxes of wooden chips, tied with ribbons of various colors. "One hesitates to say 'must' to royalty in their own bedrooms, but there are a couple of items which I would consider urgent. The hanging of Lieutenant Zeldones at dawn today is one of them."

Is it after midnight? she wondered. Then, "All right, Odilao. Who is this Lieutenant Zeldones and what are we hanging him for?"

# 11

# Crown Prince of Guhland

THE early evening snow sifted lightly down into the courtyard outside Queen Shaia's personal suite. Inside, the queen, Duke Falenda, and Odilao Rovira, the court wizard, sat around an ornately inlaid secretary, decorated with floral wreaths composed of forty-three different woods, its working surface a highly polished slab cut from a single block of malachite. They watched with resigned patience as King Grathnys fussed with his quill pen and inkwell. Finally he nodded that he was ready, and Duke Falenda pushed a stack of documents across the table to him.

"This is necessary state business requiring your signature," Shaia said, as a servant loaded firewood into the tile-covered stove.

"Must I read it, dear?"

"You should, but you don't have to," she said. "It's necessary, but it's also routine."

King Grathnys nodded and gave the gilded candlestand a turn to screw the height of the flame up to the best level. The wizard, standing behind him, leaned over to guide his hand to the correct spot on the page. Unresisting, the king signed the first two documents without reading them. The third, however, he picked up and held closely in front of his nose, reading the text with an effort.

"Ah," he said, "Doctor Wizenbeak has requested authority to issue more land titles in the Semeryan, and we are granting it . . ." He lowered the document and looked at Duke Falenda. "As I recall, you were opposed to the introduction of freeholders into the Semeryan. Don't you think we should reject this and reserve the land for the serf-holders?''

''I had been of that opinion, Your Majesty,'' said Falenda gravely, ''but I now feel that the serf-holders—including myself—would be better off buying out working farms and hiring experienced foremen to supervise them. There is no profit to be made in trying to develop the Semeryan ourselves.''

''Yes, yess . . .'' The king nodded, sucking in his breath. ''I could see that.'' He signed the third document and the fourth, and picked up the fifth for scrutiny.

''Who is Police Lieutenant Josut Zeldones,'' he asked, ''and why do you want him on your personal staff?''

''Read the whole document and find out,'' said Queen Shaia brusquely. ''Basically, we're pardoning him for assaulting a bailiff and unlawfully jailing a judge and killing several rioters in the course of carrying out his duties.''

''Heh heh, hee hee hee . . .'' chortled the king. ''And what do you want with a tiger like *him*? Isn't fat old Falenda enough of a man for you anymore?''

''The witchfinder wants to hang him,'' said Shaia, ignoring her husband's insinuation, ''when he was acting in an attempt to carry out *our* orders.'' If she let him hang, the police could no longer be counted on in any future crisis. If she gave him a full pardon, restoring him to duty, she precipitated an immediate crisis with the Syncretist church. Putting him on her staff was a compromise, an attempt to buy time. ''Just sign it.''

''Yes, dear,'' said Grathnys, affixing his signature to the document. And the next one. And then he stopped.

''What's this?'' he said, holding the ornately decorated parchment before his nose. ''Routine business, you say?''

''The proclamation of Prince Gatsack as heir apparent,'' said Queen Shaia. ''Don't tell me what I think about the idea, don't tell me what I said about it, just sign the paper.''

''Hee hee hee,'' giggled the king, bending over the malachite desk top to fix his signature on the paper. ''Won't young Kahun be pleased . . . the nasty little prick! He made his mother promise him that *he* would be the one.'' After signing, he picked up the wax dispenser from its stand over the candle, and with shaking hand started to affix his seal to the proclamation.

"Allow me, Your Majesty," said Odilao Rovira, guiding his hand so that the king poured a precise charge of red sealing wax in a neat round puddle beneath his signature. The wizard replaced the wax dispenser and handed the king the Great Seal of Guhland, which Grathnys thumped on the liquid wax. Dr. Rovira signed as a witness and pushed it across the table to the others.

"Kahun made her swear," said the king. "She didn't want to, but he persuaded her to swear on the holy ikon in the chapel nearest the throne room. The little prick!"

"Yes, Your Majesty," said Falenda and Shaia together, as they signed as witnesses.

"What he did—Kahun—was bring the ikon in and set it on a cloth-covered chest, and his mother swore that as she hoped to go to heaven, he'd be king someday. And then the little prick opened up the chest and damned if he hadn't filled it with more holy relics than you could shake a stick at!" Grathnys stretched and yawned. "God must have been very annoyed at a cheap trick like that because I recovered from my wounds and the queen died of mortification!" The queen had died years later, but nobody corrected the old man. The king yawned again.

"Your Majesty has had a tiring day," said the court wizard smoothly. "If you will just sign these two remaining orders you can go to bed."

"I don't *want* to go to bed," said King Grathnys, but he signed the documents without reading them.

"Lullaby, my little darling . . ." began Queen Shaia, singing very softly, but the king rubbed his eyes with thumb and forefinger in an effort to ward off sleep. After a few bars, it was evident that for once the spell had failed to take hold.

"Wait," said Dr. Rovira, holding up his hand, and Shaia held a minor note, letting it fade into silence. "Your Majesty," said the wizard to King Grathnys, "what *do* you want?"

"I want to make the proclamation to my court," said Grathnys. He pushed himself away from the desk, and with a great effort stood erect. "I want to make Gatsack the crown prince, and I want to do it *now*! Tonight!"

Queen Shaia and Duke Falenda looked at each other. The queen had reluctantly consented to having Gatsack named crown prince as an insurance against the witchfinder. She had hoped to keep the document a secret, a trump card, to be played when and if it became necessary. Falenda had argued with bitter vehemence that the proclamation should be made public, and at once. He had not agreed with the queen's decision, but in the end he had not broken with her over the matter.

"I am king," said Grathnys. "Summon my court, for I am about to proclaim my favorite son, Prince Gatsack, my heir apparent and the Crown Prince of Guhland!"

The servants, flustered, looked to Queen Shaia for guidance. Shaia looked at Falenda, and pressed her hands against her mouth. The duke, deferring to the queen, said nothing. Chamberlain Fudjak entered, holding a napkin he had snatched from his neck.

"You heard His Majesty," said Dr. Rovira. "Assemble the court. Prince Gatsack is to be proclaimed crown prince!" He held up the signed and sealed document. "The instrument is already signed and sealed and witnessed!"

Chamberlain Fudjak looked at the queen in astonishment. "Your Majesty . . .?"

She slumped in her chair. "Do it," she said at last, and burst into tears.

Prince Gatsack held his long sword high and just to the right of center, and advanced on Count Braley across the bare wooden floor.

"No," said Braley. "Your feet . . . you walk with a floating foot. It looks very graceful. No limp is evident. But you are not firmly set on the ground, and consequently you will not be firm in defense and may not be firm even in attack. You walk like this—" The count slid gracefully across the floor of the fencing hall. "You *should* be walking like this." He turned back and walked deliberately to his starting point, mimicking Gatsack's slight limp. "Foot firmly planted at each step, just as when you are walking purposefully."

He raised his sword in a two-handed grip and began to circle to the left. Gatsack circled to the right, taking care to plant his feet firmly.

"That's better," said the count, as they circled. "Now try—"

The door opened, and both men lowered their swords. The chief butler came in and bowed.

"Forgive the disturbance, please," he said, "but King Grathnys requests your presence at the palace. He wishes to proclaim you crown prince."

"What?" Gatsack looked startled. "When?"

"Tonight, as soon as you can get there." The butler looked up. "Do you wish to speak with the messenger?"

"Is this a trap?" Gatsack shook his head. "No. At least I don't think so. Count Braley, what do *you* think?" A second servant came in, bearing a cylindrical scroll case. Gatsack opened it.

"So? My father put it in writing. I shall be proclaimed crown prince whether I'm there or not."

"No trap," said Braley. "The consequences of failure are . . . are . . ." He sheathed his sword. "Simply incalculable. More interesting is to ask 'why?' Has the queen lost control? She didn't seek any preconditions."

"I'll take it," said Gatsack, returning his own sword to its sheath, "but what's the hooker?" He and Braley marched swiftly to his chambers, where he could select the proper dress, accompanied by a fluster of servants.

"Kahun, of course," Braley replied. "Right now, he is stronger than you. In a year—"

"In six months," said the crown prince elect. "No matter. If my father had died tonight without naming anybody, I should have fought Kahun for the throne. Shall I wear the black and red?"

"By all means," the count said. "Do you think it was an act of policy?"

"You mean as opposed to an accident?" Gatsack grinned wolfishly. "Who cares?"

"I do," said Braley. "An accident is easier to figure."

When Prince Gatsack arrived with his entourage some time later, the court assembled in the great throne room, and while the servants were still lighting the candles in the great crystal chandeliers, King Grathnys mounted the throne without assistance and ordered the proclamation read. He then drank a little wine and socialized with his courtiers for another hour, and at last permitted himself to be led off to bed.

"My father seems to be in a remarkably good mood," said Crown Prince Gatsack.

"Yes," agreed Queen Shaia resignedly, "he does, indeed."

Gatsack accepted another glass of wine from a passing tray, and studied his stepmother for a moment.

"This wasn't your idea, was it?" he asked.

"No." She shook her head. "Duke Falenda wanted it. He felt that we could climb back down from this dangerous place and go back to being what we were. *He* can, maybe."

"Why did you let him move you?"

"I wish I hadn't. But there aren't any good choices. Kahun and his damned witchfinder are out to nail my hide to the barn door." She took a sip of the sweet wine in her glass and smiled. "You wouldn't stop him for me. Can't say as I blame you. We haven't been close, you and I, but maybe we can work together?"

"I don't see why not," agreed Gatsack cautiously. "We have a mutual interest in maintaining the peace of the realm."

"What about the witchfinder?"

"Doctor Fadel? I don't have a handle on him. Maybe Kahun doesn't either. On the other hand, I shall not permit him to come after . . . after the royal family."

"I'd appreciate that," Shaia said. "Perhaps Falenda would arrange a loan to cover some of the expenses you'd expect to incur."

In deference to Archdeacon Nasar-Namatu, Prince Kahun served pure, cold well water, flatbread, and a frugal platter of pickled vegetables surrounding a block of hard yellow cheese.

"Yes," said Dr. Fadel, leaning back in his tapestry upholstered chair, "more than ever I feel that we *eventually* must bring down the Witch-Queen and all that she stands for, but it seems to me—"

"That now is a terribly dangerous time," said Gorabani, mimicking the witchfinder's high-pitched voice.

"You mock me, may God forgive your ignorance," said Fadel in his petulant whine, "but now is *indeed* a terribly dangerous time."

"That is no concern of yours," growled Kahun. He wore the black robe of a lay preacher, but no longer the ornately gilded parade armor. Instead he wore a canvas hauberk with a padded cuirass, armor intended for hard use. "*Your* only concern is witches. Find them and destroy them. And I tell you that all your work will stand as naught if you close your eyes to my wicked stepmother, the Witch-Queen Shaia."

"Doctor Fadel correctly fears precipitating a civil war," said Nasar-Namatu, brushing back his aureole of white hair. "It is *you*, Prince Kahun—"

"You old fool," said Kahun, "this civil war was begun long since, like unripe hay fermenting in a barn until it bursts into flames. The heat didn't bother you, the smoke didn't bother you, but now you say, 'Oh no, we can't have any burning!' I will not permit my gimp brother to seize the throne of Guhland, and that is final. Civil war is upon you, make the best of it!"

"The Church will not support your unholy ambition," said Nasar-Namatu. "We will not bloody our hands in fratricidal strife."

"Wrong," said Gorabani, cutting a prism of hard cheese from the corner of the block. "Our hands are already bloody. Witches bleed, even as you and I, and are they not our sisters in the sight of God?"

"They are *witches*!" protested Fadel. "And the witchmark— the Devil's teat—*that* does not bleed!"

"And the Orthodox church is a nest of unbelievers," said Gorabani, "and from witches to heretics is a short, easy step. God wants those sons of bitches dead!" He fixed Fadel with a stern gaze. "Not so, witchfinder?"

"We-el ye-es . . ." Fadel agreed at last, "but surely the righteous would suffer terribly in a civil war . . . I cannot agree with your tactics. No, I cannot agree at all."

"Tactics are not your concern, either," said Kahun, pouring himself a goblet of water. "Strategically, the Church and the Crown will divide the property of the Orthodox bourgeoisie, as we burn them one at a time. God's reward to the righteous in this life as well as the next. And witches are the kindling that will ignite the stolid heretic-burghers. And the Witch-Queen is the torch that will ignite that kindling!''

"Move against the queen and you kill your father," said Fadel. "Her black arts are what sustain his life."

"My father has been dead for years," replied Kahun. "He is now a Ghola, trotted out of the closet to do her bidding. I would but give him peace." The prince smiled at the witchfinder and bit at his thumbnail. "But what a curious argument for *you* of all people to be making."

"Move against the queen, and you set your brother, Prince Gatsack—Crown Prince Gatsack—on the throne," said Nasar-Namatu.

"That is true," agreed Kahun, "and if I wait a year or two, he might be able to hold it . . . so I must move at once."

Fadel took out a large lace handkerchief and blotted his forehead and mouth. "I can't proceed against the queen," he whispered.

"You can't *not* proceed against her," said Gorabani. "How many file drawers of affidavits do you have testifying to her true nature? Balk on us and I will, by God, have you impeached for dereliction of duty, nonfeasance, and being soft on witchcraft." He picked up a piece of flatbread and chewed it very slowly, waiting for the witchfinder's rejoinder.

When Fadel said nothing, Archdeacon Gorabani tapped him on the chest with a massively ringed forefinger. "Witchfinder? When I get through with you, a civil war will seem the lesser of *many* evils."

"I have many friends," said Fadel weakly, "friends in high places."

"Indeed yet," said Kahun. "I am one of them. Count the Archdeacon Gorabani as another."

"Go for the Witch-Queen," said Gorabani. "It is the only proper thing to do. And for you, the safest."

"Safety be damned!" said Nasar-Namatu, hitting the wooden tabletop with the flat of his hand. "Now is not the time! Push the matter now, and I shall not release the Knights of St. Tarel to fight beside you on field of battle."

"The Tarelian Order?" said Kahun mildly. "I'm counting on them. And if it should happen that I were to urgently ask them to follow me into a just and holy war, do you think they will listen to an aged windbag, an antic buffoon who says 'yes, but not now'? Even if you are the master of the order.''

"The Church should be neutral!" protested the white-haired old archdeacon.

"Horseshit!" demurred Kahun. "Which side are you on?"

"Prince Kahun, the Church *must* be neutral!"

"Between Good and Evil, there can *be* no neutrality, archdeacon! Join my brother, or join me! Which side are you on?"

"We can't join Gatsack, for God's sake," said Fadel at last.

"Well then," said Archdeacon Gorabani, eating a pickle, "that makes your choice very simple, doesn't it?"

Dr. Fadel, Witchfinder of Guhland, looked at Archdeacon Nasar-Namatu for support. The old man met his gaze for a moment, then dropped his eyes and began to tell his onyx prayer beads. Fadel sighed.

"Yes. Yes, I suppose it does. God forgive me. I shall move against her beginning tomorrow." He shook his head. "God forgive me."

Kahun rang, and a steward brought in a bottle of sweet dessert wine, its cork already removed to let the wine breathe a little before serving. The steward filled the cut crystal goblets, and Kahun stood up to propose a toast.

"Gentlemen, I give you . . . Death to the Witch-Queen!" They all drank, even old Nasar-Namatu, and Kahun threw his glass into the fireplace that it might never be used for a lesser toast. As did Gorabani, and after a second, so also did Fadel. Archdeacon Nasar-Namatu simply set his half-empty glass on the table and eased himself back into his chair.

"Aren't you going to throw your glass?" asked Fadel.

"I'm not through with it," replied the old man, taking a slow sip. When he finished, he slipped it into one of his capacious sleeves. "One of these days I'll use it for quaffing a nice draught of poison."

# 12

# The King is Dead . . .

IN front of the Royal Palace the mob was chanting and pounding. "*Death* to the Witch-Queen!" (stomp-stomp) "*Death* to the Witch-Queen!" (stomp-stomp).

Queen Shaia sat next to Count Rigano, Captain of the Palace Guard, who was handsome and quite dashing when he wasn't scared, and Marquis William Gelenian, the Chief of Police for the Cymdulock Metropolitan area. Big Bill Gelenian was paunchy, bald, and not terribly impressed by his recent ascent into the peerage. Beside him sat Duke Falenda and Dr. Rovira. At the end of the table sat Count Braley, Prince Gatsack's fencing instructor, an extremely strong swordsman and an astute strategist, whose ability was belied by his foppish dress. The chair next to him was empty. Archdeacon Gorabani had not arrived. On the other side of the empty chair, next to Count Rigano, was General Eaklor, commander of the Military District of Cymdulock. The general was tall and muscular under an overlay of fat, and bore a marked resemblance to his nephew, Inspector Eaklor, who had vanished while in pursuit of a certain wizard.

"The palace cannot be made safe," said General Eaklor. "Not with the men we have. I urge Your Majesty retire to the Citadel and wait the mob out."

"I agree." Rigano nodded. "The palace was not made to endure a siege."

"What do you think, Chief Gelenian?" asked Shaia.

"Eeh . . ." He shrugged his massive shoulders. "Right now,

the mob isn't really angry. Listen to them. The tone, I mean, not the words.'' The chanting of the mob was distinctly audible when they listened, a white noise, pitched in the upper baritone. ''They've been at it all afternoon, Your Majesty. If they were going to attack, they'd be working up to it, and you'd hear them chanting down *here*, uhrr-UHRR! uhrr-UHRR!''

''Really?'' said Braley. ''I thought mobs went rhu-bar! rhu-bar! rhu-bar!''

''That might be true in the theater,'' said Big Bill, whose long and checkered career had brought him into contact with many professions of dubious legality. ''But your tone—no offense, count . . . if you were a mob chanting like that, I'd send one man out to say: 'Shoo, you naughty boys!' ''

''You don't think we're in danger, then?'' asked the queen.

''Not tonight,'' replied Gelenian. ''Another hour, they'll go off for supper. But my information is that they'll be back tomorrow, and the smart money is betting on the day after, as well. Probably you ought—''

''We shall remain in the palace,'' said Queen Shaia flatly. ''General Eaklor, if your men have such tender feelings for their coreligionists that they are unwilling to disperse a mob, perhaps they can block off the access to the squares on Canal Street and on Park Boulevard.''

To the north Canal Street ran east to west, parallel to the Seven Locks Feeder Canal. The Park of Heroes Boulevard was built on the site of the old city wall and ran east to west, until it reached the Royal Palace, at which time it bent north toward Canal Street. The west end of the Royal Palace fronted on the square facing Cymdulock Cathedral, the east end butted against the Asare River.

''I shall deploy my men,'' said Eaklor, ''but I cannot vouch for their loyalty if the mob attacks them.''

''In deference to your considered judgment, general, I am not asking your men to attack their civilian coreligionists,'' Queen Shaia snarled. ''But if they will not stand against a mob, I do not need them . . . nor you either, you fat fool!''

Eaklor flushed but held his peace.

''We shall assume that the army will hold the squares

north and south of the palace,'' said Shaia at last. ''That leaves the square on the west. Chief Gelenian, can your men hold it?''

''We can barricade Canal Street and—what is it that Park becomes? Cathedral Street. And the little side streets and alleys.'' Big Bill rubbed his bald head thoughtfully. ''The problem is, the mob will funnel through the cathedral behind our lines.''

''Let them,'' she said, ''Count Rigano—''

Lieutenant Zeldones walked into the conference room without knocking. Shaia looked up from the conference table, startled at first and then furious, but he started talking without awaiting permission to speak.

''The king is up and arming himself,'' said Zeldones. ''Says he's going to take the army and disperse the mob.''

''Oh shit,'' said Shaia. ''If we could rely on the army, I'd have done it myself!''

''He wants to lead the Palace Guard against the mob,'' said Zeldones. ''Says he's going to call for 'no quarter' and charge the mob on foot. I said I'd get help, and he made me a general!''

''It might work . . .'' began Count Braley. The army, he was thinking, or some of them, maybe enough of them, would remember they were loyal to Grathnys. A bloodbath would reaffirm their loyalty. If he survived, he would be far stronger.

''I am surrounded by idiots!'' snapped the queen. ''Go back there and stop him!'' The old fool would spill an ocean of blood, she thought, and leave me to clean it up. If he didn't get himself killed.

''He is the *King*, Your Majesty!'' said Zeldones. ''He's waiting for me because I said I was going to bring reinforcements!''

''Yes. Right.'' She stood up, striving for composure, eyes glittering, face white. ''Wait here, gentlemen. Doctor Rovira, lieutenant, come with me.''

They walked swiftly down oak-panelled corridors, past rich tapestries and massive stone busts, to come at last to the king's bedchamber. King Grathnys was standing there in full armor, a score of pages and squires behind him, armed with spears and swords, a fierce little old man leading a commando of children to almost certain death.

"There you are, General Zeldones," he said grimly. "Where are the reinforcements you promised to bring?"

"Grathnys, darling—" began Shaia.

"Get out of the way, woman. This is warrior's work!"

"Your Majesty," said the queen. "I fear I have been remiss in keeping you informed about our situation."

"I fear you have," said Grathnys. "You keep me asleep all the time so you don't have to tell me a damn thing! Well *listen*—" He jerked his head toward the mob noise. "The witchfinder gets his hands on you, he'll scrape your pretty hide off with oyster shells and broil you over a slow fire! And you'd have it coming, you whore!" He drew his sword. "Now get out of my way, you son of a bitch!"

"Stop him," said the queen. Zeldones drew his jitte.

"Well, well, General Zeldones," said the king sarcastically, "which side are you on?"

"I'm on your side, Your Majesty," said the tall police officer. "Believe me . . . charging the mob is not the way to go."

"I say it *is*, and I am the King. Will you follow me?"

"Your Majesty is overtired," began Dr. Rovira, when the king thrust at him. Zeldones parried the thrust with the jitte, but Odilao Rovira stepped back with blood running down from a cut on his cheek.

"I aimed for the throat, you goddamned traitor," growled the king. "Now prepare to die!" He was old and he was frail, but a fell mood was on him, and seizing his sword in both hands he laid on against Zeldones, who stood his ground, parrying the first two strokes and catching the king's blade in the jitte's hook on the third. He applied torque and leverage, and the king's sword clattered on the stone floor raising a shower of sparks. The old man grinned and drew his companion sword in a single smooth motion, cutting the gilded silver chain that Zeldones was wearing on his chest over his hauberk. The chain, weighted by a small medallion of the queen, slithered across the tall policeman's chest and shoulder and fell at his feet with a musical tinkle. On the hauberk, a razor-thin cut went through the glass-reinforced outer layer but was stopped by the inner layer; a stronger hand would have cut to the heart. Zeldones returned to guard and stood his ground, uncertain whether or not to proceed against the King Himself.

"Ah, general . . ." said Grathnys softly. "I loved you like a brother." Tears began to flow down the old man's face, and then he swayed and fell backwards into the arms of his loyal followers. A page removed the short companion sword from limp fingers and stood uncertain.

"Remove his armor and make him comfortable," said Queen Shaia. "See to it, doctor!" Rovira, staunching the wound on his cheek with cobwebs taken from a lacquered box, nodded. She turned to Zeldones.

"Lieutenant, you did well to fetch me. Disperse these young men to their duties and give the doctor a hand. God! What a night!" She turned and walked swiftly back to the council chamber.

Zeldones plucked the scabbards from the sash at the king's waist, picked up the long sword and sheathed it. After a moment, the page proffered the companion sword. The tall policeman thrust both swords into his belt, and picked up the king. Despite his armor, the old man was not heavy.

"This way," said Rovira. Lieutenant Zeldones took a step and then looked back at the little cluster of pages and squires standing doubtful and irresolute. The oldest might have been seventeen. He caught the eye of the page who had given him the king's companion sword.

"You come with us," Zeldones said. "The rest of you men, go back to your regular duties."

As he followed Dr. Rovira, the king took a deep gasp, followed by a series of progressively weaker breaths, taken faster and faster, until he stopped breathing entirely. Then, after an interminable pause, the king took another deep gasp and began again.

"Here," said the wizard, opening the bedchamber door, and then, as Zeldones laid the king on the canopied bed, "His color is bad . . . terribly bad." The king took a deep gasp, less strong than his first, and Dr. Rovira sent the page for the queen.

His bag, indeed, his whole medical armamentarium was in that room, and he worked what magic he could to preserve King Grathnys' life, but by the time Queen Shaia arrived, the old man was dead.

# 13

# . . . Long Live the King!

"Do we have confirmation?" asked Kahun.

"Yes," said Archdeacon Gorabani. "We've talked to the page who was sent to the queen. Just prior to the time Rhimskaia's telltales registered the king's demise, the page reports that Grathnys had fainted and was 'breathing funny.' Then he gave the queen a written message from Doctor Rovira, and she left the conference a *second* time."

"Did he see my father dead?"

"No."

"You call that confirmation?" asked Kahun, biting his knuckle.

"What do you want? The old man's head on a pike?" Gorabani stood with his back to the embers glowing in the fireplace and studied his master.

"She wouldn't let him slip away from her. She wouldn't *let* my father find peace while she and my gimp brother needed him to buy time." Prince Kahun sat indecisive, frowning.

"Maybe one of Darussis' anti-Ghola spells worked," suggested Gorabani. As a practicing wizard, Archdeacon Darussis left much to be desired. "Or maybe Grathnys *wasn't* a Ghola, and he just—"

*"He was a Ghola!"*

". . . died."

"He was a Ghola," repeated Kahun.

"Anything you say, chief," said the archdeacon. "What are you going to do about it?"

"I don't know," Kahun admitted at last. "My father should not have found peace until the Witch-Queen was destroyed."

"Wrong question," conceded Gorabani, clenching and un-clenching his hands behind his back. His stomach was fluttering with tension. "Tomorrow—sometime tomorrow or maybe the next day—the Palace is going to announce that King Grathnys is dead. When the king dies, it is customary to have a funeral. Will you attend your father's funeral?"

"He's been dead for years."

"And now they're going to bury him, understand? *Will you attend the funeral?*"

"*They* are not going to bury my father," grated Kahun. "*I* am going to bury my father!"

Gorabani put another log on the fire, stirred up the embers with a poker, and watched the sparks swirl up the chimney.

"Charming," he said at last. "Your filial piety never ceases to astonish me. How do you propose to do that thing?"

"We storm the palace tomorrow," said Kahun. "The word goes out tonight. We don't wait for any announcement. We don't pay any attention to any announcement. We move every-thing up a day and go for it! Then we announce that with the death of the Witch-Queen, my poor Ghola father is finally at peace. *Then* I shall bury him."

"What about Crown Prince Gatsack?"

"What about him? His claim to legitimacy is tainted with the stench of witchcraft."

"True," agreed the archdeacon, nodding. "And you'd have had to fight him eventually in any case. It might work. I'll put the word out on it."

Queen Shaia stood naked in the king's bedroom and made one final incantation. Grathnys' corpse reclined on a wheeled table, half propped up by pillows, its eyes open to receive the light of special candles reflected from carefully placed tau-nabla mir-rors. As she spoke the final word of the final phrase, the light of the candles started to burn with a lurid green flame, which then trembled and went out, sending a plume of pungent smoke up into the still air in the bedroom. Dr. Odilao Rovira made a note with his stylus on the wax surface of his diptych, and shut it with a snap.

"That's it," he said. "All those antiGhola spells the Church was casting are still holding. A Ghola Grathnys would be pretty damned handy at this point, but we can't cut it."

"If we had more time . . ." Shaia sighed, setting the sharp little knife with the strange handle into its block. "Ah, Grathnys," she said, picking up the little black dog, "you really lucked out tonight." The puppy wriggled and licked her hand.

Rovira shrugged. *Without her makeup she looks totally sexless,* he thought. *Even naked, when the face is less important, you see no bust, no hips. Of course, why would she want to entice* me?

"Now what?" he asked the queen as she put down the sacrificial black dog and slipped into a red silk wrapper. "Shall we announce Grathnys' death and parley to hold a proper funeral? It might," Rovira added hopefully, "take the point away from any further rioting."

Shaia looked at him for a moment. *He's letting his hopes and fears cloud his judgment,* she thought. *The trap has closed and he hasn't admitted it to himself.* She shook her head.

"No," she said. "The news will spread fast enough. And I will not ask quarter from Kahun." She opened the door to the antechamber and roused two of her trusted servants, both women of proven discretion, from the couch on which they were sleeping.

"Grathnys is well and truly dead," said the queen. "Take his body, which I have washed with my own hands, and prepare it to lie in state in the great hall."

They nodded, and being mute, said nothing, but rolled the body on its table out of the room.

"That's it, then?" asked Rovira when the queen closed and bolted the door.

*It is as far as you're concerned,* she thought. Aloud she simply said: "I have one last string to my bow." Walking over to the rack of scrolls on the eastern wall, she reached up to the top shelf and selected an ancient black scroll case which was not dusty for she had recently consulted it. "This is Mowpater's Forty-Second Spell. The unexpurgated version. You know it?"

"Ah . . . I've read the critiques," he replied. "Isn't it dangerous?"

"Well of *course* it's dangerous. If I wasn't in deep shit I wouldn't try it." She spread the scroll on the table and snapped the keepers over the ends so it lay flat. "Now I'll need help compounding the elixir . . . everything we need is in the cabinet."

Rovira moved a black candle to give him better light and studied the scroll. Action was called for, and he could defer thinking for another time.

In the refectory it was not light enough to distinguish a white thread from a black one, but the cooks had been there for some time. One of them gave Lieutenant Zeldones a cup of boullion and some toast made from leavened white bread.

Odilao Rovira wandered in, looking worried and somewhat agitated. He picked up an apple and a couple of boiled eggs, and when he saw the lieutenant, he waved and came over to his table.

"I've been looking for you," said the wizard. "This place is a madhouse."

"You got my assignment squared away?"

"Here's your pass," said Dr. Rovira. "You'll have command of two squads of ten men each . . . Falenda's last hired mercenaries . . . not worth much, probably, but what we can spare. Your job: escort Count Whatshisname—Gatsack's fencing master—over to the Czajka Palace in a sedan chair. Take off from the Lesser Riparian Courtyard." He rapped both ends of his egg and began to peel it. "Then come back. A nice, leisurely stroll, right?"

"Maybe," agreed Zeldones, "maybe not. Don't you think the Citadel is the place we ought to be?"

"No. Nor here, neither. Were I you, I'd find some excuse for leaving the city." The wizard took a bite of his egg and washed it down with a sip of water.

"Where would you go?"

"Me?" Rovira laughed without mirth. "I'm going nowhere."

"No, seriously . . . if you could get out, where would you go?"

"North, I guess. You know Autmerida, below Merida Gap?" Zeldones nodded. "Right. Well, up on the altiplano, there is a colonization project . . . Zenburg, it's called. Fellow named Wizenbeak's in charge. I'd go there."

"Autmerida's the end of the world," said Zeldones.

"And Zenburg's two days' march beyond Autmerida," Rovira replied, finishing his egg and brushing salt off his fingers, "but it's the nearest friendly place I can think of." He stood up and bit into the apple. "It's been nice talking with you, lieutenant, but I've got to run."

Zeldones finished his bread and boullion, and presently a cook came over with a string bag of flatbread and another string bag of cold boiled tubers.

"Breakfast for two squads, to go," he said.

"Right. Have you someone to carry it over for me?"

"No, man. A bunch of the day help didn't show up. You'll just have to carry it your own self." Zeldones unfolded himself from the table where he was sitting, rising very, very slowly to his full height. It was a trick that had got him out of unwanted fights on more than one occasion. The cook watched him with growing concern. "Sir," he said at last.

Zeldones picked up the bags and headed over to the Lesser Riparian Courtyard.

Shortly after midnight Count Braley was admitted at the main entrance of the Czajka Palace, where he had arrived on foot and without escort. The captain of the guard looked him over, noting a conspicuous slash in his otherwise immaculate garb.

"Trouble coming home, count?"

"Ehh . . . I took my sedan chair without escort. I didn't choose to wait until morning."

"So?"

"My bearers were run off by a dozen of Kahun's men."

"What did they want?" asked the guard captain.

"They didn't say," replied Braley. "I killed two of them, and somebody shouted that I wasn't the one, so the rest of them ran off. If they hadn't I'd have killed them all. Take me to Gatsack, please.''

"How could you tell they were Kahun's men in the dark?" asked the guard captain. Count Braley reached into his pocket and produced two medallions with neck chains, one bronze, the other gilt silver. Both bore the right profile of Prince Kahun. The captain examined them and nodded.

"Take me to Gatsack," repeated the count, putting them back in his pocket.

"The crown prince left orders that he was not to be disturbed," said the guard captain.

"Fine. I'll be disturbing the king. Take me to him."

The guard captain's eyebrows went up. "Very well, Count Braley. Please follow."

At the door to Gatsack's chamber, there was the sound of jostling and female laughter. Count Braley rapped on the door.

"I said I was not to be disturbed!" bellowed Gatsack. "Whatever it is can damn well wait until morning!"

"Wrong again," said Count Braley. "Are you decent?"

"Oh shit," came the disgusted rejoinder. "Come on in."

Gatsack was sitting on the edge of his canopied bed in a white linen nightshirt, which he had pulled over his knees. Kneeling in front of him was a naked lady, while behind him lay another, who was languidly covering her charms with the bed sheet.

"What is it?" he growled.

"The King is dead," said Braley, "long live the King!"

"The wizard's telltales didn't show anything," Gatsack muttered.

"When was the last time Your Majesty looked?"

"Guard!" shouted Gatsack, and when the man responded, "Get the damn wizard! Tell him I want the reading on Grathnys' telltale for *right now*! Move!" After the man ran off, he turned back to Count Braley. "So," he said. "How did my father die?"

"He wanted to lead a sortie against the mob, Your Majesty. Queen Shaia overruled him, in the presence of a score of squires and pages, and he drew on that police lieutenant—the tall fellow that jailed the judge—who disarmed the king with his jitte. The king had a stroke and died shortly after."

"Any last words?"

"He is supposed to have said 'Get out of my way, you son of a bitch!' " Braley rubbed his jaw, feeling his beard. "I imagine that would have been to the policeman. In any event, Queen Shaia returned to the council meeting immediately after, to resume ordering the defense of the palace."

"The palace is indefensible," said Gatsack. "She should go to the Citadel. Especially now."

"I so advised her. Before she could make any reply, a page came in with a message from Doctor Rovira. She changed color and left at once. After a time, she sent word that the meeting was adjourned."

"So the lieutenant killed my father? Find out his name and put a price on his head."

"That may be unjust," said Braley. "He was the one who brought the word that the king was going to make a sortie, so that the queen was able to stop him."

"He would have died with his boots on," Gatsack said. "Sword in hand, facing the enemy."

"As he appears, in fact, to have done, Your Majesty."

"So I shall have to avenge him. Filial piety and all that. Pity about the lieutenant . . ." He shrugged. "See to it, Braley."

"Yes, sir." Count Braley removed a small diptych from an inner pocket and made a note on the wax. "We may, possibly, have more urgent business."

"Possibly." Gatsack stood up and began walking back and forth. "I should be surprised if we did not."

"Your majesty," came a quavering voice from outside, "Your Majesty . . . I bring news of great import . . . may I come in, please?"

"Let him in," said the crown prince, and the guards admitted a scruffy little man in a black nightshirt, with a black nightcap, wearing a mustache press carefully hooked over each ear to keep his carefully trained mustache in proper position.

"The telltales, Your Majesty, for King Grathnys . . . the telltales, I looked at them as you ordered. Just now. Your Majesty, King Grathnys appears not to be alive! My record shows that he was well at noon, today—!"

"Very good, old boy," said Gatsack, patting him on the

shoulder. "That's all I needed to know. You go back to bed and get some sleep, now, you hear?"

"Your Majesty, there are tests and procedures . . . we can fix the exact hour and moment . . . !"

"I'm not interested. Go to bed." It was a dismissal. The wizard bowed, and left.

"Well," said Crown Prince Gatsack grimly, "it is time to leave the fleshpots of Cymdulock. The fine meals. The lovely ladies. And get down to the business at hand. Which is to insure my lawful succession to the Throne of Guhland. Guard captain!"

"Here, sir."

"We move out immediately, horse and foot! Pass the word to all my officers. Have the cooks serve breakfast within the hour. My father, King Grathnys, is dead, and I must join my main force at once. Understand?"

"Yes, sir. What about the baggage train?" Putting the baggage train together typically required two days' notice.

"No. We don't have time to order the logistics. I want to move like a thunderbolt!" He felt his jaw. "Have the train assembled and I'll send for it." He looked at the two naked ladies, who were sitting up under the bed sheet, and grinned. "You *will* be on the baggage train," Gatsack said.

# 14

# Death to the Witch-Queen!

LIEUTENANT Zeldones stood in the Lesser Riparian Courtyard, watching his recently assigned command eat breakfast as the sky grew light. There was no sedan chair in sight, a fact which did not bother him unduly. The assorted gentry who rode in them often did not choose to rise this early, so you played the hurry up and wait game. In the distance, there was a sound he hadn't heard before, a chant—yah, yah!—followed by a triple drum beat—bom, bom, *bom*! Then a pause, and then the repetition. Someone out in the city was mobilizing, and it sounded ominous.

Chamberlain Fudjak, looking harried, scurried into the courtyard, scroll cases under his arm.

"Lieutenant, lieutenant . . ." he called, walking over to the tall police officer, "are you the escort for the sedan chair?"

"Yes, sir," replied Zeldones.

"There was supposed to be a whole company! I was *promised* a whole company! Where are they?"

"I was told that this was all that could be spared, sir," replied Lieutenant Zeldones patiently.

"God! What a bloody mess! The sedan chair is leaving from the Greater Riparian Courtyard . . . should have left an *hour* ago . . . follow me, young fellow!" Zeldones signalled his sergeant, who called the two squads to order, and followed the chamberlain into the next courtyard. There was another official by the gateway, throwing three-by-five inch wooden chips onto a brightly burning bonfire. He saw the chamberlain and scurried off.

Inside the courtyard, four bearers stood by the sedan chair, which rested on the unswept snow. An old woman, somebody's nurse, perhaps, was standing beside it with a pot of tea and some small cakes, trying to press them on whoever was inside. She looked upset and was trying not to show it.

"Here we are," muttered Fudjak. "You will be escorting Prince Dervian and Princess Marjia to the Citadel, where the queen expects that they will be safe . . . safer, at any rate, than here." He opened one of the scroll cases and shook out a pass. "This will take you through our lines. Do be careful. And sign here—"

"What for?"

"To acknowledge that you have received custody of the prince and princess. I must have it for my records . . . if anything should go wrong . . . I must have the complete record."

"Just a minute," said Zeldones. He walked over to the sedan chair and drew back the curtain. Inside was a boy dressed in rich clothes hung with golden chains, carrying two artfully sized swords. He might have been twelve or thirteen years of age. With him was a girl, also richly dressed, wearing ropes of pearls and holding a rag doll. She looked to be about eight. Beside her was a carefully folded blanket and a small valise.

"Hello, young lady," said the lieutenant. "Is that your brother over there?" She put her thumb in her mouth and nodded. Zeldones turned to the boy.

"Who are you?" asked the child.

"I am Lieutenant Zeldones, the captain of your escort. If you are Prince Dervian, that is."

"He is the prince," said the old woman. "I was his nurse, and I ought to know, and now the poor lamb is going out into such a sea of troubles as we never saw before, and his father dead and all—"

Zeldones laid a finger gently to her lips. "Hush, mother, let the boy tell me himself."

"I am Prince Dervian," said the boy. "And this is my cry-baby sister. Let us be off."

Zeldones closed the curtain, and signed Fudjak's release chip.

Then he formed up his two squads, one in front of the sedan chair and one behind, and marched out the gate. As he left, the official came out with another basket of wooden chips for the bonfire, the yah, yah! bom, *bom*! sounding louder and closer. Then the outer gate swung open and they marched into the city.

Technically speaking, the Royal Palace was beleaguered rather then besieged. The enemy was not at all gates at all times, and the little party passed through the army checkpoints on Canal Street without meeting any opposition. Without, in fact, meeting anybody. The streets were deserted, and the shop windows shuttered. They marched through the narrow warrens and back alleys and finally took Rubacky Road to one of the lesser bridges across the Asare River.

On the other side of the river, Rubacky Road wound back and around as it ascended the ridge leading to the Citadel. Not far from the crest, they paused to give the bearers a rest, and in the distance, from the direction of the city, sounds of strife and tumult could be heard. At the next intersection they turned left, and in less than a hundred feet came to a low stone wall overlooking Cymdulock. The Royal Palace was clearly visible, and the Canal Street square, which the army was supposed to hold, was full of people. As they watched, the mob pulled down the tall wrought iron fence and poured onto the palace grounds.

"There," said the sergeant, pointing. Zeldones followed his gaze. Along the edge of the square, where the army lines had been, was a line of pikemen wearing black and green. "Tarelians," said someone. "We must have just missed them."

"That yah, yah, bom, bom, bom was them?" asked Zeldones.

"Yeah," the sergeant said. "They do it to psych out the opposition."

After a while, black smoke began to pour from the palace windows, and someone raised Prince Kahun's standard in the main courtyard.

"Some mob," said Lieutenant Zeldones, fingering the medallion with the cut chain in his pocket. As he watched, a little knot of people was dragged out into the square. A great cheer went up from the mob, and one of them, a woman, was set upon and torn to pieces, triggering a frenzied jubilation.

"Let's get out of here," he said at last, and the bearers hoisted the sedan chair and resumed the procession to the Citadel, the mercenaries talking softly about what they had seen.

Taking the alleys and byways to avoid mobs or hostile patrols, they climbed a narrow street with whitewashed stone walls and worn granite steps, coming to a weathered wooden door with a panel broken out.

The point man waved for Zeldones, who came up and took a look. On the other side of the door was a small plaza across the moat from one of the side entrances of the Citadel. The drawbridge was up, and the plaza was lined with soldiers. After a moment, Zeldones was able to make out their device, a golden boar's head on a black field. Kahun's men. The Citadel was under siege.

He turned around and they went back down the stairs to a cul-de-sac off the main alley with tightly shuttered windows and tightly shut doors. They grounded the sedan chair and paused to take stock of their situation.

"Well, then," said the sergeant, "what'll we do now, chief? Call it every man for himself?"

"Not yet," replied the lieutenant. "We're on the right side of the river . . . if we head for Duke Falenda's chateau as a unit, we'll have a decent chance of getting there."

"We'll 'ave an even better chance without no bleedin' officer!" said one of the men in the second squad.

"He's right, you know," said the sergeant. He drew back a step and gestured to the bearers. "That's it for today, boys . . . run along home!" The bearers looked at each other, hesitating for a moment, until one of the mercenaries drew his sword and flourished it; then the four of them ran off.

"Now I like you, lootnant," the sergeant said, "but our ways are parting right here. Why don't you chase after them bearers?"

"I've signed for the prince and princess," said Zeldones, stubbornly, "and I'm not leaving them."

The sergeant looked up at the tall man facing him, weighing the odds. They could take him, but somebody might get seriously hurt in the process.

"Anybody would lock a judge up in his own jail, ain't nobody to mess with," said the sergeant amiably. "But see, the royal palace is burning. Like as not the queen is dead. And we saw the Citadel is under siege. It's like we're enlisted on the wrong side, and we don't know where our next meal is coming from. You understand?''

"Then leave," said Zeldones, resting his hand on his jitte. He had a companion sword thrust into his belt also, but the hooked truncheon was his weapon of choice. One of the men in the second squad drew his sword.

"Hold it," said the sergeant. "You can have the kids. We need a little walking around money, is all . . .''

"The kid's gear is worth a blooming fortune," said the man in the second squad. "We can split it an' go home!'' He took a step forward. "And you ain't stopping us, see?''

"Easy, Bill," the sergeant said. "Him and us don't want the same thing. Talk nice, we can cut a deal.''

"Bill's right," said another mercenary. "Enough of the talk, here. Let's take the loot and get the hell out!''

"You're good, lootnant," said the sergeant, "but there's twenty of us. We can take you. We maybe lose a couple guys doing it, but you're dead. And the kids, too, after that. We'll cut their throats . . . I swear it!''

Bill ran his sword over the top of the mat that concealed the inside of the sedan chair, cutting the fastenings, and it fell to the cobblestones. Inside, Prince Dervian was holding his sister underneath the blanket, trying to comfort her.

"Step back, Bill," said the sergeant firmly. "And put up your steel." Bill stepped back, and sheathed his sword. The sergeant was giving orders.

"Now you throw out the bag, laddie." The sergeant was giving orders to Prince Dervian, too. The first order was easy.

Inside the sedan chair, Prince Dervian picked up the valise and threw it out onto the snow-covered cobblestones.

"Dom, see what's in it." A man from the first squad opened the bag and dumped it on the street. It was old clothes, well worn and mended. As if to be worn in a prison cell or as a disguise. He pawed through them, and kicked them aside.

"Now the two swords." Dervian looked at Zeldones, as if for confirmation of the order. Being a child and a prince, he was quite prepared to die fighting if he was told to do so.

"Give him the swords, Your Highness."

Dervian removed the swords and laid them on the other side of the sedan chair. Dom reached over and picked them up, and snatched off the blanket as well.

"Now *that's* more like it," he said. Dom spread the blanket on the snowy ground, covering the old clothes, and put the valise and the two swords on it.

"Now *you* get out, prince," said the sergeant. "Move!"

Prince Dervian stepped reluctantly out of the sedan chair. Dom and Bill marched him over to the edge of the blanket and held his arms, while two other mercenaries stripped him to the skin, piling his gold chains and rings and tooled leather boots and cut velvet and silk clothes on the blanket. He was silent until the very end, when Dom inserted a finger in his anus to search for hidden treasure, and he cried out.

"That will do," said the sergeant, and pushed the boy over to Zeldones. "Now you, princess."

He beckoned, but the little girl shook her head and wouldn't come, so Bill grabbed her by one arm and dragged her over to the blanket. She was weeping and fussing when they stripped her, but fell grimly silent when first Dom and then a second mercenary checked her body for treasure.

"Let her go, Dolgar," growled the sergeant. Oh hell, he thought, in a minute the stupid jerk is going to drop his pants and the lieutenant is going to kill him. Hell and damnation! What am I going to do?!

"It's not often you get to feel up a genuine princess," said Dolgar, grinning with wet lips. And he kept at it.

Oh God, thought Zeldones resignedly, in a minute the silly son of a bitch is going to drop his pants and I'll have to kill him. He drew his jitte and short sword and stepped forward, jitte held extended, short sword reversed with the blade covering the underside of his forearm. Dolgar was holding the naked princess with one hand and untying the rope that held up his pants with the other.

"Turn her loose or die!" barked Zeldones. The mercenary looked up, startled, immobile. *"Now!"*

Oh shit, thought Dolgar, if I draw my sword my pants will fall down. ''Come an' get me, copper!'' he snarled, but he let her go, and Princess Marjia ran over to her brother.

''That will do, soldier!'' said the sergeant, using the voice of command. ''Fall in!'' Dolgar glowered as he retied his rope, and shuffled back to his squad, cursing under his breath.

Then Dom and Bill folded up the blanket with their treasures and tossed it in the sedan chair. Four mercenaries picked it up, two from each squad.

''There, lootnant,'' said the sergeant cheerfully. ''We got what we want, and the kids ain't hurt a bit. Take care o' yourself.'' He waved, and the mercenaries trotted off with the sedan chair.

When they had rounded the corner, Zeldones walked over to the old clothes lying in the snow, picked them up and brushed them off.

''Here,'' he said, ''it's too cold to stand around bare-ass naked. Put these on and let's get out of here.''

## 15

# The Struggle for Succession

WITHIN a little gaggle of courtiers, staff officers, and body-guards, Prince Kahun walked along the carriageway leading to the Royal Palace, inspecting the heads that lined the low wall of dressed stone. Behind him, Archdeacon Gorabani crossed names from an enemies' list as he spotted one or another of the heads he was looking for.

Kahun paused at the great double doors that had been smashed open by a ram that lay halfway across the threshold.

"A good morning's work," he said. "What do you think?"

"It's too cold for the wax to take a proper impression," replied Gorabani, looking up from his diptych. "You make one scratch and it turns up a little feather, you make two and it chips and splinters."

"No, no," said the prince. "Who are we missing?"

"Duke Falenda, for one."

"He's in the Citadel. We'll have him in good time." Kahun stepped over the log and walked into the grand foyer, now soiled with blood and soot. The great crystal chandelier that had graced the lofty ceiling now lay on floor, smashed and ruined. He kicked one of the cut glass pendants, sending it clattering across the floor.

"Prince Dervian and Princess Marjia, for two more."

"You're sure?"

"They aren't here."

"Pity. When do you think they slipped out?"

"It must have been last night. The only sedan chair that left this morning went through Count Glenclow's men, and that was Gatsack's fencing master . . ." Gorabani hesitated, reaching for the name. "Bralet? Braley."

Outside a rider pulled up his horse and dismounted. After conferring briefly with Kahun's officers, he was escorted into the presence.

"What news, fellow?" asked Kahun.

"Sir, Prince Gatsack left the Czajka Palace with his house guards early this morning. He crossed the Eastbridge about nine, and is now out of the city." Kahun thanked the messenger and dismissed him before turning to one of his generals.

"We have four hundred men holding the Eastbridge Gate!"

"We sent them over immediately after the fall of the palace, Your Majesty," replied the old warrior. "By which time, it was already too late."

"Damn! How could Gatsack have moved so *fast*?" Kahun paced back and forth. His units had moved immediately from the sack of the palace to secure the gates of Cymdulock, at least partly in the hope of trapping his brother.

"Count Braley might not have been in the sedan chair that left this morning," said Gorabani. "Last night, one of our patrols watching for Falenda stopped an unescorted sedan chair and got creamed. One man, but very strong. *That* could have been Count Braley. In which case, Gatsack had timely news of Grathnys'—" the archdeacon hesitated a moment, seeking a euphemism that would not displease Kahun "—departure from this world. At that point he would naturally want to leave Cymdulock, and as soon as possible."

"Damn," muttered Kahun. "The one sedan chair. If not Braley, then *who*?"

"Your infant half brother and half sister, I should imagine," replied Gorabani. "With twenty mercenaries, four bearers, and a junior officer, they won't get very far."

"Could the Witch-Queen have been with them?"

"No, Prince Kahun." Gorabani sniffed; the smell of burnt wood and charred flesh was heavy in the air. "A dozen witnesses saw her die."

"Yes. But her head . . . you'd hardly recognize it as human!"

"Queen Shaia is dead," said Archdeacon Gorabani flatly.

"She and her unholy entourage. And *if* she were alive, which she is not, she'd be betrayed before she could turn around. Put her from your mind. Forget her. Get on with the business of burying your father so you can proceed to your coronation!"

"You're right." Kahun nodded. "Put out a reward for Dervian and his sister. Alive, for the time being. A pity the mob plundered Father's corpse, but we'll give the old man a fine funeral."

"Yes, Prince Kahun. Where did you have in mind?"

"The Cymdulock Cathedral? It's traditional, after all."

"So it is. You walk out the door and look at the Royal Palace. Are you sure that's a good idea?"

"The Royal Palace is a mess," agreed Kahun, walking around the ruined chandelier. "Perhaps if we cut out the three days lying in state?"

"No, no . . ." said Gorabani, "that would look like unseemly haste to ascend the throne. The Gydejii Church is nice, but a little small. What about the Ehudin Church?"

"Big enough," Kahun conceded, "but miles from anywhere." He rubbed his nose. "It might do."

"The Ehudin Church," said the archdeacon, making a note, and blowing a little feather of wax off the tip of his stylus. "I'll see to it. What about Gatsack?"

"First the funeral, then the coronation, then my brother," said Kahun. "And *then* we can start to work on our agenda for Guhland."

"Oh? You'll want to talk to the witchfinder, then."

"Doctor Fadel? What for?"

"He's hellbent to set the witch fires burning. He is, in fact, talking about setting quotas for the counties—so many witches to burn each month."

"So?"

"Don't you want to take care of Gatsack first?"

"First or second, what's the difference?"

Archdeacon Gorabani sighed. "You want to be King of Guhland. At least, that's what you told me. *Don't*, for God's sake, start off your reign by doing small, repeated injuries to your subjects while a rival to your throne is still in the field! Is that so hard to understand?"

Kahun laughed. "Right. You *are* right, old fellow. Of course, we're going to be distributing the witches' property, so we're doing small, repeated benefits . . . to our followers . . . at the same time." He rubbed his nose. "I'll talk to Fadel. I owe him for the riot, but certainly he ought to be able to hold off until after our coronation."

"Splendid. And your brother will have *his* coronation, too. Then what?"

"Then we go out and kill the son of a bitch," said Kahun. "No way is God going to let my gimp brother be Guhland's king."

The freezing rain began late in the afternoon, and Zeldones and the royal waifs took shelter under the arch of a stone bridge. He took three of the faggots Marjia was carrying, and set them together to form a kind of tripod. Underneath, he put some carefully preserved tinder and a few sticks of dry kindling, and struck fire from his flint and steel. The third or fourth attempt, the tinder caught, and the kindling began to burn.

"Won't they see us?" asked Prince Dervian, huddling close to the fire for warmth.

"Who'd be out looking in *this* weather?" asked Zeldones. "And if they see a fire, so what? Vagrants and tramps hang out in these sorts of places." He took the cloth sack that held the coarse ground boiled grain left over from breakfast, and passed it around.

"How can you tell?" asked Princess Marjia, taking a handful.

"What? They do, you know." He looked at the stones of the arch overhead. "Look. They leave messages to each other. The star, there, is for the local sheriff, and the two arrows on each side show that he's really mean—they all point down. Now here's the bridge, and this line is the road north. And the squares—that shows the houses on the road. The first three have jagged lines, like lightning. That means they'll sic the dogs on you. The next one has a crescent, points down. You can get a handout, but they grudge it. Then a couple of dogs, and then a crescent with the points up. The—what is it—the seventh house up the road will give you a handout and not grudge it."

"Let's go there," said Prince Dervian, handing back the sack that now contained very little. "Maybe we can sleep in the barn, too."

"Ah, luxury," Zeldones said, scraping the last of the meal out of the sack. "Not only do you want a free meal, you also want to sleep on dry straw! Some people are just *so-oo* spoiled you wouldn't believe it."

"Don't make fun of my brother," said Marjia. "I think we should go there, too. Sleeping under bridges is no fun."

"When the rain lets up," agreed Zeldones. "Or when our fire burns out. Whichever comes first."

"Why can't we go right now?" whined the boy. "Anything to make crybaby here shut up!"

"Listen to my big, manly brother," said Marjia, who had, in fact, behaved uncommonly well the whole trip. "*He's* the one doing all the complaining!"

I should hit them a few times, thought Zeldones with a flash of irritation, *real* hard! Then he shrugged.

"Hey, hey, prince. Remember the three virtues you need to survive? First, patience. Second, patience. Third—"

"Patience," said the children in unison.

"That's right," he agreed, "and don't you forget it! Now, then. If we wait until suppertime before moving out, we have a better chance of getting fed. Meantime, enjoy the fire while you can."

By the time the fire burned down to gray ashes, the freezing rain had turned to snow flurries as the temperature dropped in the gusting winter wind. The three of them left the meagre shelter of the bridge and started up the road in the last light of day.

The seventh house was a small cottage with a thatched roof and a stable leaning off the farther side. Zeldones knocked at the door, and an old peasant woman opened the door's top half.

"What do you want?" she asked.

"We'd like to sleep in your stable tonight, ma'am," he said.

"We? Who's we?"

"Me and my stepchildren," Zeldones said, using their carefully rehearsed story. "I married a widow with a little money and a couple of kids, and when she died . . ." He shrugged.

"I'm taking them north to live with their aunt." Through the top of the dutch door came the smell of baking bread.

The old woman looked out in the gloom and saw the children standing behind him. "Oh, for goodness sake," she said, opening the lower half of the door, "come on in. You'll freeze out there."

Her name was Guiora, and her husband had died twenty years ago, and her children had all married and gone off and nobody wanted to help her with a little place like this. She had chickens and goats and cats, and some fruit trees, and she rented five acres to the neighbors, but there wasn't enough for her children to live on, and she didn't blame them for leaving a little town like this, and there wasn't enough in the pot to feed all you people.

So Zeldones went out with her to the root cellar behind the stable, a trench about six feet deep, with the excavated dirt piled high on the peaked wooden roof. Inside, the temperature remained at about fifty degrees, winter and summer. He held the lantern for her, while she went down the stairs into the earthy smelling cellar to select various tubers, onions, and assorted vegetables. She took them upstairs into the kitchen, where she refused his offer to help, and peeled them and cut them up and put them into the black iron pot sitting on the blue and white tiled stove.

And while the supper was cooking, he told her about what was happening in the great city of Cymdulock, and although his last news was far from current, it was still exciting and ample repayment for their meal. She remarked on the good manners of the children, and praised his wife for raising them so well. Then she offered them the wooden shelf over the stove to sleep on. Zeldones didn't fit—the shelf was well short of six feet—but he put Marji and Derk on the shelf, and made himself comfortable sitting up against the wall as she went off to her bed in the other room.

At midnight there was a knock on the door. Pounding, rather. Firm, vigorous, repeated. Zeldones awoke and slipped his jitte and short sword into his belt. Guiora got up, slowly, and lit the candle on the kitchen table with a splinter she thrust into the banked coals in the stove.

"I'm coming, I'm coming," she said, and opened the top half of her door. Outside were standing three men, a rather portly sheriff with an expression as if he had bit into a lemon of such surpassing sourness that it had frozen his face. With him were two lean deputies, mercenaries, one with an eye patch, the other with severe acne scars, partially hidden by a patchy beard. The second deputy held a lantern.

The sheriff reached inside and opened the bottom half of the door, while the mercenary with the eye patch held the top half of the door open.

"Widow Guiora," said the sheriff grimly, "you have been accused of witchcraft. You must come with us to Branhamn Jail where our local witchfinder will pass on the truth of the accusation."

"I'm no witch . . ." she said stepping back. The scar-faced mercenary grinned and stepped over the threshold.

"Then you ain't got nawthin' to be 'fraid of," he said. His accent marked him as coming from the south. Around his neck he wore a bronze medallion depicting the right profile of Dr. Fadel.

The other two entered and closed the door, as the old woman retreated toward the kitchen. The deputy hung the lantern on the top door latch, and stuck his thumbs in his belt.

"Now look here, Tom Riphka," the widow told him, "you know good and well I'm not a witch! Get out of my house!"

For all the dyspepsia that was in him, Tom averted his gaze.

"Get dressed, you old bag," said the one-eyed mercenary. "You're going to 'ave a liddle session wid tha witchfinder!"

"Get out! Get out of my house!"

The one-eyed mercenary hit her across the face, knocking her down. "Get dressed, bitch!" he growled.

"What's this," said Zeldones, stepping into the archway between the rooms, "making your arrests at night so you won't disturb the neighbors?"

"Shut up, you son of a bitch!" growled the burly sheriff, then, defensively, "this is no business of yours." Then, as the first touch of doubt began to rise in his mind, "Who are you, anyway?"

"Call me Don," said Zeldones. "Since I accepted the hospitality of this house, abuse of my host makes it my business."

The one-eyed mercenary drew his long sword. "You look lak a vagabond to me, Don . . . if'n that's your *real* name. Ah think we gonna take you in along with the witch heah."

Zeldones drew his jitte in his right hand and his short sword in the left, holding the sword reversed so that it covered his forearm. The scar-faced mercenary drew his sword, stepping up on the right side of his comrade and thrusting at the tall policeman's face, as the other slashed at his knee.

Parrying the thrust at his face with the steel edge along his forearm, Zeldones parried the slash at his leg with the shaft of his jitte. With his sword hand, he made a left cross, flexing his wrist to extend the short sword, which cut across the base of the scar-faced mercenary's throat, severing veins, arteries, and wind-pipe. The one-eyed mercenary made a two-handed cut, hampered by the confined quarters, and Zeldones caught the blade of his sword in the jitte, bending it downward. The mercenary heaved with all his strength, the lieutenant twisted the jitte, and the sword broke. Drawing his short sword, the one-eyed mercenary was hit on the side of the head with the steel-clad truncheon.

He stumbled backwards over the body of his partner, and went down hard. Zeldones took a deep breath and stepped toward Sheriff Tom Riphka who held his trembling sword before him as he sidled backwards. Desperate, the sheriff grabbed Widow Guiora and pressed his sword against her neck.

"Surrender, or I'll cut her throat!" he snarled, "And I really mean it!"

"I believe you." Zeldones nodded, lowering his jitte and taking a long step forward as he swung his sword upwards and out, with a left uppercut. Riphka's right elbow moved as his shoulder muscles drew the sword across Widow Guiora's throat, but his forearm, holding the sword, fell to the floor. The old woman twisted out of his grasp as Zeldones reversed his grip on the sword and cut the sheriff over the heart.

The one-eyed mercenary was sitting up, groping for his sword, when the lieutenant stepped on his hand.

"Mercy, comrade, mercy . . . I yield!" screamed the one-eyed man, and the lieutenant kicked the short sword out of reach.

"Pity," said Zeldones. "Tell me, how long has a little place like Branhamn had its own witchfinder?"

" 'Bout a week, Don," said the mercenary, holding his hand and attempting to smile in an ingratiating manner. "We come up with him from Mewis . . . that's a wee bit south of Cymdulock."

"Mewis. Right. And how many witches does our boy have to burn this month?"

"Four."

Zeldones' eyebrows went up. "A quota?" he said softly. He had guessed, but he hadn't really believed. "What if there aren't four witches in the district?"

"The witchfinder says it's better to burn ten innocents than let ary a guilty one 'scape justice."

"I see. So Widow Guiora here . . . you take her in, and she's guilty. Right?"

"That's for the witchfinder to decide," protested the one-eyed man. "Me, I'm just obeyin' orders."

"Hunh. So you obey dirty orders and stay clean?"

"Don, Don . . . I have to live. Don't you see, I don't have ary a choice!"

"Yeah," growled Zeldones, "but you looked like you were enjoying your work. Come on . . . you got some cleanup to do."

He led the one-eyed mercenary into the root cellar, where the earthen floor was unfrozen, and made him dig a grave for his comrades.

"What are you going to do with me, Don?" the mercenary asked when the second body was dropped into the ground. He must have known, but hope springs eternal.

"My name isn't really Don, it's Zeldones, and I'm a Lieutenant of the Cymdulock Police." The tall man laid his hand on his sword. "I escaped from the Royal Palace with Prince Dervian and Princess Marjia . . . they're asleep in the cottage."

"But why—" began the mercenary as Zeldones cut him down.

The tall policeman wiped off his sword and returned it to his sheath, and then began to shovel the dirt back into the grave.

"Why? I'll tell you why. I couldn't kill you for being a little rat. I couldn't kill you for enjoying your work. I couldn't even kill you for knowing that I killed your buddies, though you could hang me for it. But you had to die." The tall man shrugged and picked up the spade. "So I told you. I just *couldn't* let you go knowing what I'd told you."

After tamping the dirt down, Zeldones unhitched the three horses from the front of the house and led them back to the stable, rubbing down each one in turn, and seeing that they were watered and fed.

When he returned to the cottage, the dawn star had risen a hand's breadth above the eastern horizon, and the old woman had cleaned the blood off the floor.

"Wake up," he said, shaking the children. "We have a long way to go today."

"Do we havta?" asked Prince Dervian, sleepily.

"Yes. However, there are three horses in the stable, so we'll make time, for a change."

Widow Guiora built up the fire, and fixed them a country breakfast, as well as packing them lunch to carry along.

"Do you want to come with us?" he asked, mounting the sheriff's black gelding. "Marji could ride postillion."

"Why would I leave?" she asked with a shake of her head, as she stood in the doorway of her cottage. "Branhamn is my home."

As they rode off on the three horses, the first light of dawn was showing in the sky.

The coronation at the Ehudin Church in Cymdulock was austere as King Kahun, facing the reality of civil war, had the crown set upon his head before his generals and fourteen of the seventeen dukes of Guhland. Missing were Duke Falenda, who had declined the offer of a safe conduct to the ceremonies, and the dukes of Mihaly and Jamreaux who had chosen to attend a rival coronation.

The rival coronation was held on a snowy field, before the walled fortress city of Rosano, a Kahunist stronghold that had never fallen to siege or storm. "Austere" took on new meaning as Gatsack addressed his armies at the beginning of a winter campaign in what the weather wizards promised would be the harshest winter in living memory.

In the privy council chamber, a long, narrow room panelled with carven hardwoods and hung with banners, Kahun, Gorabani, Nasar-Namatu, and the generals Allojhi and Macedak studied the map spread out on the table.

General Allojhi, a smooth, handsome courtier in his late fifties, leaned over and pointed a graceful finger at the map.

"The Pretender's forces have surrounded Rosano, and are at present concentrated there—" his finger traced the river line "—and on the western bank of the Asare River, where our patrols report that they are cutting the ice, which is more than a foot thick, and hauling it away."

"What? My gimp brother is trying to keep us from crossing the river against him, do you think?"

"We have not been able to ascertain the purpose to which the ice will be put," said the saturnine General Macedak. "I believe that we ought to march at once to the relief of Rosano."

"I agree, Your Majesty," said Archdeacon Gorabani. "At present, the Pretender's army is about fifty-five thousand men, including the levies from Jamreaux and Mihaly. Counting the Tarelians—" he glanced at old Nasar-Namatu, who merely nodded "—we could take the field with seventy thousand."

"A winter campaign?" Kahun rubbed his finger against his nose. "I don't like it. I don't like it at all."

"There is no reason to engage in one," said General Allojhi. "Rosano is in no danger of falling." He smiled confidently. "There was a good harvest, much of it brought into the city. The garrison also is well led and up to strength. The city wall I inspected last spring. There are no weaknesses, believe me."

"You think we should let my gimp brother break his teeth on Rosano and come after him in the spring?" asked Kahun.

" 'Break this teeth!' " Allojhi laughed. "That's well put indeed, Your Majesty. Yes, yes, that is exactly what I should suggest."

"I disagree," said Nasar-Namatu. "I am not happy to sit passively while the Pretender lays siege to one of our cities. Suppose he takes it?"

"Then he would have to garrison it, of course," said Allojhi.

"Out of his army, subtract, say, a third—not counting any losses he might suffer in the actual conduct of the siege—and he would face us weaker than ever."

"By that argument, if the Pretender takes enough of our cities we win without fighting," growled Gorabani. "I, for one, do not believe it!"

"General Allojhi is right, though," said Kahun, sitting back in his chair. "Gatsack has made a monumentally dumb move. Whether or not he is able to take Rosano, he loses. And Rosano has *never* been taken!"

# 16

# The Fall of Rosano

OUTSIDE Gatsack's tent lay five pikestaffs with notches cut on them. The notches were lined up under a taut string and the shafts were about six feet apart. A group of officers stood around in the beaten snow, waiting.

"*That's the moat,*" said Count Braley. "That is, that line of pikestaffs *represents* the moat. Each pikestaff is the width of one sled from the next, and each pikestaff is notched to show how high you have to pile the ice on the sleds." He walked to the center of the line, the snow crunching under his boots. "The deepest point, here, is nine feet. We've cut the ice off the moat, and we've cut the ice off the river, and what we haven't used for the glide path should be more than enough for the causeway across the moat. Now the moat is skinning over, but it won't be more than an inch thick when we move out tonight." He picked up the poles one at a time and handed them to the captains standing around him.

"You each have your order, you each have your sled. Load the sled with ice up to the notch on the pole, and be ready to move out by midnight!"

"The causeway is the last step," said King Gatsack. "The siege towers are already built and mounted on sledges. The ice glide path is already built and complete up to the moat and around the base of the wall where we intend to move. Tomorrow's dawn will see us at the walls of Rosano!"

The ice sledges were twenty feet wide, and loaded with rocks for ballast as they were piled with great blocks of ice to the required height. When slid into place, they would form a solid causeway of ice, reaching all the way down to the bottom of the moat. Each layer of ice was tied to the sledge with long strips of cloth, and finally each sledge was slid onto the glide path of ice and eased into the icy waters of the moat. The first sledge went in, and the second sledge went over it, and the third sledge went over the first two, rising about a foot above the surface of the causeway. Blocks of ice were added, and the fourth and fifth sledges were slid into place.

Then, working by torchlight, behind wicker shields to protect them from the archers on the wall, Gatsack's men raised the height of the causeway and brought it level with the glide path at the base of the wall. By dawn, the causeway butted against the wall, and the glide path extended fifty feet on each side of it.

King Gatsack sent out his herald under a flag of truce.

"To the garrison and the city of Rosano, mistakenly loyal to the Pretender Kahun," shouted the herald, "I bring this offer from my master, Gatsack, King of Guhland." When the derisive laughter on the wall died down, he continued. "If you surrender, the garrison may march out with their weapons and banners, and the city itself will be spared sacking." More laughter and jeering from the lofty walls. "Refuse, and we shall offer no quarter!"

After a moment, a powerfully built warrior with a red and white plumed helm came to the wall and motioned for silence.

"Tell your master, the Pretender Gatsack, to . . ." he made several impolite and vulgar suggestions, causing great hilarity on the walls.

"Does this mean that you refuse our terms?" asked the herald.

"Yes!" bellowed the captain of the garrison. "Get you gone, sir herald, your mission is ended!"

The herald ran nimbly back across the causeway, and when he was out of bowshot, King Gatsack raised his hand. When he dropped it, the drums beat the "No Quarter" and the siege towers began to slide easily forward as hundreds of willing hands pushed them and teams of horses, laboring on the tow paths on either side of the ice glide path, pulled mightily. Once over the little rise, the siege towers slid onto the causeway and moved silently toward the wall, crews of men with ropes now pulling to restrain them, as the horses were unhitched. The first two in that silent procession overtopped the towers in Rosano's wall. The first siege tower came to the wall and slid right for fifty feet to come butting up against a round masonry tower; the second slid left. Then came two more towers, lower but fatter, overtopping the wall, arriving in place simultaneously with the first two. The fifth tower reached the wall moments later, not a fighting tower, but the front end of a tall wooden stairway.

Gatsack's army poured over the wall! The garrison, taken by surprise, was destroyed piecemeal as they tried to make a stand. No prisoners were taken, and by sundown Rosano was turned over to rape and pillage. The next day, Gatsack ordered the walls and towers of Rosano pulled down, and the citizens were put to that task.

Four days later, when the walls were breached, the towers burned and tumbled, the great gates smashed and broken, King Gatsack assembled his army and marched on a second Kahunist stronghold, the walled city of Mewis.

Archdeacon Gorabani, wearing his red and black robes and golden chains, trotted down the spiral staircase into the dungeons below. A guard with a lantern preceded him, and another followed him, but the staircase was well lit; at every hook on the dank stone wall a brightly burning lantern hung. A clear indication that His Royal Highness remained down below.

At the foot of the stairs he came to the intersection of three corridors, where a dozen guardsmen stood at ease with their weapons. The guard nearest the stairs checked the archdeacon.

"No passage," he said brusquely. "King's orders."

"I am Archdeacon Gorabani," was the cool reply, "with urgent state business. Let me pass."

"That's Gorabani, all right," said one of the men in the back. "Should we let him through?"

"Urgent state business?" asked the corporal. The archdeacon merely nodded. "Let him pass, then. King's third door on the right."

Gorabani motioned his guards to wait, and strode down the

dank and noisome corridor. A woman screamed, perhaps a witch.

A guard was posted in front of the third door.

"You can't go in, sir," he said. "The king gave specific orders he wasn't to be disturbed."

"I have urgent state business," repeated the archdeacon.

"I'm sorry, sir. My orders was very specific. Nobody is to disburb the king. Just *nobody*."

"Get out of the way, you stupid son of a bitch!" snapped Gorabani.

"No, sir." From behind the door came another scream, ending in a racking cough.

"TREASON!" shouted Gorabani.

"My God, no . . . I'm just doing my duty," protested the guard.

The door opened, and King Kahun stepped out wearing a plain linen smock, freshly spattered with blood.

"Was that you bellowing 'treason', Gorabani?"

"Would I bellow, Your Majesty? We have urgent news. The messenger is waiting in the privy council chamber."

"Huh. Whatever it is can wait till morning. What is it?"

Gorabani stepped forward to whisper in the king's ear and Kahun pushed him away.

"What is it, asshole?"

"Rosano has fallen, Your Majesty. The messenger is upstairs. You might, perhaps, be interested in the details."

"Rosano has *never* fallen!" shouted Kahun.

"Yes, Your Majesty," said Archdeacon Gorabani, stepping back and bowing. "I shall return to the privy council chamber and inform the messenger that he is mistaken."

"Imbecile! Buffoon! Get out of my sight!"

The archdeacon made a deep bow and backed away from the presence down the dungeon corridor. He picked up his guards at the foot of the stairs and returned to the open air above.

Kahun arrived at the privy council chamber half an hour later, having changed into plum colored velvet with a fur lined cape. Archdeacon Gorabani stood up and smiled politely.

"Your Majesty, may I present Captain Boukolkin, of the Rosano garrison." Boukolkin, a small wiry man with battlestained

armor and a bedraggled red and white plume, made a deep bow
to his monarch. A plate with a half-eaten beef sandwich sat on
the council table beside a stein of beer. "He and a few others
fought their way clear when the city fell, and he took it upon
himself to ride day and night to bring you the news."

Kahun nodded. "What news, captain?"

"The city," faltered Boukolkin, "it was taken by storm. The
drums beat 'No Quarter' and the siege towers came sliding down
the ice causeway, right up to the wall. So fast and quiet, men
said it was the Witch-Queen's doing . . ." He shook his head.
"Siege towers . . . they go slow, slow, squealing like pigs. I
said it wasn't the Witch-Queen, but they came on faster than a
man could run, with hardly a sound, and the garrison panicked.
They were coming down one after another, like great trolls sliding over the ice—"

"They crossed the moat?" asked Kahun.

"Yes, sir, one after another—"

"Siege towers are *heavy*," said Kahun. "Push one on the
moat, it would crash through the ice! They could *not* cross the
God damned moat!"

"They built an ice causeway in the night," said the little man,
"and maybe the Witch-Queen did help them, because they
crossed the moat and glided up to the wall, one after the other,
like great fearsome monsters with the morning sun behind them.
We fought them as best we could, but the drums had beat the
'No Quarter,' and then . . . and then . . . Gatsack's men came
pouring over the wall. . . ." He blew his nose.

"We couldn't stop them. I joined some men making a stand
at XII Tower, and we raised our banner. The White Company,
it was . . . our old rivals in the garrison . . ." The corners of
his mouth turned down suddenly. "The Wh-Wh-Wh—" He put
his face in his hands and cried like a child.

"Excuse me, Your Majesty," he said when he recovered.
"The White Company held XII Tower until the Pretender's flag
went up over the citadel. Then they opened a sally port and
charged through the enemy's line . . . which wasn't hard. By
then, most of them were inside. We made it to the edge of the
woods and bivouacked for the night, building fires against the
freezing cold. Many were wounded, few had blankets. We

shared around what food we had, and in the morning, we'd strike out for Mewis, about a day's march to the north . . ." He paused for a moment.

"In the morning, we took one last look at Rosano. All the towers were burning. The citadel too. And men were working on the walls, pulling them down."

"Hunh," grunted Kahun. "Razing the defenses?"

"So your brother won't have to split off a garrison," said Gorabani. "We can have Rosano back anytime we want it, but it won't be much of a stronghold. Go on, Mr. Boukolkin."

"That's about it. We ambushed a couple of Duke Mihaly's scouts and took their horses, and the captain sent me here to bring the news."

There was an urgent knocking at the door. Kahun looked up and glared.

"Enter," he said.

The guard admitted a smoothly groomed General Allojhi and a travel-worn dispatch rider.

"This fellow has news for your ears alone, Your Majesty," said Allojhi. "I told him the hour was late, but he said his message brooked no delay, and I felt it best to bring him to you."

"What news, fellow?" asked Kahun wearily.

"I come from Mewis, Your Majesty," said the messenger. "The Pretender's army has laid siege to it. Count Lastra, the commander of the garrison, fears that if you do not come to relieve the siege . . ." he hesitated.

"What does he fear?" asked Gorabani.

"He fears that his men will accept terms. Survivors of the Rosano garrison arrived a few days before the Pretender."

"Do you wish to question these men further?" asked the archdeacon. Kahun shook his head. "Guard," said Gorabani, "see that these two men are fed and quartered."

"What now, Your Majesty?" asked Allojhi. Kahun sat with his elbows on the conference table, cracking his knuckles.

"I would suggest that we relieve the siege of Mewis," prompted the archdeacon.

"What, has the Pretender given up on Rosano, then?" asked the general.

"Weren't you listening, General Allojhi?" asked Gorabani sourly. "Rosano has fallen, and the Pretender, deciding that he didn't wish to garrison it, has razed the walls."

"Is this true, Your Majesty?" asked Allojhi with a note of sincere concern in his voice. Kahun cracked his knuckles and said nothing.

"It is true," said Gorabani. "I fear that we shall have a winter war whether his majesty likes it or not."

"That is for the king to decide!" snapped Allojhi, who didn't much relish a winter campaign himself. The woolen underwear made him look bulky and fat.

"Yes, general," agreed the archdeacon patiently. "A winter war is unpleasant. It would have been less unpleasant, however, than losing Rosano. And to lose Mewis on top of losing Rosano would be intolerable."

"Mewis isn't all *that* important," protested the general.

"No," agreed Gorabani, "but how many dukes do you think would defect to the Pretender if we just sit around in Cymdulock, keeping warm by burning witches?"

"Demcio, perhaps," said Kahun, looking up. "And maybe not him. But then . . . *then* if we do not go out to fight Gatsack, they'll *all* go over. The treacherous sons of bitches. And if we fight—*when* we fight—we'd better not lose, not so much as the opening skirmish."

"Do we relieve Mewis, Your Majesty?"

"It would mean fighting a winter war," replied Kahun. "What would you advise, general?"

There is nothing a courtier hates worse than being asked to choose the lesser of two evils. Nevertheless, Allojhi was as quick as he was smooth, and *he* remembered that his advice not to relieve Rosano had turned out badly. There were worse things than a winter campaign and being hung was one of them.

"Mewis is not important, Your Majesty. We should go out with the intent of destroying the Pretender's army." Gorabani stood behind him, miming applause. "Mewis, however, is where we shall find it." Allojhi struck a modestly heroic pose. "We should march, Your Majesty, to victory!"

"Then make ready. We should have left yesterday."

General Allojhi saluted crisply, and left to wake General Macedak who would take care of the details.

"The Witch-Queen," said Kahun. "That fellow said she spread panic among the garrison."

"What?" Gorabani looked up, startled. "At Rosano? Shaia is dead. Forget her."

"Then her ghost was at Rosano," Kahun muttered. "That's even worse."

"Gatsack was at Rosano," said the archdeacon, "with some crackerjack engineers. You want to worry, worry about your gimp brother!"

# 17

# The Witchfinder
# of Autmerida

THE weekly water wagon pulled out of Zenburg hours before dawn, a routine mission delivering water to the bivouac at the top of Merida Gap, otherwise Camp Merida, and relieving the half squad that was stationed there. Today, Janko Jankura and Nick Sejenics also rode on the wagon, and Lasco Genzari and Dr. Wizenbeak rode beside it, the one on a white stallion, the other on a gray mule.

The wizard wore a hooded horse blanket, natural wool with a green dyed stripe, the ruana of the altiplano. Under the horse blanket, and under his beard, was a fur muff suspended by a cord from around his neck. Inside the muff, Gruchka, who didn't like the cold at all, was curled up asleep.

The bivouac at the top of Merida Gap had started out as a few tents, with a corral and a haystack. It had turned out to be convenient for dealing with the village of Autmerida, so that in the natural course of events the tents were replaced by adobe barracks, and the haystack was replaced with an adobe barn. Lacking a well, the local aquifers being hundreds of feet deep, water was carted in on a regular basis. A temporary solution for a temporary facility. In addition to the regular barn and barracks, there was also a transient barracks, where applicants for land out in the Semeryan could wait until Wizenbeak interviewed them, and where mercenaries seeking employment could wait until Genzari decided hire or no hire.

They reached Camp Merida at sunset, and as the men went to unload the barrels of water from the wagon, Wizenbeak and

Genzari rode to the edge of the bluff overlooking the rolling hills around Autmerida far below. The sky was a luminous green, streaked with brilliant golden clouds on the horizon, and red and purple clouds high above. The shadows were pouring over the ground below, isolating the hilltops as little islands of light in a sea of rising darkness.

"That's really beautiful," said Wizenbeak, "so calm, so peaceful. I love this vista."

"Me too," Genzari replied. "High ground is very soothing to the nerves."

"You have the soul of a strategist," said the wizard. "When we saw the dragon, you were asking if it could spy out enemy troop concentrations. Where's your sense of wonder?"

"In the morning," said Genzari, "when I'm shaving, I look at myself in the mirror, and think about the various fights, duels, skirmishes and battles I've been in. Then I wonder why I'm still alive."

"And your conclusion?"

"Why, that I don't have any better way of making a living, Doctor Wizenbeak. I wonder about other things, too."

"Such as?" prompted the wizard.

"Such as how much longer we're going to be able to draw on the royal line of credit," replied Genzari. "Last week there were reports that the witchfinder was preparing to challenge the Witch-Queen to a duel to the death. The witchfinder is the sentimental favorite, but the betting was six to five on Shaia. Comes the revolution, how are we going to pay our bills?"

"Ahh . . ." sighed Wizenbeak, exhaling a cloud of white vapor. "Some things it doesn't pay to worry about until they happen. If you had worried about all your battles and duels and so forth when you were a youth, you might today be a farmer. Perhaps a farmer in this very village. In which case, you could worry about being paid. Which worry would you prefer?"

"I'm going down to buy pickled beef, and cobgrain for the horses, and flour," said Genzari. "What if the man wants cash?"

"I'll have a talk with him, of course." Wizenbeak rubbed his long nose. "Don't worry about it."

"Right." Genzari wheeled his horse around. "You think something will turn up?"

"If it doesn't," said the wizard, "I'll *make* it turn up."

They stabled their horses in the barn and walked slowly into the whitewashed adobe mess hall.

Mrs. Fajon, the cook, was a large plump woman whose husband worked in the barn. "Mr. Boukhaf's here to see you, Doctor Wizenbeak," she said. "You want supper first?"

"No," said the wizard, "send him in. I can eat and listen at the same time."

"Should I set a place for him, too?"

"Of course," replied Wizenbeak. "Otherwise I might feel obliged to feed him off my own plate."

The visitor who was brought in was Guilly Boukhaf, a small, balding fellow from Autmerida, where he worked in his brother-in-law's glazing shop. Wizenbeak had dealt with him a few times buying mother-of-glass. Mrs. Fajon sat him across the table from the wizard, and served him flatbread, pickles, and two kinds of cheese. Wizenbeak had three kinds of cheese, and beer as well.

"So what can I do for you?" asked the wizard after the plates were reasonably clear.

"My old aunt—Miz Amy," said Boukhaf, "she kept the troll-bats in the shop, you know, and talked to them like they were people. She liked you." He reached into the pouch on his smock and took out a troll-bat kitten. "She wanted you to have this; she said you were looking for a—a—I forget what she called it, but she said this was what you wanted."

Inside the muff, under the wizard's beard, Gruchka stirred. Wizenbeak could feel the sudden surge of tension pass through him as Gruchka detected the presence of a possible rival.

"Come here, Janko," said the wizard. "This is what we were coming into Autmerida for." Jankura's face lit up when she saw the little animal.

"Isn't it *adorable!*" She sat down and laid her arm out on the table, hand near the candle, and began talking very softly to the little troll-bat. After a while the troll-bat got up and very casually strolled over to Jankura's hand, and sat down on the back of it. Slowly, slowly, she raised her hand and brought the tiny animal to her breast. Gruchka put his head back inside the muff, and

Wizenbeak could feel the tension drain out of him as his familiar went back to sleep.

"You're very good with animals, young fellow," said Boukhaf. "Most people are afraid of troll-bats, and with good reason, too, I'd say. The ones making the mother-of-glass have pretty nasty dispositions. And vicey-versey, too, of course. I've never seen a kitten take to anyone like that."

"How much do we owe Miz Amy for the little darling?" asked Janko.

"Nothing," was the reply. "She said you should have it."

"You didn't have to come *here*," said Wizenbeak. "We would have come down there . . . and by the way, how *is* Miz Amy?"

There was a long pause. "She's dead," said Boukhaf at last. "We have a witchfinder in Autmerida now, and someone told him about Miz Amy talking to the troll-bats . . . so they took her in, that would have been a Sunday . . . and they burned her on Volsday."

"I'm sorry to hear it."

"You have no idea the trouble it caused . . . the troll-bats were very upset, and everybody was afraid to soothe them. We'll likely have to go out of business if things don't settle down." He hesitated for a moment. "She was my mother's oldest sister, Miz Amy, and she went to church every sabbath . . . every Volsday."

"Ah," said Wizenbeak. The Orthodox sabbath fell on Volsday, the Syncretist sabbath fell the day before, on Sunsday. "Perhaps we ought to pay Autmerida's witchfinder a courtesy call." He ate the last slice of pickle reflectively. "I'll talk to Mr. Genzari about it."


Autmerida was built around the intersection of Military Road, which ran due north and south to the foot of Merida Gap, and Cobblewash Road, which meandered alongside a shallow stream bed, filled with cobbles and large pebbles. A block south of the intersection, was First Street, a block south of that was Second Street, and a block *north* of the intersection was Third Street, a later development, dating from the golden age of Mambrino.

The Autmerida city hall, the mayor's palace, the jail, and the

Mercenaries Hall were on Military Road. The Syncretist church complex, including tithe barns, two monasteries, a convent, and the deacon's house, occupied Cobblewash Road and Third Street.

South of the masonry bridge where Military Road crossed the Cobble Wash, was the older section of Autmerida. The mills, dependent on the fall of water to turn their grindstones, had never moved, nor the grain elevators. An Orthodox church, downgraded to a school was on First Street, off Cobblewash Road. A second Orthodox church had been converted to a brewery.

Dassenji and Sons, Glaziers, was on the far side of the Cobble Wash, south of Second Street. A wooden footbridge gave access into the town. Wizenbeak paused for a moment, watching the vertical waterwheel slowly turning in the frigid morning air.

"That's the glazier's place," he said. "I don't know how long I'll be in there, and it's too cold to just stand around."

"Don't worry about it," said Genzari. "I'll post the squad on the sunny side of the street."

"You think that will be warm enough?"

"Of course, sir. It's sheltered from the wind, and we aren't going to be gone *that* long."

"You have business too?" asked the wizard.

"Just up the street," said Genzari. "The mill for flour, the warehouse for cobgrain. I'll pick up the pickled beef on the way out of town." The wizard nodded, and his strategist posted the squad of men to watch up and down Cobblewash Road, and along Second Street.

"They see anything," Genzari said, "they'll send a runner in to you, and a runner to get me." He smiled faintly and fingered his closely clipped mustache. "Not that I expect any trouble, but it'll keep them awake, right?"

Wizenbeak nodded, and went over to the glazier's shop. The door was locked with a sign that said: CLOSED DUE TO DEATH IN THE FAMILY. He knocked, and knocked again.

Finally a stoop-shouldered man with a gray beard and a black skullcap came down to the door.

"Go away," he said, "we are not open for business."

"Open the door, Mr. Dassenji," said the wizard. "I want to talk to you." The old man peered through the glass.

"Oh, it's you, Doctor Wizenbeak." He unbolted the door and let the three of them in. "You heard about Miz Amy?"

"Yes, Mr. Boukhaf went up the hill to let me know. That was very kind of him to take the trouble."

Dassenji nodded. "He's afraid, and I don't blame him. Do you know how much the fine we had to pay for—for keeping a witch on the premises was? That much cash we don't have, and they wouldn't take mother-of-glass. Look, don't just stand there . . . come on in back." He raised his voice. "Marji, Doctor Wizenbeak is here, with a couple of friends. Come down and make some coffee for us, would you be so kind."

They wound up seated in the red and white painted kitchen at the meticulously scrubbed table, as Mrs. Dassenji ground the coffee beans and spooned sugar into the little copper brewer, and then added water and put the brewer on the stove, to which she added a fresh stick of kindling. Presently the pot of coffee began to pop and crackle, and she removed it and poured it into tiny cups.

"What I had in mind," said Wizenbeak, taking a sip of the sweet and potent drink, "was to offer you the possibility of moving to Zenburg. The farming looks promising at this point, and we'll need glass to build houses for the new people coming in. Would you be interested?"

"That's really very kind of you, doctor," said the old man, "and I only wish that some of our neighbors would take as much interest, but Autmerida is our home. My grandfather's grandfather built this mill, and we have always been glaziers here. This trouble will blow over, just as the trouble in Mambrino's time did."

"I'm glad you think so," said Wizenbeak. "However, I'm concerned with the development of the Semeryan, and perhaps one of your sons, or even Mr. Boukhaf might be interested. Is there any reason why we couldn't make mother-of-glass on the altiplano?"

"Well, for one thing, you have no power," said Dassenji. "The troll-bats don't do it all themselves, they tap onto the shaft power from the waterwheel. They need the power to make the ingredients combine properly."

"We don't have falling water," agreed the wizard, "but we could build windmills. The winds are strong and persistent, and we could tap *them* for power." He reached inside the muff and petted Gruchka's ears. "My little baby. Do you have a piece of fruit for Gruchka?"

Mrs. Dassenji giggled, and returned with a small handful of dried fruit on a platter. "We should keep forty or fifty troll-bats and not have a little fruit on hand?" She sighed. "If the witchfinder has his way, we won't be able to afford fruit, not even this little."

"A pity," said Mr. Dassenji, bowing his head. "The fine he levied for burning poor Miz Amy. Ai."

"A real pity," agreed Wizenbeak, handing Gruchka one piece of fruit, and taking a second for himself. "But if we build a windmill, as I'm sure we could, would you have any problems about coming up to the antiplano to be with the troll-bats?"

"Well, maybe . . . maybe not," replied Dassenji. "I take care of my troll-bats, and they give me my livelihood. Anywhere they thrive, I thrive. You'd have to keep them warm."

"We have to keep them warm here, too," said Mrs. Dassenji. "And didn't you once tell me that troll-bats originally came from the altiplano, that they were bred to keep dragons aloft during the Dragon-Human wars?"

"Something to that effect," her husband conceded, "but Doctor Wizenbeak here is a loremaster, he knows the old tales about how men and dragons both came from the stars to win this most beautiful of worlds."

"The wars I know," said Wizenbeak, offering Gruchka a second piece of fruit, "but there are many, many tales relating the origin of troll-bats." When the little animal declined, he ate the fruit himself. "In any event, everything you need for mother-of-glass we can get in the altiplano. You'd just be moving closer to the mines, is all."

"Everything except the alcohol," conceded Dassenji.

"So you'd have something to trade for," said the wizard. "An excuse to go into town, right?"

"The alcohol we could reuse," said Mrs. Dassenji. "Get

some cobgrain good and dry, and it will pull the water right out of the vapors of the spent liquor.''

"Drying the cobgrain would be no problem," said her husband, "not on the altiplano, but could you grow cobgrain up there?"

"Maybe not a lot," the wizard said, thinking of the problems of irrigation, "but some."

"Yes, yes," said Dassenji, "if you have some, you can redry it and redry it, and use it over and over. No reason you couldn't set up a little shop, if you could find someone to handle your troll-bats. That fool Boukhaf! They were so upset when Miz Amy died you couldn't imagine, and he wouldn't go in to calm them down. I and Mama went in to them, and they were jumping around and crying, and making such a fuss—"

There was a sharp knock at the door. Sejenics went, and came back at once.

"The sheriff is coming with a force of twenty men," he said. "Plus there is a sedan chair as well. Some official, perhaps."

"The witchfinder!" said Mrs. Dassenji, putting her hands to her mouth.

Up the street, at the elevator, Lasco Genzari plunged a wooden handled grain-thief into a bin of cobgrain and withdrew it, dumping the grain into a wicker basket over a porcelain bowl. He put a cover on the basket, and shook the grain vigorously for a few moments. Then he removed the basket and inspected the bowl.

"Rat turds, rat hairs, weevils, miscellaneous dirt . . ." He looked up with bemused scepticism. "This is really your top number one cobgrain?"

"That bowl is hardly dirty at all!" protested the merchant indignantly. "Scrape it all together, it wouldn't cover a single silver denny!" He reached into his pocket and produced one of the tiny coins, setting it on the counter. Genzari picked up a horn spatula and began scraping the crud out of the bowl and onto the coin.

A runner came racing up. "Excuse me, sir," he said breathlessly. "The sheriff and an official in a black sedan chair are coming down Cobblewash Road. They have twenty men with them. Corporal sent me to tell you at once!"

Genzari nodded, and finished scraping the bowl onto the coin. The dirt covered the coin completely, and spilled over the edges.

"Number three, possibly four," he said. "Don't you agree?" The merchant looked at test results and shook his head.

"Number two," he said.

"Same terms as before?" asked the strategist.

"For number two. For number three, pay cash."

Genzari glanced at the messenger. "Twenty mercenaries?"

"Yes, sir. Plus the sheriff on his horse, and the official in the sedan chair."

"I see." He looked at the merchant. "I have pressing business. Number two, on terms, one hundred bushels. I'll bring the wagon around."

"Done," said the merchant, writing it down on his slate. Genzari made a note in his diptych, and shook on the deal.

"Excuse me, please," said Genzari. "I'll be back." He walked swiftly out the door, and turned down Cobblewash Road to where he had posted his squad.

The sedan chair and the sheriff's horse were in front of the glazier's shop. As he walked, he tried to count the number of men confronting his squad in the street. Eighteen, plus a sergeant, so that one or two had gone into the glaziers with the officials.

He slowed his pace a little to bring the runner abreast with him, the packed snow creaking under foot in the bright, cold morning sun. The sergeant, who was walking back and forth bullyragging the Wizenbeak men, seemed very familiar. At ten paces distance Genzari recognized him, and stopped.

"Good morning, Riffscut."

There was a heeltap of silence, and Sergeant Riffscut turned. He was about the same height as Genzari but heavier in build and less calm in disposition. His face was florid, his eyebrows and mustache thick and black, theatrically fierce.

"You, Lasco?" he said, and drew his long sword. There was a sudden flash of steel in the morning sunlight as everybody on both sides drew steel.

"Yes, Lasco Genzari at your service at last." Genzari smiled with genuine enthusiasm. "Since our duel does not concern our present employers, may I suggest that your men and mine sheathe their swords?'' His hand rested on his own long sword, which remained in its sheath. "Your employer could not be pleased to walk out onto the street to find even a few dead bodies."

"True," said Riffscut. "Put up your swords, men." His mercenaries stepped backwards, sheathing their swords. Genzari nodded and his squad did the same. Then Riffscut took a two-handed grip on his sword, holding it in front of him, the point level with his eye and slightly to the right. Genzari drew, also taking a two-handed grip, but holding his sword drawn back to the right, the hilt alongside his ear. Genzari stood perfectly still, watching the whole body and sword of his opponent. Sergeant Riffscut advanced with little dancing steps, his feet floating lightly over the packed snow.

At a distance of about three paces he stopped advancing and began to circle, darting his sword forwards and backwards in little feinting maneuvers designed to confuse and frighten the enemy.

Genzari simply turned to face him, sword poised and ready.

Neither man said a word. Riffscut continued to circle slowly to the left, feinting thrusts at Genzari's face. Genzari continued to turn. The mercenaries on both sides watched the duel with total fascination.

Suddenly Sergeant Riffscut gave a fierce cry and leaped forward to attack in earnest!

Inside the glazier's shop, Janko admitted Benzho, Sheriff of Autmerida, an official with the silver medallion, and two mercenaries wearing the bronze medallions of Dr. Fadel. The sheriff and the mercenaries looked dour to bored, men doing a job that had to be done. The witchfinder looked alive, excited, even exalted, a man doing the will of God.

"Good morning, Sheriff Benzho," said the wizard affably, "and who might this gentleman with you be?"

"Hunh. This is Witchfinder Wrascha. Witchfinder, this is Doctor Wizenbeak, heading up the settlement thing in the Semeryan."

"We have heard of the good doctor," said Wrascha, "but today our business is not with him. Mr. Dassenji, have you the money to pay your fine?"

"Ai! No, no I don't, your honor . . . the banks wouldn't loan

me the money, but I have friends yet . . . if you'll give me a
little more time.''

''That is out of the question,'' said the witchfinder. ''We have
received only last night the most serious accusations against
Mrs. Dassenji. Had you the money ready, I might have disre-
garded them—''

''Ai! Ai! Ai! I don't have the money, I swear it!''

''How unfortunate,'' said Wrascha pleasantly, folding his
black gloved hands over his ample middle. ''Sheriff, there is the
lady in question. Arrest her!''

Mrs. Dassenji took a deep breath and covered her face with
her hands.

''You don't have jurisdiction,'' said Wizenbeak.

''What?'' said the sheriff.

''You don't have jurisdiction,'' repeated the wizard. ''I have
asked Mr. Dassenji to come to Zenburg and set up shop there.
He has agreed in principal to do so. Therefore, he is a subject
of the Village of Zenburg and not of the Village of Autmerida.
Unless, of course, he decides he doesn't wish to leave Autmerida.''

For a moment there was total silence. Then, from the street
outside there was a fierce warcry.

Riffscut lunged and Genzari cut, as Riffscut's sword missed
its intended target by a hair's breadth. Cut to the heart, Sergeant
Riffscut sank slowly to his knees and fell on his side, the spurt
of blood from the aorta staining the white snow for more than
six feet. Genzari bent over and wiped his sword on the hem of
the sergeant's cape as the sheriff and the witchfinder emerged
from the door of the glazier's shop, with Wizenbeak close behind them.

''What happened?'' asked the wizard.

''I just settled an old unfinished duel,'' said Genzari, replacing the sword in its sheath. ''Any number of witnesses will
testify that it was a fair fight.'' He smiled and bowed. ''Now if
you will excuse me, I have to arrange to pick up some cobgrain.''

''Go ahead,'' said Wizenbeak.

''Aren't you going to arrest that man?'' asked the witchfinder.
''He just killed an officer of the court!''

''It was a fair fight,'' said the sheriff, ''a duel.''

"You have twenty men, sheriff! Arrest him!"

"I wouldn't if I were you," said Wizenbeak.

"Do your duty!" thundered the witchfinder.

"Take him in, boys," said the sheriff. Once again there was a flash of steel in the street, but nobody moved. Sergeant Riffscut had been by far the strongest swordsman of his group, and nobody was keen to engage his conqueror.

Inside the house Mrs. Dassenji screamed. One of the witchfinder's mercenaries lay dead on the floor, the second stumbled toward the door, and fell into the witchfinder's arms. Neither one of them had drawn steel when Sejenics cut them down.

Sejenics walked toward Witchfinder Wrascha, sword in hand. His sword had a faint pinkish film on it, which he would wipe off at the earliest possible moment.

"Witches!" squeaked the witchfinder, letting his dead mercenary slide to the floor. "I'm surrounded by witches!" He rolled his eyes up into his head and fainted dead away.

"Dear me," said Wizenbeak mildly, "witches seem to be everywhere. Sheriff, you don't really want to arrest Mr. Genzari for duelling, do you?"

Sheriff Benzho looked at Sejenics patiently, waiting to be done using his sword so he could wipe it and put it away.

"Ah . . . no."

"Tell your mercenaries, then," said the wizard.

"Put up your swords, you men," shouted the sheriff. On the street, the tension dissolved. In the house, Sejenics wiped his sword on a piece of silk and sheathed it.

"Well done, sheriff," Wizenbeak remarked. Then, turning to Mr. Dassenji, "Have you decided whether you'll come to Zenburg?"

"Ah, why, uh—uh . . . Autmerida is my home," began the old man, but he put his arm around Mrs. Dassenji. "Uh, ah . . . we'll be up as soon as we can arrange transportation for our goods. Maybe three or four days."

"Splendid," said Wizenbeak approvingly. "Sheriff, I wonder if we could borrow the witchfinder to purge Zenburg of any witches that might have infiltrated our little settlement?"

"It's fine with me," replied Sheriff Benzho. "The witchfinder can go wherever the hell he wants."

"Good, good." The wizard smiled. "Mr. Sejenics, you and
Janko load the witchfinder on one of our wagons. Make him
comfortable. Keep him snug and warm. Stay with him to be sure
he wants for nothing. When he wakes up, I want you to apologize for killing those two men of his. You understand?"

"Yes, sir."

"*Sincere* apologies, Mr. Sejenics. I know he started it, but
don't rub it in." He turned to the Dassenjis. "I hope we'll see
you in Zenberg very shortly." He turned to the sheriff. "We
*will* take good care of Mr. Wrascha, here. I *do* hope his absence
won't inconvenience you."

# 18

# Mewis Field

MEWIS Field, Volsday, 9 Hoarst 33. Late in the afternoon, King Kahun's army of sixty-three thousand men took up a position on a low ridge, overlooking the city of Mewis, and raised a great bonfire to signal their presence. Around the walls of Mewis, King Gatsack's army of forty-nine thousand saw that fire, and knew that siege operations were at an end.

"Look at 'em," said General Macedak. "They're spread all around the city! Give the order; we can take 'em before dark, Your Majesty!"

"I don't know," muttered Kahun, wrapping his ermine lined robe of royal purple about his shoulders. "The day is almost done, and we aren't in the order of battle."

"Strike while the iron is hot, Your Majesty," said Macedak. "Don't worry about *our* order of battle! Think of the trouble *Gatsack* will have getting lined up!"

"His Majesty is right," said General Allojhi smoothly. "With less than two hours of daylight remaining, we'd hardly have time to strike a decisive blow."

"Give the order to attack, Your Majesty!" urged Archdeacon Nasar-Namatu. "See how they move . . . Gatsack is coming swiftly to the support of Duke Mihaly, who has turned to face us, but Duke Jamreaux remains on the far side of the city. Strike now, the shifty son of a bitch will change sides!"

"If he'll change sides now, he'll change sides tomorrow," Kahun replied. "No. Make camp on the ridge, here. Tarelians on the right, by that piney wood. General Allojhi here with my personal regiments and the baggage train. General Macedak down the hill to the stone farmhouse, over on the left. We'll advance in that order at dawn.''

"You're throwing away a chance for an easy victory," said Nasar-Namatu, grimly. "We'd taken Gatsack by surprise. We could have had him.''

"I don't agree," said General Allojhi. "We would have had an indecisive fight which darkness would quickly end. In the morning we will crush him!''

From before the walls of Mewis, King Gatsack looked up.

"My brother appears to be making camp," he said, knocking crusted snow from his boot with his scabbarded sword. "What a pity.''

"Just as well," said Count Braley. "Granted he showed up where you said he would, but to engage their whole force while Jamreaux came around the city and took them in the rear would have been pretty damned risky.''

"Not if Kahun had bit . . .'' Gatsack grinned and shrugged. "He'd have come down the hill pell-mell, everybody charging that little redoubt on the east, and Jamreaux would have brought his cavalry west on that path of beaten snow . . . talk about panic! You know that my brother is prone to panic, don't you?''

"You've told me several times, Your Majesty.''

"So I have.'' Gatsack walked over to the campfire and warmed his hands. "Well. Here's Duke Mihaly. When Duke Jamreaux arrives, we'll arrange our order of battle for tomorrow.''

"What about the garrison?" asked Mihaly.

"They won't come out. Tonight we'll pile the cut ice for the causeway in front of the gates and pour water on it," said Braley.

Gatsack grinned. "Another couple of days, we'd have had them. Those poor slobs were sitting in there, working themselves up to surrender when we offered terms. They've got no heart to fight, so with any sort of an excuse, they won't. Ice up the gates, that's all they need.''

Mewis Field. Sunday, 10 Hoarst 33. Sunrise was marked by lurid crimson and scarlet clouds moving in ordered rows from the northeast.

In the center, General Allojhi faced Gatsack, as Kahun stood behind him with the strategic reserves. On Kahun's right, Archdeacon Nasar-Namatu led his Tarelian Order against the pikemen and archers of Duke Mihaly. On Gatsack's right, Duke Jamreaux stood with light and heavy cavalry against General Macedak's collection of assorted mercenaries. Battle was engaged before the red orb of the sun was fully clear of the horizon.

By nine, the wind was blowing from the northeast at twenty knots, and the clouds were thickening. By ten, a fierce snowstorm was raging, as both sides fought with the utmost tenacity. At eleven, Kahun, guided by the sound of the battle, committed his reserves to the fight, because he could no longer see what was happening a hundred yards away.

The battle continued for nearly ten hours, surging back and forth, until the Tarelians broke Mihaly's line of pike, and Gatsack's army began to fall back, under heavy pressure. The intended line of retreat was toward Mewisford Bridge, but in the storm they missed it by a quarter mile and tried to cross the Osino River, where they had cut the ice to lay siege to Mewis.

Count Braley stood in the blizzard, at the extreme right of Gatsack's center, where he had been sent to maintain contact with Duke Jamreaux, wondering where in hell Jamreaux had got to. On his left he heard a "bom, bom, yah, yah, yah! bom, bom, yah, yah, yah!"

"Coming closer, sounds like," grunted one of his captains.

"Right," Braley agreed. "Swing the goddamned line around to face left. We're going to make a stand!" His captain shouted orders, and the left wing of Braley's command, which was not engaged, fell back to form an angle, with Count Braley standing just behind the apex. To his right, his men were skirmishing with General Macedak's mercenaries, as Macedak pressed his attack against the area Duke Jamreaux was supposed to be holding.

A warrior came stumbling through the snow storm, one of Gatsack's Elite Guards.

"Hold up there, fellow," shouted Braley. The man turned toward him, mouth open, eyes unseeing. "What's happening?"

"Tarelians," was the halting reply. "They're rolling up the center. Listen."

From the left came the drumbeats and chanting, "Bom! Bom!
Yah! Yah! YAH! Bom! Bom! Yah! Yah! YAH!" and then another Elite Guardsman, weapons gone, running for his life.

"Goddamnit, raise a shout!" yelled Count Braley. "GAT-
SACK!" he thundered, and his men picked it up. To their left
front they were answered by scattered cries of "Gatsack!" but
they were drowned out by the "BOM! BOM! YAH! YAH!
YAH!" of the advancing Tarelians. Some of the retreating warriors made a stand with Braley's line, but most simply ran on
past.

Then the Tarelians hit them. The left half of Braley's line
buckled and went down.

A hooded figure with a spear emerged from the snowstorm
and yelled "Kahun!" Braley parried the spear thrust and cut
him down. Two more appeared, one thrusting at Braley's face,
the other swinging his spear low in a cut at the legs. Braley
leaped over the one spear as he dodged the other, closed with
the thrusting Tarelian and cut him diagonally across the abdo-
men with a two-handed stroke. The second man swung his spear
again, checked, and lunged in a vicious one-handed thrust.
Braley pivoted to let the spear slide past him and stepped forward, lunging in turn with his long sword. His man dropped the
spear and stepped backwards, clutching his chest with both
hands.

Count Braley took a deep breath and looked around. Nothing
but blowing snow and dead bodies. The Tarelian drumming and
chanting now appeared to be coming from his right. His left
wing was broken, his right wing seemed not to be there anymore.

"Well," he said, to no one in particular, "I guess I'd better
rejoin the battle, if I can find it." He turned and marched toward
what had been his rear earlier in the day, arriving eventually at
the Osino River. The river was choked with the bodies of men
and horses, and Count Braley made his way across on the bodies
of his comrades in arms. They slipped and shifted as he put his
weight upon them, and more than once he plunged into the icy
waters of the Osino as he made his way back. He emerged on
the other side, scrambled up the icy riverbank to stand knee deep
in drifted snow, soaked to the armpits in ice water, teeth chat-

tering, facing death by exposure if he couldn't find fire or shelter.

Looking around, he saw a dim light, possibly the reflection of a fire. Shivering and shaking, he made his way toward it with grim determination. As he drew closer, he saw the light was reflected off the trunk of a tree, probably from a bonfire in the shelter of a hedgerow.

A voice asked: "Do you want to go again?"

"No," was the reply, "I'm finished, sergeant."

"Good. When Bill's done, we'll hang the whore and move on."

"Do we have to kill her?" asked a third voice.

"Yeah, Noll," said the sergeant. "Orders. All the camp followers get it." Count Braley reached the corner of the hedgerow and peered around.

Beside a small bonfire, three soldiers watched their comrade topping a woman lying on her clothes in the snow. By the green nabla on their black capes, they were Tarelians. One of them, the sergeant, by the remains of the plume on his helmet, was fashioning a noose out of a hempen rope.

"But this one was a noblewoman," said Noll. "Look at all the shit we took off her."

"Then she was in bad company," said the sergeant.

The count clenched his jaw to keep his teeth from chattering, took a firm grip on his sword with numb hands, and stepped around the corner, cutting down Noll with one stroke and Bill with the second. The sergeant, a stocky, thickset man with a short beard looked up. He dropped the rope, and drew his companion sword, bringing it up just too late to parry the cut that split his forehead. God, thought Braley, I'm really slowing down. I should have had the son of a bitch before he could have let go of the rope.

The fourth soldier, hearing the commotion, raised himself up on his forearms, but the woman wrapped her arms and legs about him, and before the man could disencumber himself, Braley cut him across the nape of the neck, severing the spinal cord. The man collapsed in a heap, and the woman rolled him over and off.

"I'm much obliged, Count Braley," said the naked lady, sit-

ting up on her ermine cape and smiling with genuine warmth.
"I'm kind of sore, but you can have anything I've got."

Oh shit, thought Braley, his teeth chattering. A romantic in-
terlude with a goddamned woman is just what I need! "Exc-c-
cuse me, Lady Rad-d-doji," he said. "Right now I'm chilled
to the bone." He walked stiff-legged to the bonfire and wiped
his blade with hands that shook so badly that it required three
tries to sheathe it. "Mainly, I want t-t-t-to warm myself at your
fire." He held out his hands to the blessed heat. "You were
with Gatsack's personal baggage. How did you get over on this
side of the river?"

She sat up and slipped on her silk chemise. "When the Tarelians rolled up the center, some of Kahun's people overran the
baggage train. I heard them coming and started to run, but I
tripped and fell in the snow. Maybe my ermine cape helped me
get away . . . I lay there, and I couldn't see what was happening, but there was a lot of screaming."

She shivered. "When it became quiet, I got up and slipped
over the river, trying to make it away from there." As she spoke
she pulled on her fur-lined boots. "That's where these men
caught me . . . they were taking a little break from the battle.
This is their fire, really."

"It's our fire, now," he said. "What happened in the center?"

"The last word we had was that Gatsack had fallen," said
Lady Radoji. She gathered the purses of the dead Tarelians and
emptied them on the snow, recovering her jewelry, plus a few
small coins, dried fruit, sausage, and flatbread. "I fear it may
be true."

"Damn," said Braley. "From what I saw at the river, it could
have happened." He thrust one of the Tarelian spears into the
ground, a second into the hedge, and tied the butts together with
a piece of the sergeant's noose. Then he draped his wet cloak
over it, so that it would shelter the fire from wind and view, and
stripped dry clothes from the dead bodies.

"These boys must have crossed over Mewisford Bridge," he
said, removing his soaking and frozen boots as he sat on the
sergeant's body. "They didn't get wet at all, the lucky bastards." He kept his own hauberk, which was of better quality

and better fit, and his own swords, but for the rest, he wore Tarelian issue from the skin out.

"Now what?" asked Lady Radoji, holding her hands to the bonfire.

"Tomorrow is going to be too late," said Braley. "On the other hand, we can't go anywhere tonight. If you think of something, let me know." They sat huddled together by the fire, and he laid his head on his knees.

"Would you like a piece of sausage?" she asked. There was no answer; he was sound asleep.

The next day, Kahun raised a pyramid of 41,722 heads, setting his brother's head in the place of honor, with the heads of Duke Mihaly and Duke Jamreaux just beneath it. A vigorous search was made for the few survivors in the days following the battle, and many more heads were eventually set at the foot of the pyramid.

# 19

# Autmerida Revisited

"Look, Doctor Wizenbeak," said Lasco Genzari as they rode slowly up the road into Merida Gap, "I'm your strategist, right? You can tell *me* for God's sake! What in *hell* are you going to do with that goddamned witchfinder?"

"I don't know, exactly," conceded the wizard. "It seemed like a good idea at the time. I guess I didn't want him bothering the Dassenjis after we'd gone."

Genzari made a rude noise. "Right. And when word gets back to Cymdulock that we have kidnapped an official of the Church, *then* what?"

"I suppose I'll have to write a nice letter to Queen Shaia explaining things," said Wizenbeak. "Fortunately, she is not totally sympathetic toward witchfinders."

"Oy!" said Genzari, "What is it . . . 'Put not your faith in princes'? That would go for Queen Shaia, too, chief. She'd throw your ass as a sop to Kahun, or use your mangy hide as a makeweight for some deal with the clerisy."

"Hunh," grunted the wizard, shifting his leg around the side-saddle. "You were the one that started all the tumult, duelling in the street. What do you suggest, Mr. Strategist?"

"Well, for sure you can't turn him loose. I mean, it would be better to kill him, which also wouldn't be very good, as a practical expedient. So what can we do?" Genzari fingered his thin mustache as the other hand guided his horse between the wagon and the edge of the road, which dropped precipitously.

The late afternoon sky was overcast with clouds marching

southwards in grayish white windrows, line after parallel line. On the ground, however, the snow barely frosted the fields, which lay brown and sere, waiting for spring.

"All I can think of is to stall for time," said Genzari at last. "As far as Witchfinder-in-Chief Doctor Fadel knows, Autmerida is copacetic as long as he keeps getting the weekly reports. So you have to intercept the mail and keep him happy."

"Forge Wrascha's reports? What good would *that* do?"

"Would you rather be hung sooner or later?" asked Genzari.

"Hunh," repeated the wizard, feeling the scrawny neck under his beard, "I'd rather not be hung at all."

"That's not one of your options," replied his strategist. "Go for later?"

"The later the better, I guess."

"Right. So. We'll keep Witchfinder Wrascha up at Camp Merida, and you'll have to be there with him."

"Why me?" asked Wizenbeak.

"Who can you trust to do the job when you don't know what it is?" asked Genzari. "And *I'll* have to be there to see that you don't screw up."

"Are you implying that I might exhibit judgment that was anything less than superb?"

"It wouldn't be the first time, Doctor Wizenbeak. Also, impersonating a witchfinder promises to be a fulltime job. You'll need to be in Autmerida almost on a daily basis."

"So I'll rent a room in Autmerida."

"Wrong. You go in and take over the witchfinder's quarters, and if anybody objects, we put 'em down. You are, for God's sake, supposed to be an official. Act like one!"

"But what if they object?" asked the wizard.

"Who? The sheriff? By my count he has seventeen men. We have fifty. Fifty-one, counting Janko. Come down in force, you won't have to fight, you understand?"

"Ye-es," conceded Wizenbeak. "I'll take over from Witchfinder Wrascha, lock, stock, and barrel. Then what?"

"That should take us through the winter," said Genzari. "At which time we might go off to explore the Semeryan, for example."

"We'll think of *something*," said the wizard. "Couldn't we just apologize to the man and send him on home?"

"And if you just lie nice and still," came Jankura's voice from under the canvas wagon cover, "I won't have to cut *anything* off."

"You're right, you're right, you *are* right," said the wizard, giving the reins an irritated twitch, "it won't do to—easy boy, whoa boy—have the son of bitch get loose."

Two days later Wizenbeak and Genzari rode down into Autmerida at the head of a column of fifty men, stopping first at the jailhouse.

"Good morning, Sheriff Benzho," said the wizard looking down from his mule. "It seems to me that as the local representative of secular authority, you are seriously understaffed to deal with the alarming threat of witches in the vicinity."

"What?" Benzho looked blank.

"So I have here letters authorizing me to take over the function of Witchfinder of Autmerida." Wizenbeak produced an official looking parchment and flourished it. "By the powers vested in Brother Wrascha, and through him in *me*, I am authorized to assume command of both you and your deputies, seventeen good men and true."

"Sixteen," said the sheriff. "One of the boys just up and left after that dust up the other day."

"Whatever," said Genzari. "Fall 'em out! I want to take a look at the stupid sons of bitches you have left!"

"Wrascha never did anything like that," protested the sheriff.

"Times change," said Genzari. "Fall 'em out."

After taking over the local constabulary, Wizenbeak and Genzari paid a call on Mayor Perjics, who perforce introduced them to Deacon Oxtoby and the village council, assembled in the rectory behind the Syncretist Church on Third Street.

"As you know, Witchfinder Wrascha is a saintly man," said Wizenbeak. "It grieves his soul to harm any living thing, even a witch. So he has asked me to act as his deputy."

"Wrascha did *what*?" asked Deacon Oxtoby.

"He asked me to be his deputy," said the wizard, flourishing the parchment which Wrascha had signed under threat of torture.

"He will take care of matters of policy, while I attend to the myriad of all too painful details."

"Wrascha loved to fiddle with details," said Oxtoby. "I want to hear it from his own mouth!"

"Do you doubt Doctor Wizenbeak's word?" asked Sejenics.

"Oh, no," protested Oxtoby, "I just find it hard to believe."

"Believe," said Sejenics softly, laying one hand on his long sword. "Sometimes one requires a little effort to keep the faith, but the effort is, as you people like to say, worth it."

"Now here," said Wizenbeak, removing a stack of chips from his sleeve, "we come to the nub of the matter. Brother Wrascha was deeply grieved to have a weekly quota of witches to burn, even though his master, Doctor Fadel, suggested names of people that might be ignited with impunity."

"But this is half the business community," protested Mayor Perjics.

"The Orthodox half, I imagine," said Wizenbeak. "Right, deacon?"

Deacon Oxtoby looked at the list and nodded. As the list went round the room, there was no sound but the soft clicking of prayer beads.

"But my wife is Orthodox," said the mayor, plaintively.

"No wonder poor Wrascha was so distressed," murmured Wizenbeak. "He would have burned them one at a time, and when would the demands have stopped? A saint, I tell you, a saint the man is!"

"What are you going to do about it?" asked Deacon Oxtoby at last.

"I shall execute the orders of Witchfinder-in-Chief Doctor Fadel to the letter, with the utmost fidelity and total devotion," said Wizenbeak, running his fingers through his long white whiskers. "Never doubt it. This, of course, in *addition* to my regular duties which require me to colonize the Semeryan, as commanded by Her Majesty, Queen Shaia."

"Ah, pardon, your excellency," said Deacon Oxtoby. "We have just received word that King Grathnys is dead, and that Queen Shaia is deposed, if not actually slain."

"I hadn't heard," replied the wizard, twisting a strand of white whiskers around one finger. "However, as it happens, my master, Prince Gatsack—who assigned me to work for Queen Shaia—is in favor of the project, and since he is heir apparent, I expect we'll have no trouble.'' He looked around the room and smiled through his whiskers.

"This is really terribly irregular," said the deacon, "*extremely* irregular! I really must protest this—this—''

"Just do as you're told," said Lasco Genzari, "and nobody gets hurt, not even the witches.''

In Autmerida, Wizenbeak took over the old Derajian Monastery, which the witchfinder had been using as a residence and place of business. The ground floor had mortared cobble walls two feet thick, faced with split cobbles to give a flat surface, patterned with multihued stone circles, all pretty much the same size. The second and third floors were adobe covered with a cream-colored stucco, the second floor having tiny hooded windows so the monks could have light without being distracted by a view. The low-pitched hipped roof was weathered green copper sheeting with skylights on the northern side. In front, a low masonry wall enclosed a flagstone courtyard facing Cobblewash Road. In back, there was a decrepit wooden barn, set at an angle to Third Street. In the basement, Wrascha had been furnishing a torture chamber, the sawdust and wood shavings still unswept on the floor, fresh cut oak and beodar highlighting the dank earth odor.

Wizenbeak billeted two squads on the first and second floor, and two squads at Camp Merida on the top of the hill. He took the abbot's former quarters, a spacious suite on the northern side of the building, with tiny slit windows to view the world, a huge skylight to illuminate it, and a great old fashioned fireplace, into which Wrascha had set a modern grate of cast iron, the better to warm the room. On the reflecting plate of the grate was a buxom witch casting her eyes heavenward as cast iron flames leaped about her. Other than that, Wrascha had done nothing in the room.

Wizenbeak moved in cots and field chairs for Janko and himself, and replaced the drape covering the skylight. Before the fireplace he set up his field desk, and improvised a table from the rack in the basement, nailing the three main planks together into a broad flat surface and setting them on sawhorses. The bedroom was comfortable and spacious, the office bright and cheerful.

"Well, Lasco," he said when Genzari entered the room, "pen and sword, in accord, just like you said. This might not come off too badly, you know?"

"Mewis Field," said his strategist. "We're starting to get the reports."

"What?" the wizard looked blank.

"Mewis Field. Your master, King Gatsack, was either taken or slain, and his army routed or totally destroyed, depending on who you believe."

"I don't understand."

"There was a battle," said Genzari. "At Mewis Field. Our side lost decisively. A fact which can hardly help our standing in the local community." He pulled a wooden armchair over to the improvised table and sat down. "Have you ever considered shaving your beard and becoming . . . oh, say, a peddler or a dancing master?"

"Not really," said Wizenbeak. "Are you so all-fired eager to become a peddler's assistant?"

"No," admitted Genzari. "I like my job, I like *you*, crazy as you are. But." He shrugged, and sat back in his chair, folding his hands across his middle. "It looks like time is running out on us."

"Hunh," grunted the wizard. "Time has been running out on you since the day you were born." He sat back and twisted a strand of white whiskers around his forefinger, tugging absently at his upper lip as he gazed out the window. "Still . . . I can see what you mean." He sat back and propped his slippered feet on an upended block of firewood.

"Got any ideas, chief?"

"Hunh. The gentry of Autmerida can't really get rid of us, since they accepted us, you know. That makes them . . . oh, accessories after the fact." Gruchka leaped from the mantel over the fireplace where he had been sleeping, and landed deftly on the wizard's field desk, skidding on little chips of wood. Wizenbeak picked him up and petted him absently.

"What are you thinking?" asked Genzari politely, after a few moments.

"Archdeacon Heiby, and those two officials that came after me, and that freelance witchfinder in Huitmire, and now this crazy bastard Wrascha that we've got locked up. I could be in serious trouble with the Church." Wizenbeak rubbed his long nose. "And me fresh out of friends at court."

## 20

# The Royal Refugees

LIEUTENANT Zeldones paused at the bridge where Third Street crossed the Cobble Wash, and looked around.

"That must be it," he said to the children riding the gray mare he was leading.

The house on the right was an imposing stucco and masonry dwelling with a stone lion sitting at the front gate, its mouth open to receive anonymous denunciations. A neatly carved sign of painted wood was posted on the wall behind the lion, proclaiming OFFICE OF THE HOLY INQUISITION, in gold and black, and underneath in discreetly smaller letters, MASTER WRASCHA, WITCHFINDER. A wooden chip wedged in the lion's mouth bore the message: PLEASE BE PATIENT WHILE WE ARE REORGANIZING. A sentry stood at the gate looking bored.

"Excuse me. I'm looking for Doctor Wizenbeak . . . I was told he might be at this address."

"He's inside," said the mercenary. "You have an appointment?"

The tall man shook his head.

"Corporal of the Guard!" shouted the sentry. After a moment, Nick Sejenics appeared.

"This bumpkin wants to see Doctor Wizenbeak," he said. Sejenics looked the man over. He carried a jitte and a short sword, he was big, and he looked tough. He might even be competent; the jitte suggested police training.

"Come in, please," said Nick, "I'll announce you. Have the kids wait around back."

"They come with me," was the reply. "They are, in fact, the reason I'm here."

"Oh?" Sejenics raised his eyebrows. "Hey, Simat—walk the man's horse over to the stable." The mercenary took the horse's reins, and the tall man helped the children dismount.

Sejenics led them into the house, and up two flights of stairs, pausing at a split door, the top half of which was open.

"Doctor Wizenbeak appears to be in," he said softly. "Who shall I say is calling?"

"I am Police Lieutenant Zeldones, lately assigned to the staff of Her Majesty Queen Shaia." He reached into his pocket and produced his silver medallion, which bore Shaia's profile on one side, and his own name and rank on the reverse.

"That proves nothing," said Nick. "You could have picked it up on the street or in a pawn shop."

"You wanted a name to announce," replied Zeldones, "I gave you one."

"Indeed?" Sejenics took a step backwards. "Assume guard position, please," he said, drawing his long sword, and holding it before him in a two-handed grip.

Zeldones drew his jitte with the right hand, and his short sword with the left, holding the sword reversed, the blade guarding the forearm, as the children stepped behind him.

"Cymdulock Police Academy, eh?" said Nick, sheathing his sword in one smooth motion. "You studied under Tsejedi?"

"My first two years," replied Zeldones. "He then assigned me to his pupil, Master Ramial."

Sejenics rapped on the low door. "A Lieutenant Zeldones to see you, Doctor Wizenbeak," he called. The wizard looked up and waved for them to come in. Nick reached over the door and unfastened it from the inside. As they entered, he took a position opposite Genzari, between the wizard and the tall lieutenant.

"What can I do for you, sir?" asked Wizenbeak, leaning forward on his table. "And who might your young friends be?"

"Ah, ah . . ." Zeldones had rehearsed his opening speech a hundred times, and now his mind had gone blank. "Ahh . . . Prince Dervian."

The boy, dirty and travel worn, in shabby clothes, stepped forward and made a formal bow. "An honor to meet so distinguished a wizard," he said gravely.

"And Princess Marjia."

The girl, in no better case than her brother, made a formal curtsey. "Delighted to meet you, Doctor Wizenbeak," she said sweetly, as she stepped forward to the edge of the table and presented her left hand, wrist elegantly limp. "You may kiss our hand," she added, in precise mimicry of her mother.

Dumbfounded, Wizenbeak stood up, and leaning over the converted rack, took the child's hand and kissed it, bending as low as he could manage in the circumstances.

"Holy shit," said Genzari softly. Then he stood up and bowed from the waist. "Your Highnesses are a long way from home," he said, as Wizenbeak stood there, taken aback, and wondering what ought to be done next. "May we offer you refreshment?"

Dervian smiled. "Please do," he said. "Travelling gives one an appetite."

Genzari went into the next room and sent Janko down to the kitchen for some bread and cheese and fruit.

"Hunh," said Wizenbeak at last, recognizing that his guests were standing. "Nick, pull up chairs for our guests, please. Lieutenant, what in God's name made you decide to come *here*?"

"Doctor Rovira," said Zeldones, easing himself into a wood and canvas chair. "Just before the palace fell, I asked him where he'd go. He said—"

"Odilao Rovira? The Queen's beautician? I hardly knew the man."

"He said the settlement beyond the end of the world, the one you were running in the Semeryan, was the nearest friendly place he could think of. Then I was left with the kids, and I couldn't just turn them loose—" He shrugged. "So I came here."

"I see," said the wizard. "How are you going to prove that these two are the prince and princess?"

"I don't know," said Zeldones. "*You* knew them, didn't you?"

"Ye-es, but I'd met them at the Royal Palace. Don't they have any identification?"

Zeldones took the silver medallion from his pocket and slid it across the desk. "Like that, you mean? The pawn-shops are full of all sort of identification. Theirs included."

He was giving an account of their escape from Cymdulock, when Janko walked in with a pot of tea and a platter of bread and cheese, dried fruit and pickles.

Princess Marjia looked up as she came in, and saw the slender young woman with close-cropped hair, dressed as a soldier, passing as a young man.

"Mommy?"

There was a brief silence. Then Lieutenant Zeldones removed his medallion with the cut chain from his pocket, and studied it, his eyes flicking back and forth between the silver image of the late queen and Janko Jankura.

"Ah . . . there *is* a resemblance, young man," he said at last. "If you smeared a little cream on your lip and let the cat lick off that mustache, it would be quite marked."

Janko woke up to find a troll-bat sitting on her face. "Is that you, Gruchka?" she mumbled and sat up. "What time is it?" There was a light outlining the doorway to Wizenbeak's room, a pallid yellow marking out blocks of black door and dark brown wall. It must be before the first cock crow, she thought, and got up to see if the master was all right. At the door she hesitated, then knocked.

"Come in," said Wizenbeak. He was sitting at the head of his bed in his green and white striped shirt, laying out some sort of solitaire on the counterpane.

"Did you send Gruchka in for me?" The troll-bat perching on her shoulder leaned against the side of her head, and made no move to return to the wizard.

"No," he said, "but you were on my mind." He pulled

the cards together and gestured to the bed. "Sit down, please."

She nodded and sat down on the edge of the bed.

"I've had a long session with Genzari," he continued. "The consensus is that trying to run a counterrevolution with the kids is hopeless. If you were to act the part of Queen Shaia, however—"

"There's hope?"

He snapped his fingers. "C'mere Gruchka," and the little troll-bat languidly walked across the bed to his master. "Not exactly," said Wizenbeak, gently rubbing Gruchka's ears. "With Queen Shaia, even a false Shaia, it isn't obvious that we lose in every possible case. That's hope?"

"It's something," Jankura replied. "You think I could be a false Shaia?"

"Up to a point, probably. There's a down side, too, you know."

"What? That Kahun and his witchfinders will get all exercised about it?"

He nodded, and fingered his beard. "That too, of course. I was thinking that if we just faded into the woodwork, nobody would come looking for us. Not really. Once we proclaim you Shaia there'd be no going back."

"We don't have to decide right away, do we?"

"No, of course not." Wizenbeak leaned back on one elbow.

"Good," she said, smoothing her close-cropped black hair with one hand, "why don't I just try to find out how to do it, in case we *do* have to decide right away? That way you'd have an option."

"Right." He nodded approvingly. "I could appoint you . . . oh, 'Stategic Liaison' to Prince Dervian. Talk to him and the lieutenant about how we're doing, and let them tell you all about life at the palace. What do you think?"

"The little princess might know more about the queen than both of them put together," said Jankura. "A girl watches her mother with an eye to imitate."

"Hunh. Some do, at that." He squared his deck of red-backed cards and put them on the night table. "Janko . . ."

"Yes?"

"Is this something you want to do?"

"Yes, Master Wizenbeak." I may go down, she thought, but the witchfinders will know they've had a fight.

"Very well." He sighed. "I'll set it up in the morning."

# 21

# The Spoils of Victory

IN Cymdulock, the victory at Mewis Field set the church bells tolling and pealing all over the city in joyous celebration. Archdeacon Gorabani, whom Kahun had named acting Governor of Cymdulock, ordered a course of masses said to praise God for the victory, and pledged the construction of a splendid altar in the Cymdulock Cathedral by way of commemoration.

Across the plaza from that cathedral, in the city hall, Dr. Fadel and his assistant, Dr. Rehbeinji, a small, wiry man with intense black eyes and a missing front tooth, entered the acting governor's palatial office, noting with envious gaze the arched and lofty ceiling decorated with carefully tinted plaster molding, the polished parquet floor, the exquisitely tasteful chandeliers, the elegant secular murals, the beautiful suite of matched furniture. A small ikon behind the desk was the only overt evidence of Gorabani's presence.

"Nice place you have here," said Fadel, casually treating the archdeacon as a peer.

"Yes," agreed Gorabani, ignoring an implied claims to place or status. "My late predecessor had superlatively excellent taste in interior decoration. He had the misfortune to be loyal to the late Shaia, however, and I now sit in his place."

"He *chose* to be loyal to the Witch-Queen," said Rehbeinji, dragging a chair over to the edge of the desk and seating himself without invitation, "and God has punished him for his transgression!"

"Indeed, Doctor Binji?" said Gorabani politely. "I had not thought that loyalty to one's master constituted a transgression."

"Don't call me Doctor Binji!"

The archdeacon shrugged. "Surely you had some business that brought you here?"

"Yes," said Fadel, taking a little stack of wooden chips from his tall hat. "Now that the victory has been consolidated, we want to move against the forces of iniquity . . . not only witches, but their friends and supporters as well. We have a number of accusations here, which we have total confidence in. Sign them, please."

"His Majesty gave me the strictest instructions not to sign anything without reading it," replied the archdeacon, taking the stack of chips and sorting through them. "I trust you implicitly, of course, but orders are orders."

Most of the chips he stacked in a neat pile, a few he set aside for further review, two he kept in his hand.

"You might wish to reconsider these," he said softly, pushing the smaller stack across the desk.

"As you wish, archdeacon," said Rehbeinji, taking the little stack of reprieves. Gorabani turned over one of the chips he was holding, and looked mildly distressed.

"And to forget about Archdeacon Darussis!"

"The man is a dabbler in the black arts," said Fadel, brushing lint off his velvet sleeve. "Unworthy of the high trust he holds."

"Utterly unworthy," added Dr. Rehbeinji.

"Indeed," said Gorabani. "However, he is a fellow clerisiarch, and to my knowledge he has done nothing to warrant even so much as a reprimand." He took the wooden chip accusing Darussis and broke it into pieces.

"Do you defend this—this—warlock, this consort of witches, this covenmaster—" sputtered Fadel indignantly. Gorabani cut him off.

"He has supported Kahun to the best of his ability, witchfinder. And you may be sure that my master did not win at Mewis Field in order to burn his *friends*!"

"We are prepared to make formal charges," sad Rehbeinji, his humorless grimace showing the missing tooth.

"Good," replied the archdeacon. "We'll need to put the question to your witnesses before the matter goes any further."

"*What!?*"

"You heard me, Binji. Archdeacon Darussis isn't some little old lady you swept up off the street." Gorabani dropped the pieces of broken wood into the wastebasket beside his desk, and studied the last chip before him.

"Doctor Wizenbeak?" he said at last.

"Yes," said Rehbeinji sullenly. "Is he another of Kahun's creatures?"

"No, no . . . there is no love lost on that one." Gorabani hesitated a moment. *Probably* the man had not murdered Heiby. The disappearance of the officers sent after the wizard was circumstantial . . . no bodies had ever been found. Even so . . .

"Then sign it," said the witchfinder, leaning forward.

"The crown has invested considerable money in the colonization scheme," temporized Gorabani, "which ought to accrue to Kahun's benefit. Assuming it works, of course," He folded his gloved hands on the polished wood of his desk and studied his amethyst and garnet rings. "It wouldn't hurt you to wait half a year—"

"Money!" Rehbeinji almost spat the word. "This Wizenbeak is a limb of the Devil, the spawn of Evil, and *you* want to recover the money the Witch-Queen spent on his perfidy!"

"You object to colonizing the Semeryan?"

"It can be done without this Wizenbeak," said the little man, his black eyes blazing.

"How do you propose to take him?" asked Gorabani. "Assuming that we let you have him, of course."

"The nearest arm of the Inquisition is Witchfinder Wrascha, at Autmerida, perhaps fifty or sixty miles to the south," said Rehbeinji. "We shall order him to seize this Wizenbeak as a known witch. Wrascha is an enthusiast and energetic, and we don't care *where* the son of a bitch is burned, after all, as long as the fire is well and truly lit."

"I suppose not, Binji," agreed Archdeacon Gorabani, sitting back in his elaborately carved and gilded wooden chair. Wizenbeak already had established a record for being resourceful and tough, and he was out in the Semeryan with fifty mercenaries, but that was Wrascha's problem. "You think your local witchfinder can take him?"

"Wrascha is my smallest finger," said Dr. Fadel, extending his hand with the little finger curled upwards. "If Wrascha fails—" His hand opened into a claw and closed into a fist. "We'll still rend that limb of the Devil!"

"Very good," said Gorabani. He put Wizenbeak's chip on the large pile and rang for his secretary. When the man came in, he gave him the pile. "Here. Stamp each chip with our seal, and make a list of the names."

"Why don't you just sign the chips?" asked Fadel.

"My hand would get tired, witchfinder."

"No, no . . . why do you make a list of what is actually none of your business?"

Gorabani stood up and walked over to the window, looking out onto the plaza below. "Ah, Doctor Fadel," he said softly. "Each one of those chips is a human life I have wasted . . . how can that *not* be my business?" He clasped his hands behind his back. "Besides, it keeps you and Binji, here, from temptation."

"Temptation?" The witchfinder lifted his eyebrows up his high forehead in a gesture of puzzlement. "What temptation?"

"The temptation to cut red tape," said Archdeacon Gorabani. "To slip in a few unauthorized names, perhaps even the ones I asked you not to. In order to do God's work without bothering the secular authorities."

"Since when is a clerisiarch a secular authority?" asked Dr. Rehbeinji. "You should support us with the whole heart!"

"I wear two hats," said Gorabani, "and I *do* support you with the whole heart, Doctor Rehbeinji. When Wrascha fails to catch Doctor Wizenbeak, you all come by and *see* the support I'll give you!"

The Steering Committee for the Congregation of Clerisiarchs met at the rectory behind Cymdulock Cathedral. Kahun sat at the head of the plain wood table, Gorabani and Nasar-Namatu at his right, Dr. Fadel and archdeacons Eaklor and Najile at his left. A burning log in the fireplace lit the room while providing a measure of warmth in the large, drafty chamber.

"I *am* King," said Kahun, "and I *will* be Patriarch. The only question is when, and that is the only question we are going to take up tonight."

"Then it will be later rather than sooner," said the redoubtable Nasar-Namatu, his white hair making a halo about his head in the firelight. "You don't have the votes."

"We can wait," said Gorabani, serenely. "Let the clerisy handle the idea, sniff it, chew it over. When it has been around for a while, when they've gotten used to it, *then* we shall push for the votes. In six months it will fall like ripe fruit."

"Perhaps," said Archdeacon Najile, a smooth-faced man with the cold, calculating gaze of the moneylender that he was. "Perhaps not. A patriarch would sensibly diminish the clerisy's influence and power. When that is understood, the clerisy will not freely elect a patriarch."

"Would *you* vote Kahun for patriarch?" asked Gorabani.

"It would be against my interest as a clerisiarch," replied Najile with cold politeness, "but I have other interests."

"Of course," said Gorabani, propping his chin on one hand. "As do all the others . . . the clerisy being the educated rich, using their education to make themselves richer in the name of God."

"Blasphemy!" said Fadel the witchfinder.

"I agree, actually," replied Archdeacon Gorabani, "but that's the way they do it."

"Yes," agreed Kahun, scowling in the firelight. "That's the way they do it. And I'm not going to bribe the lot, and I'm not going to wait for the bastards to talk it out either . . . even if it looks like they might come round."

"What did you have in mind, Your Majesty?" asked Eaklor, pouring himself a glass of water.

"To call the congregation into special session for the purpose of selecting me Patriarch of the Syncretist Church," said the king. "A simple plan is the best."

"They won't select you," said Nasar-Namatu, "and the Tarelians didn't crush Gatsack at Mewis Field to let you ride rough-shod over the Church!''

"Well, well," murmured Kahun, smiling ever so slightly. "You'd add 'Kingmaker' to your titles and tell me what I may or may not do?"

"You cannot simultaneously be king and sit in conference with your peers," said the old man.

"Well God damn!" growled Kahun. "First you tell me I don't have any clout because I'm not king, and when I *am* king, you tell me it's not nice to use it!"

"Gently, gently," said Gorabani. He got up and stirred up the fire with a black iron poker, finally adding another piece of kindling. "Suppose we let the matter sit for a day or two? There can be no profit in pressing further tonight."

"I want it settled!" said Kahun.

They then rehearsed the ground they had covered a few more times with minor variations.

As they were at last preparing to leave, Gorabani drew Kahun to one side. "Look, Your Majesty . . . you don't want to be patriarch for a while, yet."

"Wrong as usual, but what's your argument?"

"Doctor Fadel. He's burning up witches like leaves in autumn and he's started on the Orthodox. I think it's crazy, but that's your policy, so all right. Eventually, however, you'll have to stop the man . . . they *are* your subjects he's incinerating, remember."

"So?"

"So when you're ready to stop him, *then* is when you make your push for patriarch. Any opposition in the clerisy, you can denounce as witches and the man is dumb enough to go for them." Gorabani hesitated for a moment, then continued.

"When the witchfinder's work is done, when he's run his course, *then* you move to become patriarch so you can hang the son of a bitch, and everyone will cheer you as their savior from Fadel's reign of terror."

"That's good thinking," said Kahun, "and if I wanted my subjects to love me, that's how I'd do it. As king, I can hang the son of a bitch any time I want, right?"

"Ye-es," conceded Gorabani.

"So there's no need to wait to become patriarch."

"Wrong, Your Majesty. By pretending to honor the autonomy of the Church, you validate your claim to become patriarch when you act to stop the burning."

"Burning witches is very popular," said the king.

"Not on the scale Fadel wants to do it," was the reply. "Give him his head, he'd burn every woman in Guhland over the age of puberty!"

# 22

# Peejisford Bridge

Out at Zenburg, some unsung genius had taken the standard plow and split it, mounting a pair of half-plows so that they would throw the furrow in the same direction. A simple idea, it made contour plowing possible. In the Semeryan, contour plowing—two furrows ploughed, your furrow's width left uncultivated save to remove the weeds—was the key to agricultural success. As if by magic, the spring rains collected in the plowed land to raise a fine crop of spring barley, rows of greenery spread out along the contours of the gently rolling hills.

"It looks good," said Genzari, as they rode back toward Castle Wizenbeak. "With the rain we had, I wouldn't have expected anything."

"It does look good," agreed the wizard, as the wind ruffled his whiskers. "See how it wiggles!"

"You were never a farmer, chief?"

"No. Actually, I was thinking about what to tell Witchfinder-General Fadel, back in Cymdulock. You'd think he had it in for me, the way he writes."

"He wants you dead," replied Lasco Genzari, shrugging. "You never *have* decided what you are going to do about it."

"I wanted to talk him out of it," said Wizenbeak, rubbing his long nose. " 'Wrascha' wrote all those nice things about me, and what happens? The poor son of a bitch gets the sack, even though he reported burning his quota of witches each and every month." He fumbled in his pocket and produced a letter, three wooden chips tied together with red tape, bearing the seal of the Inquisition.

"My relief—that is, Witchfinder Wrascha's duly appointed replacement, is on the way—'With a company of mercenaries to execute the duties you have been so singularly unable to perform.' "

"You told me," said Genzari. "When is this replacement witchfinder supposed to arrive?" The wizard handed over the letter without a word, and his strategist studied it for a few moments.

"So," he said at last. "We have maybe ten days. And they'll be coming up Military Road. What do you want to do? Turn Witchfinder Wrascha loose and let him try to explain matters?"

"Ah . . . no," said Wizenbeak, pulling at his beard.

"I told you you should have burned *somebody*," the strategist observed. "Maybe that old bitch who kept denouncing her daughter-in-law. I'll bet she blew the whistle on you, and when they asked around, they found you hadn't done any of the stuff you were reporting."

"You gain merit in heaven for burning a mother-in-law, but I think it has to be *your* mother-in-law." The wizard sighed. "Anyway, that's water over the dam." He shaded his eyes against the bright spring sunlight for a moment. "Play for time, you said. Now what?"

"You can run, hide, or fight, chief—whatever you like."

"Come on, Lasco. What would *you* do?"

"I'd fight," said Genzari. "Just because you'll lose is no reason not to fight." Entering Zenburg, their mounts slowed down to a leisurely walk. "Besides, you want more time, right?"

Wizenbeak nodded as they rode past the rows of adobe houses, with the line of newly planted trees along the street showing a few pink and white flowers and budding leaves.

"So we arrange for a 'third party' ambush to wipe out Wrascha's replacement," the strategist continued. "That ought to take you into summer, right?"

"Hanh," grunted the wizard, as they crossed the wooden bridge over the ditch surrounding the motte. At the gate, a sentry presented arms as they passed inside, and Genzari returned the salute.

"So we'll fight." Wizenbeak sighed at last. "Maybe something will turn up. You really think we'd make it into summer?"

"Let me put it this way, chief," replied Genzari, "if you *don't* take out this new witchfinder, you have maybe two weeks."

After lunch, a strategy planning session was held in Wizenbeak's bedroom, the wizard sitting cross-legged on his bed under the drawn-back canopy, Genzari sitting on the folding chair by the camp desk, Jankura sitting on one end of her cot, while Lieutenant Zeldones sat on the other. The corporals and assistant squad leaders stood at the back of the room. Nick Sejenics, heading the garrison in Autmerida, was absent.

"We have received intelligence that Witchfinder Wrascha has been replaced," said Wizenbeak. "This is most unfortunate, since he has been very little trouble to us locked up in the well house. Worse, the new witchfinder is coming up with a company of mercenaries, and presumably with instructions to deal with us in a 'firm and expeditious manner.' "

He paused for a moment to rub Gruchka's ears. "That, of course being the policy repeatedly urged upon Wrascha, poor fellow. So. I believe that our best response is to fight. How would you suggest that we proceed, Lasco?"

"Since Mewis Field we have hired a number of mercenaries, anticipating retirements, resignations, and so forth," Genzari said. "We are, at the moment, somewhat over our authorized strength, but not enough to take on a full company in a fair fight. I would suggest an ambush." From the back of the room there was a murmur of approval.

"I agree," said Wizenbeak firmly. "Where and when?"

"This company will be coming up Military Road, sir," said Zeldones, "and about fifty miles south of Autmerida, the bridge is out—that is, the masonry is tumbled. They have a wooden bridge in place, but it's in bad shape. It's a natural site for an ambush. Wait till half their force is across, and hit 'em. There's good cover on both sides, woodlots, orchards, low stone fences.

As for when, they figure to be marching thirty miles a day, roughly, so that puts them at the bridge about two days out of Autmerida.''

"I know the place," said Jankura. "Peejisford Bridge. There's a bivouac ground about eight miles south, just outside Peejis Village."

"Right," said Genzari. "If we can believe what Cymdulock is telling Wrascha, they'll be there on the twenty-ninth, bright and early in the morning—eightish, say—depending.''

"Good." Wizenbeak twisted a strand of whisker around one finger. "How many men will you take?''

"Everybody, of course." Genzari smiled and nodded at Jankura. "Even the boy, here."

"Agreed," said the wizard. "However, I have my own plans for Janko.''

Zeldones and Sejenics arrived in Peejis Village on the evening of the twenty-seventh, where they took bed and board at Mandol's Inn. As Zeldones tended to the horses in the stable, Sejenics took the two cages of carrier pigeons up to their room. A walk around town after supper showed no adverse troop concentrations but a rather large number of unattached mercenaries.

The next morning they went down to the local Mercenaries Hall, a former Orthodox school converted to secular purposes. On the blackboard was posted a hiring notice.

MERCENARIES WANTED! We have vacancies for ablebodied archers, spearmen, and swordsmen of good character, for billeting at Autmerida. Interviews will begin on the morning of Grasday, Ajril 28. By Authority of Witchfinder General Fadel. signed, Wdr. Regeonay

As they stood reading the notice, a greasy little man in the black robes of a lay preacher swaggered up to the bulletin board, and smudged out the twenty-eight to chalk in twenty-nine.

"Just got word that they're running a day late," he said. "You fellas looking to sign up with Regeonay's company?''

"Possibly," conceded Zeldones. The lay preacher looked them both over for a moment.

"You *look* fit enough," he said. "If you know how to use those swords you're carrying, we might find a place for you . . . the recruiter is over yonder." He gestured toward a small tent at the edge of the yard, where a couple of officials were watching a spearman demonstrate his skill on a dummy. Inside the tent was a table set with a barrel of ale and stoneware mugs.

"Hired or not, you get a mug of ale."

"No, thank you," said Sejenics, "I don't drink."

"What about you, shorty?" asked the man, looking up at Zeldones.

"I fear I am disqualified on the grounds of 'good character,' " replied the tall lieutenant. "However, I never refuse the offer of a free drink." The three of them walked over to the recruiting stand.

"Got us a prospect, Dom?" asked the recruiter, a portly red-faced man in his late thirties.

"You know it, Moriz," said the lay preacher. "Shorty here says he never refuses a free drink."

The recruiter looked him over, and drew a mug of ale which Zeldones accepted.

"A jitte man?" asked the swordmaster. "We can't use you, I'm afraid."

"It's good ale," said Zeldones. "Would you like a demonstration?"

"Not with the jitte," said the swordmaster. "We had a chain and sickle man the other day. Really good, too, but we couldn't use him." He scratched his chest. "Sword or spear is what we need now."

The recruiter pushed a wooden sword across the table. "Try a pass with Instructor Retsji, here?"

"No thanks," said Zeldones politely. "The jitte, alas, is my weapon of choice."

"Try a pass with my swordmaster," repeated Moriz, scowling.

"No, thank you," said the tall lieutenant.

"You drink my ale and you won't demonstrate your skill?"

"I *told* Dom that I didn't pass on the requirement for good character," Zeldones said patiently.

"All right, shorty." Moriz shrugged. "What about your friend, here?"

"Thank you," said Nick. "I do not choose to join small groups."

"Mercenary's privilege," conceded the recruiter. "At least you didn't cadge a drink."

"Here, now," said Dom, "this ain't no small group! We've signed up nearly fifty first-rate fighters already, and another fifty's coming up the road!"

"I'm not interested," repeated Sejenics. "Good day, Instructor Retsji, gentlemen."

Early the next morning, as the mists were rising, Sejenics and Zeldones rode across the Peejisford Bridge, where they met Lasco Genzari standing beside a low stone wall.

"Good morning, gentlemen," said the strategist. "Any late word to add to what you sent by pigeon?"

Sejenics nodded. "They filled out the ranks last night . . . a big party for warriors—meat, drink, women . . . everything. They picked up eleven men. I watched from my window across the street."

"They made their century, then," Genzari mused. "So. They'll likely put the last recruits in front, where they can watch them, the old hands in the rear, and the officials in the middle. You didn't see their order of march, did you?"

"No," said Zeldones. "They were at breakfast when we rode past. They seemed to be moving very slowly."

"That figures. Well, we'll just wait for them," Genzari studied the metalled road on the other side of the river. It ran straight and true, cutting past a copse of hardwood trees before it came to the ramshackle wooden bridge sitting on the stone pilings of its predecessor, and fading into the morning mist.

"How have you disposed of our men?" asked Sejenics.

"One squad in reserve with Wizenbeak. Two squads on the left in the ditch behind that low stone wall, the other two on the right about fifty yards back." He fingered his closely cropped mustache. "On the right, there's a depression—a dry stream bed, with tall grass. When the Witchfinder reaches this side of the bridge, we hit 'em from the left with archers and spearmen, and charge in from the right. The battlecry is 'Dervian,' of course."

"Very good," said Zeldones. "Where do you want us?"

"On the right, I think. Go for the officials. We want the witchfinder dead. If there's a payroll, we'll want that, too."

"Probably in the second wagon," said Sejenics, pulling and chewing on the end of a stem of meadow grass. "They kept tight security on it all the time."

"We'll see," agreed Genzari. "The mercenaries—if they run, let 'em go." Sejenics and Zeldones trotted over to the depression on the right, where they joined the two squads waiting there.

Genzari faded back toward one of the last year's haystacks, where Wizenbeak, Jankura, and the strategic reserve sat patiently watching the road across the river. Jankura was wearing a carefully fitted hauberk of exceptional quality, the massive gold chain she had had from Deacon Manjiver, a "borrowed" velvet cloak worked with gold and scarlet embroidery depicting the royal coat of arms, and a tall, black crested commander's helmet. The gonfalonier, sitting at ease in the warm grass, carried the device of the house of Grathnys, emblazoned with an ornate *D* for Prince Dervian.

"Do you *really* think that an ambush yelling 'Dervian' is going to distract people from the killing of a witchfinder?" asked Wizenbeak as Genzari knelt down beside him.

"It will sure as hell distract Kahun," replied the strategist, "and flashing Jankura at them as—just possibly—Queen Shaia is going to sorely confuse the sons of bitches when the word gets back to wherever the hell it gets back to."

"I hope you're right," said the wizard, stroking Gruchka absentmindedly. "A red herring is better than a poke in the eye with a sharp stick, isn't it, darling?"

"Sir?"

"I was talking to Gruchka."

A long time later, although it was barely midmorning, they heard an owl hoot. Wizenbeak raised his eyebrows.

"Oh?" he said.

"Sir?" asked Genzari.

"The owl is a night bird," said the wizard.

"What owl?"

"You didn't hear it?"

"No, sir."

"Here they come," said Jankura, looking around the hay-stack. Wizenbeak adjusted his glasses and peered down the road, where, in the distance, he saw a horseman, followed by two lines of men. Then three wagons flanked by marchers, followed by another horseman and two more lines. The lead horseman bore a gonfalon fixed to the center of his back and rising three feet above his helmet, a black device, marked with a golden nabla. When he came to the bridge, he raised his hand, calling the column to a halt.

Leisurely, he rode across the bridge, inspecting it, noting, perhaps the missing handrails and the loose planks. Then he took up a position on the left side of the road at the northern end of the bridge, and waved his men on. The mercenaries marched across the wooden bridge, followed by the first of the three wagons, the Witchfinder Regeonay's personal conveyance, and after an interval of about half the width of the bridge, the second wagon.

As the second wagon pulled onto the bridge, which was too narrow to permit the passage of men *and* wagon, someone sounded a horn in the woods, and a wave of green-clad men emerged on the far side of the river, shouting and loosing arrows with deadly accuracy as they advanced on the mercenaries in the rear guard.

"What are they shouting?" asked Wizenbeak.

"The wind's wrong . . ." replied Genzari, holding a handful of hay over his helmet as he looked toward the bridge, "I can't hear."

The horseman on the far side of the river tried to rally his troop of newly hired and hung-over mercenaries to the sup-port of his comrades on the south side, and as they started back, passing the wagons on the bridge in single file, Zel-dones picked up the stranger's battlecry and led the right wing against the rear of the witchfinder's mercenaries on the northern side.

"*Sha-i-ia!*" he yelled, and his men echoed the cry.

After a moment of hesitation, the left wing advanced from their ditch to the stone wall, showering the men on the bridge with arrows and yelling "Dervian!" The gonfalonier, the redoubtable Instructor Retsji, turning to face this new attack, rallied his men to make a stand at the north end of Peejisford Bridge, as Moriz with the other group pulled the third wagon sideways across the road to make an improvised defense on the southern side of the river. A cluster of perhaps twenty men in the black and green of the Tarelians were standing around the wagon in the center of the bridge, Witchfinder Regeonay among them.

"What a mess!" muttered Wizenbeak.

"Wrong again, chief," said Genzari. "It's time to hit 'em with our secret weapon!" He mounted, and Wizenbeak mounted, and they rode around the haystack with Jankura in the place of honor between them, her massive golden chain shining in the morning sun, her troll-bat on her shoulder, as her gonfalonier raised the red and gold standard of the Grathnys, the royal banner of Guhland. They were advancing down the road before they were seen.

"It's Queen Shaia!" said Instructor Retsji.

"The Witch-Queen!?" shouted Witchfinder Regeonay. "She's dead! She's burning in hell!"

"I'll not raise steel against my queen," said Retsji and sheathed his sword.

"We have no quarrel with mercenaries," prompted Wizenbeak softly. "Say it so they can hear it."

"We have no quarrel with mercenaries!" proclaimed Jankura in a strong, clear voice, "But death to the witchfinder who hounded us from our throne!"

The fighting at both ends of the bridge stopped, and abruptly the mercenaries of Regeonay's company laid down their arms.

"Witchlovers!" shouted Regeonay. "Traitors!" An arrow pierced his tall black hat, as a volley of arrows landed among his personal guard of Tarelians. "Traitors!" he shouted again.

"Stand and fight!" Squeezing past his wagon, he drew his sword, waving it over his head, and urged his Tarelians to follow him. When he had rallied eight or nine men, he began to run toward Jankura, who sat patiently on her white horse. Sejenics stepped in front of him. As the witchfinder raised his sword to strike, Sejenics cut him down.

Then the left wing charged the remaining Tarelians and wiped them out as the newly hired mercenaries stood by their grounded weapons.

"That takes care of the witchfinder," said Wizenbeak, pulling at his long nose. "Now let's see who gave us the hand."

The three of them—Wizenbeak, Jankura, and Genzari—rode to the center of the bridge and paused. After a moment, a green clad warrior, wearing a panache of white cock feathers on his helmet, came walking up.

"Your Majesty?" he said. "I thought you died at the sack of the royal palace."

"As you see," said Jankura gravely, "we are not dead." The man knelt before her.

"Count Braley, at your service, Your Majesty."

Jankura dismounted and took him by the hand. "Rise, Count Braley," she said softly, and as he stood up. "How did you come to be calling my name in battle?"

"Kahun—the son of a bitch—frets that you may be alive. We were shouting 'Shaia' to annoy *him*, mainly." He swallowed. "That, and pretending we weren't bandits."

"Good enough," said Genzari. "Will you join us?"

"Will you have me?" asked Braley.

"Of course," said Shaia, "but you must swear fealty to my son, Prince Dervian, rightful Heir to the Throne of Guhland!"

"I do so swear!" said Count Braley. "And for my men as well!"

"Lasco," said Wizenbeak leaning over toward his strategist, "what the hell is *this*?"

"Good luck," replied Genzari. "Don't you recognize good luck when you see it?"

"Yes. And this is absodamnlutely *not* what I had in mind for a diversion, Lasco!"

"You're thinking small, chief—" Genzari said with a faint smile. "In a civil war, who's going to be looking for a stray wizard?"

# 23

# Restoring the Patriarchy

AFTER the victory at Mewis Field, King Kahun moved swiftly to consolidate his secular gains by reinstituting the patriarch's hat, which would be set firmly on his own head. The Congregation of Clerisiarchs, always a bickering and contentious body, sat for the rest of the winter debating the issue, and failed repeatedly to reach the two-thirds majority necessary to restore the patriarchy. The most tenacious and outspoken opponent of that restoration was the hero of Mewis Field, Archdeacon Nasar-Namatu. Accustomed to the tradition of free and indeed vitriolic debate that prevailed in the Congregation of Clerisiarchs, Nasar-Namatu displayed the barest minimum deference toward the reigning monarch whose royal will he was so flagrantly flouting. His utterances, privileged though they might have been, were scrupulously noted and reported to the king by various participants. The most notable of these being Witchfinder-General Dr. Fadel, who lusted after the title of archdeacon which Kahun casually dangled in front of him.

As winter turned to spring, King Kahun, exasperated at his failure to become Patriarch, and exasperated beyond measure at the manner of that failure, took direct action to remedy the situation. Having acted, he then proceeded to discuss the matter with Archdeacon Gorabani in the privy council chamber.

"The son of a bitch is guilty of high treason!" shouted Kahun. Gorabani sighed and said nothing, folding his arms and sitting back against his carved wood chair. The King walked around the table and leaned over him. "Or don't you agree, Archdeacon of the Syncretist Church Gorabani?"

"Nasar-Namatu is not guilty of high treason, Your Majesty," he replied, "and you were a fool to arrest him for it."

"Calling me a fool is *also* treason, Gorabani!" said the king, scowling.

"Tell the truth and shame the devil, Kahun!" snapped the archdeacon with a flash of spirit. "Nasar-Namatu led the Tarelians against the Royal Palace at *your* request, and he led them at Mewis Field to fight for *your* cause! He is your ally and your friend, and you have no cause to arrest him!"

"He conspired against me in the Congregation of Clerisiarchs," Kahun said dourly, "else would I have been named patriarch long before now."

"You never had the votes," replied Gorabani. "And his opposition was open, aboveboard, and principled. He did not conspire against you!"

"You lie! I have the direct testimony of witnesses!"

"How much did you pay them?"

"Enough. Getting justice can be very dear, even for a king." Kahun poured himself a glass of wine from a crystal decanter and held it up to the candle to admire the ruby color. He inhaled the bouquet and took a slow sip, savouring the fruity flavor. Then he set the glass on the table and went back to his chair.

"Show a little mercy, then," said Gorabani. "You can afford to show mercy once in a while."

"To my enemy?"

"Nasar-Namatu isn't your enemy; he was *never* your enemy."

"You could have fooled me," growled Kahun, picking up his wine glass. "Anyway, if he wasn't my enemy before, he is now. What should I do?"

"*Now* you ask!" Gorabani studied the rings on his gloved hands for a moment. "Turn him loose?"

"Never! It is over between that man and myself!"

"If you can make a deal with Duke Falenda, you can make a deal with Nasar-Namatu."

Kahun took a sip of wine, and studied his glass in the candlelight for a long moment. "Falenda gave me the keys to the

Citadel, the gold in the royal treasury, and his sons as hostage. In return, I let the smooth-faced bastard keep his life and land. What sort of offer do I get from Archdeacon Nasar-Namatu? He invites me to martyr him. He *defies* me to martyr him! What sort of a deal can I make with a holy idiot?"

"Give up on becoming patriarch."

"No." The King shook his head. "Never. I'll give up the crown of Guhland first."

"Put it off a little, then." Gorabani picked up the decanter and poured himself a glass of wine. "Defer your gratification. A year or two isn't so terribly long to wait, is it? Let the man go; the patriarch's hat will come in time."

"What, release that old fool with an apology and wait for him to die? His father is still alive, for God's sake!" Again the king shook his head. "He won't deal, so there will be no deal."

"Well, *don't* try him on fabricated charges of high treason, then," said Gorabani. "There is a serious question of what court he should be tried in—"

"Lawyer's debating points," said Kahun, clenching his fist. "I have his ass in my hand!"

"You must be seen to do justice, Your Majesty. You are not so firmly rooted on the throne that you can willy-nilly set the law aside when it pleases you to do so."

"Oh shit." The king refilled his glass from the decanter. "You could be right. You were never so happy as when you were telling me I couldn't do what I wanted."

"Your Majesty never wanted to *wait* for anything."

"And you, you son of a bitch, you never wanted to stop studying the problem and *move*!" Kahun took a sip of wine and put the glass down on the table. "Well. What I want is Nasar-Namatu dead! What I don't want is a lot of tumult over it."

"Arresting him was criminal," said Gorabani. "Killing him would be even worse!"

"Listen to my little counselor," sneered Kahun, "so steeped in the law he can hardly move! What's worse than a *crime*, for God's sake?"

"A blunder, Your Majesty!"

"Then we won't kill him; we'll let the Church kill him."

"They won't do it."

"Witchfinder Fadel will be happy to oblige," replied Kahun gently. "The only question is which of Nasar-Namatu's supporters will go to the stake with him."

Archdeacon Gorabani sat twisting the large signet ring on his forefinger—carved bloodstone set in massive red gold, his formal seal of office—and said nothing. Later, to his private confessor, he would bitterly regret the lack of courage that kept him from resigning his high position and standing by the master of the Tarelian Order.

"I expect you're right about Fadel," he conceded at last. "If you must have Nasar-Namatu dead, that's the way to go."

"I knew it," said Kahun. "I knew it, I knew it, I *knew* it! Who else?"

"The nephew, William Namatu . . ." Gorabani sighed. "He was his uncle's chief lieutenant at Mewis Field."

"Write it down," commanded the king. "Mewis Field . . . the snow has long since melted there." The archdeacon removed his diptych from an inner pocket and made a note with his stylus. "Who else?"

"Deacons Papakostas and Ochois . . . and *maybe* Garoji." Reluctantly, the archdeacon wrote down their names, putting question marks before and after Garoji.

"Go on."

"That should suffice," said Gorabani sadly. "The threat of further prosecutions deriving from these should serve you better than any wholesale burning."

"You could be right," agreed Kahun. "Once Nasar-Namatu is replaced—by someone a little more tractable—I expect the clerisy will be much more agreeable to naming me patriarch."

"You'd wade through blood for the patriarch's hat?"

"As I did for the crown. Hat and crown together, I'll have all the fools I need to clean and polish my boots!"

"History will judge you harshly," said Gorabani. "Kahun the Terrible, they'll call you."

The king laughed. "Wimp historians! Puny scholars, bitching and creeping as they mumble the bones of antiquity . . . why should I value *their* opinion?"

"Because in a hundred years, all that men will know of you is what those wimp historians set down."

"They'll get it wrong, you can depend on it." Kahun's dark eyes looked sad for a moment. *"They'll* think Nasar-Namatu died because the Tarelians constituted a challenge to my army."

The weather was perfect for a burning. Overcast, breezy, a bit raw, but no rain after early morning showers that settled the dust in the plaza before Cymdulock Cathedral. The crowd gathered two and three hours before the ceremonies were scheduled to commence in order to assure themselves of a good view.

Besides Nasar-Namatu, his nephew, and his three deacons, Dr. Fadel had selected ten female witches so as to put two women and a man at each stake, bound elbow to elbow, facing outwards as they stood barefoot on their pile of faggots.

As bands played and choirs sang, lay preachers came up and offered absolution to each trio before burning them. All the participants on the first three stakes accepted absolution, and one of the deacons, Garoji, made a moving plea for forgiveness.

At William Namatu's stake, one of the women refused absolution and spit in the lay preacher's face. William himself refused his opportunity for salvation in order to futilely protest his innocence. He was gagged with a block of wood and sent to hell in a cloud of greasy black smoke.

Both women attached to Archdeacon Nasar-Namatu refused absolution, one of them simply shaking her head, the other screaming hysterically until gagged, then rolling her head back and forth from side to side, until the lay preacher hit her.

"Well, father," he said at last, "will you ask forgiveness for all the wickedness you have done and accept absolution from Mother Church?"

Nasar-Namatu opened one swollen and puffy eye and looked at the man. "No," he said softly.

"For the second time, father," said the lay preacher, "will you ask forgiveness for all the wickedness you have done and accept absolution from Mother Church?"

"No," said Nasar-Namatu, "but I'll tell you something—"

The lay preacher took out the wooden gag with the rope running through it. "I don't want to hear it," he said. "Now, for the third and last time, will you ask forgiveness for all the wickedness you have done and accept absolution from Mother Church?''

"Queen Shaia lives," said Nasar-Namatu. It was, he knew, a lie. But he was in pain, and he wanted to strike at Kahun. "The Witch-Queen has made her way back from the land of the dead." Kahun and Gorabani and Fadel were all up there on the reviewing stand watching. Laughing and scratching and eating fruit, and they'd want to know what his last words were, the bastards. Well, let Shaia's ghost trouble the sleep of Kahun, King of Guhland.

The lay preacher looked baffled and uncomfortable. The old man had departed totally from the script, and while his mind wondered how the king would receive the news, his mouth said, "Will you accept absolution from Mother Church?" omitting the request for admission of guilt.

"Thank you," grunted the old man, closing his eye, "I accept."

"Wait, you've got to ask forgiveness for your wickedness!"

"Absolution offered and accepted cannot be withdrawn," said Nasar-Namatu, recalling the texts of his youth. "Go away."

"Well, old fool," said the lay preacher, spitefully, "you *haven't* been absolved, you haven't, you have *not*!" But the old man paid him no heed, and he backed off the pile of faggots to let the climactic burning of the day begin.

From the reviewing stand Witchfinder Fadel looked down uneasily, sensing that something had gone awry at the last stake.

"What's that imbecile of a preacher doing?" asked Gorabani.

"Send him to us afterwards," said Kahun. "I want to know what that old fool had for his last words."

Then the lay preacher stood at the foot of the pile of faggots, and his assistant handed him the burning torch that would dispatch the three witches. He looked up at them for a moment.

"You have *not* been absolved, you old idiot!" he shouted, thrusting the torch into the base of the pile as the bands played a martial and spirited air.

At the refectory in the basement of Cymdulock Cathedral after the royal party absented themselves from the rest of the entertainment prepared for the crowd, a messenger arrived with dispatches for the king.

"The Witch-Queen is dead, Your Majesty," Archdeacon Gorabani was saying patiently, "the late and utterly unlamented Nasar-Namatu was simply rattling your cage, if you'll excuse the expression."

"But what if he *knew* something?" growled Kahun. "What if he really *was* a witch, and knew something?"

"Dispatches from the north, Your Majesty," said a courtier, leading the messenger through the crowd.

"Here, fellow," said Kahun with royal composure.

The messenger reached into his pouch and handed the king a neatly sealed stack of wooden chips. Kahun broke the seal and untied the ribbon.

"So, Fadel," he said, "one of your witchfinders got himself killed at Peejisford Bridge in an ambush. I thought you said they were real popular up north?"

"They are, Your Majesty," protested Dr. Fadel, his pale blue eyes bulging with sincerity. The king turned to the next chip.

"By a force shouting 'Shaia!' as their battle cry. Hunh." He turned to the next chip. "Queen Shaia herself appeared on the battlefield and ordered the mercenaries spared." Kahun looked up. 'Here, Gorabani," he said, handing over the last chip. "Read it. Read it out loud."

"Several mercenaries—he lists names—who knew the queen refused to fight her after she appeared on the battlefield. Subsequently, they joined her forces." Gorabani turned the chip over. "Counseling her was the wizard Doctor Wizenbeak, reputed to be a necromancer. What utter garbage!" He looked up and saw Kahun's deathly pale face. "We will, of course move to deal with any and *all* pretenders, Your Majesty, including this one." He leaned over and spoke softly into the king's ear. "For God's sake, Kahun, stop looking like that! You'll scare the horses!"

After the incineration of Archdeacon Nasar-Namatu and his "coven" the Congregation of Clerisiarchs met to consider the question of the restoration of the patriarchy with a newly sharpened appreciation of what was possible.

King Kahun, rather than lobbying himself as an equal among equals—an initial approach suggested by the witty and elegant

Gorabani, who may, as Dr. Fadel suggested, have placed the interests of the Church above those of his master—withdrew from the process and left matters in the hands of Dr. Fadel and Archdeacon Gorabani.

The Witchfinder-General, Dr. Fadel, did not appreciate subtlety.

"You are handling these people altogether too gently, Gorabani!" he protested when he and the archdeacon had withdrawn to a small conference room behind one of the altars in Cymdulock Cathedral to caucus and discuss their strategy. With them were Dr. Rehbeinji, Fadel's gap-toothed assistant, Gorabani's confessor and secretary, lay preacher Odgeanni and several assistants and helpers of one sort or another, assigned to the detail of lobbying the Congregation of Clerisiarchs for the restoration.

"We should tell them, *tell* them," insisted Fadel, bitterly, "not wheedle and plead and beg for their vote!"

"The numbers look satisfactory," replied Gorabani calmly, taking the tall carved wood seat at the head of the table, as the others settled in around it. "And if Kahun becomes patriarch— as seems very likely—and he makes *you* an Archdeacon—as he has promised—what will the title be worth if you have crushed the institution?"

"What will the title be worth if it keeps me from doing God's work?"

"God's work! Burning Nasar-Namatu was God's work?"

"Yes." Dr. Fadel's bulging blue eyes were utterly sincere. "The Church is corrupt, as you, yourself are corrupt, and Kahun is the scourge of God that will purge that corruption from the body of the Church! And the sooner the better!"

"Metaphorically, Doctor Fadel, one does not purge with a scourge!" snapped Gorabani. "Or do you mean to suggest that His Majesty is 'an enema of God'?"

The echo of the phrase "an enemy of God," which was customarily uttered when casting a witch out of the body of the Church, was deliberately shocking. It served to release the tension in the room and provoked a burst of laughter totally unwarranted by whatever feeble humor it might have possessed.

"Laugh, you fools," raged the witchfinder, "but it's the Devil's work you're doing!"

"I am doing the king's bidding," said Gorabani. "More than that, I am trying to get him what he wants . . . what he truly wants. Do you stand by your statement, Master Fadel?" Abruptly, Fadel was aware he had gone too far.

"Ahh . . ." He shook his head. "No. No. You put words in my mouth, Gorabani." He took a handkerchief and blotted his high forehead, licking his thin lips with a pale tongue.

"I would have chosen different words, witchfinder," said the archdeacon. "With all due respect, why don't you go off and burn yourself some witches? Truly, you haven't been helpful in dealing with the situation."

"The king offered to make me archdeacon—"

"Conditional on his becoming patriarch. Yes. You've done your part." Gorabani folded his gloved hands on the table and studied his rings in the colored light from the stained glass windows. "You've given me all the leverage I need to threaten the recalcitrant. They *are* scared of you. But if you front them directly, as you've been doing, well . . . corner a rat, he'll fight."

"What do you mean?"

"They already know what you can do, you and the king. Nasar-Namatu's ashes were dumped into the sewer yesterday. They haven't forgotten, you may be sure."

"So?"

"So sit back and stop making horrible faces at them, Fadel! That speech you were going to give this afternoon—"

"They would have collapsed in a heap!"

Gorabani pressed his velvet gloved fingers against his eyes for a moment.

"I think not, Doctor Fadel. If you really believe that, however, send your speech to the king for approval. I'll tell him what I think about it, and let His Majesty decide. If he says yes, and the clerisy buckles, I'll resign."

"And if they don't buckle?" asked Dr. Rehbeinji.

Archdeacon Gorabani simply smiled. Again, the witchfinder-general wiped his high forehead.

"Do it your way, then," said Fadel. "I'll not wager my position on such a small matter."

"One's professional judgment is not a small matter," replied Gorabani, "at least mine is not. What I want you to do is simply

sit in this bright and pleasant chamber here. A presence. Not
dark, not brooding, simply there. Our boys here will come in to
you and tell you what's going on, and then they'll go out again.
You won't say anything, you won't do anything, but your presence will be far more effective than anything you could say. You
understand?''

"No." Dr. Fadel shook his head.

"As a threat, you are far more effective than anything you
could actually do in the real world.''

"I burned Nasar-Namatu!"

"After Kahun seized him. And handed him over. His Majesty
may come to regret it, and if he does . . ." Archdeacon Gorabani shrugged and settled back in his chair. "That is out of our
hands, Fadel. Will you play bogeyman for me?''

"You think it will work?''

"I don't know. Your way . . . it won't. Positively.''

"I see." Fadel nodded. "How much time should we give this
farce, Rehbeinji?''

"A week," said the little man. "Ten days at the outside.''

"That should be more than sufficient," said Odgeanni pleasantly. "Sweet reason will prevail, I have no doubt.''

"I honestly think a patriarchy is a bad idea," said Archdeacon
Darussis, a small, bald man with pale blue eyes and a wispy
fringe of white hair, "and as a matter of conscience, Gorabani,
I simply cannot vote for it.''

"Indeed?" replied Archdeacon Gorabani politely. "You were
aware that Doctor Fadel proposed sending you to the stake because of your wizardly sorceries? No?'' The lean and handsome
archdeacon smiled benignly and placed his gloved hands together in an attitude of prayer. "I should have said something,
I suppose. I told Doctor Fadel that you were a loyal supporter
of the king and that we had not taken the fearful risks necessary
to secure the crown of Guhland in order to burn our friends.''
The right hand washed the left in a slow, silent gesture. The
little archdeacon paled slightly but said nothing.

"Doctor Fadel was not happy," continued Gorabani, "but
he had, in the end, to concede my point. I do hope that we can
continue to count upon your support." He smiled and put his

arm around Darussis' shoulder. Unspoken was the fate of Nasar-Namatu, the hero of Mewis Field and longtime friend of Prince Kahun, but he hung like a pall of greasy black smoke over the deliberations of the congregation.

Three days later, the Congregation of Clerisiarchs restored the patriarchate, and the following week, to avoid the impression of unseemly haste, the patriarch's hat was proffered to Kahun, King of Guhland.

Who, of course, refused. It was offered again, and refused again, Kahun proclaiming that he was all unworthy of this high honor. The citizens of Cymdulock were mobilized and brought out into the streets and plazas to pray that the king accept this burden on their behalf. The king was deeply moved by this tangible expression of devotion, and when the patriarch's hat was offered him a third time, he wept and accepted it in a tasteful display of public humility.

His first nonceremonial act was to name the good and faithful Witchfinder-General Dr. Fadel as archdeacon, replacing the late Nasar-Namatu as Captain-General of the Tarelian Order.

Kahun held court in the ballroom of his father's summer palace, a vast expanse of polished parquet hardwood flooring under a cathedral roof of soaring wooden beams, whose architectural integrity had been preserved by encasing the wooden staves supporting the ceiling inside a wooden falsework supporting a prismatic display of mirrors up to a height of nine feet, and a gessoed and gilt decoration for six feet above that. At that point, the stave, lightly carved, and polychromed, rose another six feet to join the purlins that defined the edge of the room. On each side, a lean-to roof defined two suites of rooms, decorated in red on the right and green on the left, which ran the length of the ballroom. Kahun's throne was set near the south end, facing the windows that opened on the lake in the north.

The throne itself was set on a low dais, framed by four posts at the corners. These posts supported a cloth-of-gold canopy, rather like a tent, with the drapes of cloth gathered and bound to the posts. From the lofty ceiling, a giant replica of the crown of Guhland was suspended, supported by chains, and the point of the canopy was attached to the nabla at the crest of the crown.

The courtiers stood about the dais, approaching the king as they had business with him, or as they were summoned.

King-Patriarch Kahun sat on his throne, resplendent in the gold and white silken robes of the patriarch, which he wore over the utterly plain black hauberk which he had worn at Mewis Field. On his head was the patriarch's hat, not the formal hat, stiff with jewels and tradition, but a lesser version, a cap, almost, white silk, decorated with gold wire and pearls. Looking about his court, Kahun caught the eye of the freshly minted Archdeacon Dr. Fadel, Witchfinder-General and master of the Tarelian Order. Kahun crooked a finger, and Fadel at once mounted the dais and stood at the side of the throne.

Archdeacon Fadel, wearing the newly tailored scarlet robes of his rank, and golden chains, and signet rings with seals cut into precious stones, stood next to his master before the eyes of the court and felt such a rush of exaltation that it made his head swim.

"Well, now, Fadel," said Kahun, "as the new master of the Tarelian Order, how do we propose to proceed?"

"Ah, why, I imagine it would be to put my own people into the key positions in the Tarelian Order, father."

"That can wait," was the reply. "In the north, as you may have heard, a rebellion is being raised against us."

"The false Shaia? No problem. We'll catch her and her wizard too, and burn the lot."

"You'll have to wear two hats, then," said Kahun, "Captain-General of the Tarelian Order to catch her, witchfinder-general to burn her. The rebels have killed a score of witchfinders and intimidated the rest. A witch at the stake dies crying 'Long Live Shaia!' and the fool in charge of the execution has a nervous breakdown."

"The help you get these days," Fadel sighed.

"Amen." sighed Kahun, contemplating his witchfinder. How much should I tell this fool? he wondered. He's happy chasing after the False Shaia. Does he also need to know that the alleged Prince Dervian has been positively identified as my very own half brother? Probably not. The fewer people that know, the better. Besides, he'd only get upset at Darussis for using magic to make the identification. And if Fadel knew that "Prince Dervian'' was real, well, if he caught the little son of a bitch he might hesitate about killing him.

"The rebels have raised the standard of Prince Dervian," he continued gravely, "who has, in theory, at least, as good a claim as mine own to this throne I sit on."

"Surely a false prince as well as a false queen, Your Majesty."

"Father. Make life simple, and call me by the hat on my head," said Kahun with the faintest of smiles. "Trying to figure out my metaphorical hats could be confusing."

"Yes, Father."

"Good," said Kahun, nodding. "Now the false Shaia . . . there is, witchfinder, some doubt about Shaia . . . she may be necromantical, though Darussis swears she is not."

"How would he know?"

"What? Oh, she moves too competently, she talks without prompting and makes sense . . . that sort of thing."

"Hunh," grunted Fadel, "all that proves is that this Wizenbeak is a stronger wizard than Darussis."

"Darussis goes by the book," said Kahun, "and necromancy is one of the things he knows about. He may be weak on practice, but he knows the theory." He looked out over the court at the lake beyond the glass doors, his dark eyes brooding. "I want the Tarelians to go up north and wipe them out. You understand?"

"Yes, Father. What help can you give me?"

"Nothing." The king shook his head. "We are very tight for cash right now. Tap that enormous war chest that I am sure the Tarelians kept full of gold and silver."

"No, no . . ." Fadel held up his hands in an imploring gesture. "I've never commanded an army before. Or even stood on the field of battle. I'll do what you ask, but help me to not disgrace myself."

"That's different." Kahun almost smiled. "You deserve credit for knowing your limits. So many men don't. Well." He folded his hands together, and sat back on his throne. "What I'll do, I'll let you have my best general. Make him your lieutenant and trust him, you understand?"

"Yes, father, I shall do so, and at once. Now if I might have a minute, a little minute of your time, I have a complaint against Archdeacon Gorabani—nothing serious, a very trivial complaint, hardly worth mentioning, except as it belittled your own dignity . . .''

# 24

# Tarelians to Autmerida

TWITTERING and chirping the troll-bats swarmed over Jankura, seeking the tiny seedcakes and dried avricods which she carried. She laughed, but Mischka, her familiar, stayed seated on her shoulder, contemplating the antics of his relatives with beady black eyes. In the doorway of the glazed courtyard, Wizenbeak stood with Gruchka, watching. Beside him was Master Dassenji, whose establishment, newly translated to Zenberg on the altiplano, made mother-of-glass.

"Now I would be afraid to do that," said Wizenbeak. "I have confidence in Gruchka, here, but to immerse myself . . ." He shivered slightly. "Even the kittens are dangerous."

"Especially the kittens," agreed Dassenji. "A kitten can draw the support of all the adults in a second, and they'll tear you to pieces without thinking about it . . . they'd be sorry afterwards, of course, but that doesn't help *you* much."

As they watched, a kitten leaped up and pulled Jankura's head to one side with a roughness quite disproportionate to its size. There was a tiny crackle of electricity, and the kitten gave a little yip and bounded to the floor, closely followed by its mother. The mother scolded for a second, washed her wayward infant with her tongue until it started to complain, and then went back for another seedcake.

"Amazing," said Dassenji. "What did she do?"

"Nothing," replied the wizard. "She let Mischka do it for her. Adult troll-bats have ways to keep the young ones in line, and Mischka protects her without disturbing the others."

"With troll-bats I've worked all my life, Master Wizenbeak, but this is something I've never seen."

"Of course," agreed the wizard, stroking Gruchka's ears very gently. "You wanted them to make mother-of-glass, which is dull, boring work for a troll-bat unless they get liquored up a little bit. So you never had much to do with the *sober* ones, and for good reason. But Janko is training them to . . . to work in a pack, something they did naturally in the wild—"

"There you go again," said Dassenji. "Troll-bats never existed in the wild; troll-bats were always the creatures of dragons, who—"

"Are we back to the old tales again, Master Dassenji?" Wizenbeak grinned, twisting a strand of whisker around one finger. "For whatever reason, Janko is able to train them with utterly amazing success. And for now that is what is needed." As they watched, Jankura picked up a wooden board and laid it across the clay pots holding two fragrant citron trees, so that it was supported at each end. She gestured, and one of the older bats with velvety smooth brown fur shading to gray around the ears and muzzle, leaped on the board and laid one wing on top of the other.

"Now, babies . . ." whispered Jankura softly, and each of the troll-bats turned and watched the older bat sitting on the board with intense, unnerving concentration. Even Gruchka. Wizenbeak could feel the slight tugging at his back muscles, and he held up a finger to his familiar. Gruchka chittered, but the back muscles relaxed.

Until the board broke with a sharp snap under the troll-bat's overlapped wings; then Wizenbeak felt a slight stab, as if he had made an involuntary contribution to the impulse that broke the board.

"Very good, Manghar, very, *very* good," said Jankura, and when the gray-muzzled troll-bat came to her, she reached into her pocket and gave him a dried avricod, stroking his back and ears as he ate. After fussing over for him for a bit, she set another board out and repeated the process with a second troll-bat, and a third.

"Well, Master Wizenbeak," she said, picking up the half boards, "this is our finale." She laid out the boards so they spanned various pots, or in one case, a couple of adobe blocks, and turned to the troll-bats. One after another, six of the little animals, none of which had performed before, took their places, one at each board. Jankura drew herself up and very slowly raised her right arm, as Mischka, sitting on her left shoulder chattered softly, almost conversationally. Hey now, thought Wizenbeak, I can damn near hear the drumroll.

The three troll-bats that had gone first huddled together briefly, and then began to go around to the others who hadn't performed, somehow encouraging them in what they were doing. Gruchka climbed down from his master's shoulder and joined one of the groups that was supporting the board breakers. There was a tense pause, and then Jankura dropped her arm, as five boards broke simultaneously, and the sixth broke a fraction of a second later.

"Ya-hai!" she yelled, as the troll-bats leaped around the glass-enclosed courtyard, swinging from trees, bouncing off the walls, enjoying the release from tension.

"I'm impressed," said Wizenbeak. "I really am. The little monsters performed beautifully. Will they do it for you in the real world?"

"Of course," said Jankura. "Little Mischka will make sure they all understand, won't you Mischka?" Her familiar chirped softly, and she caressed his ears.

Witchfinder-General Dr. Fadel rode into Autmerida on a great black horse, General Macedak, his able lieutenant, beside him on a bay mare. Behind them rode Fadel's staff and personal bodyguard; before them the mounted scouts had already established that the village was undefended. In the van marched eleven thousand Tarelians, wearing the traditional green and black of the order. Fadel had wished to redesign the uniform, but Macedak (and Kahun) argued against it as an unnecessary and frivolous expense, and since time was also a consideration, Fadel had deferred issuing the new uniforms for the time being. Now they marched and countermarched across the northern tier of counties, seeking the elusive forces of Shaia, the Witch-Queen.

A few villagers stood on the streets, gaping and cheering as the horses clattered over the stone bridge spanning the Cobble

Wash, and followed Military Road up to Third Street, which went left, only.

At the intersection, General Macedak called the army to a halt, and with several staff officers and a few scouts rode down Third Street toward the headquarters of the Holy Inquisition. The gate hung open on one bent hinge, displaying the desolate and empty stable yard. One of the scouts rode in, dismounted, tied his horse to a hitching post, and ran up a ladder to the loft of the barn. After a moment he looked out from the hay gate and waved his comrades to come in. As Macedak sat watching, several scouts rode around the premises looking for witches, witch lovers, or stray mercenaries. Nothing. Eventually, one of them went up to the main entrance where he knocked at the door. After a long time, an old woman with a broom opened it and he stepped inside, holding the door open for his comrades.

"General, sir," he said when he returned, "I asked the old bat to take me to Witchfinder Wrascha, and she led me down into the dungeon where there was one bearded old idiot in one of the cells. She said that was him. Otherwise the place is empty."

"I see," said Macedak. "Perhaps it *is* him. I'm going to investigate. Would you invite the witchfinder-general to go in with me?"

After a moment Fadel rode up with his retinue.

"What is it you want, Macedak?" he asked.

"I thought you might wish to go into your local headquarters with me to meet Witchfinder Wrascha," said General Macedak politely. He did not add 'My best man in the whole Northern Tier.' Fadel, after all, would have a hand on his future advancement.

They dismounted and went inside, looking around the gutted interior. Everything of value had been removed, and some of the fixtures had been ruined in the effort. A scout led them to the dungeon stairs, and lit a lantern for them as they went down.

"Something's wrong," said Fadel. A dungeon typically has a stench of excrement, blood, and adrenaline. This cellar smelled of dank earth and cut wood. As if it had never been used. On the far side of the room was a row of tiny cells, the kind in which the prisoner could neither sit, stand, nor lie. The very last cell was closed with a padlock, and in the cell crouched a sad-looking man with a three-day growth of beard. There were no keys nor tools to break the lock, and the rack, stocks, ladder, and whipping posts had all been removed. One of the scouts came in with an iron bar and broke the padlock. The door swung open and Wrascha crawled out.

"How long did they keep you prisoner?" asked Macedak. Wrascha blinked at the lantern, but his eyes adjusted quickly enough.

"Since last winter, excellency . . ." he said. Then, turning to Fadel, "Oh, master, the villains took me prisoner after I'd hardly begun!"

"Stand up," said the witchfinder-general, uncomfortable at his subordinate's abasement. One of the scouts lifted Wrascha by one arm and steadied him as he tried to stand straight.

"We have been relying on *his* reports?" asked General Macedak, looking at the witchfinder-general. Fadel said nothing, but after a long time he nodded.

"They made me sign them," cried Wrascha piteously. "They kept me in chains, and in the cold, cold well house, and when the wizard wanted me to sign, he'd threaten me with terrible things!"

"You could have chosen martyrdom," said Fadel.

"Wizenbeak's assistant *wanted* to . . ." Wrasha said. "Janko wanted to . . . to . . ." his voice sunk to a whisper. "When I was taken prisoner, he threatened to cut off my pizzle. Janko really *hated* me. He would have done it, too, if Wizenbeak had let him. The wizard wasn't mean to me . . . I was never afraid of *him* . . . but his assistant . . ." His voice trailed off.

"Well," said Fadel. "You have seriously inconvenienced us by signing all those false reports." He turned to General Macedak. "What should we do with him? Hang him?"

"He's *your* subordinate," Macedak replied. "But why hang him? For being unlucky?"

"For cooperating with the forces of evil."

"Oh, horseshit, Doctor Fadel! He cooperated under duress, and when he became useless, they abandoned him. Is failure to achieve martyrdom on demand a hanging offense?"

"No. But, Wrascha, you're compromised, you're useless, you're finished with the Holy Inquisition!" Fadel, white-faced with rage, hit him across the face with the back of his hand. Wrasha recoiled, almost fell, as the scout by his side steadied him. "You're *fi-ired*, Wrascha! Do you understand?"

Wrascha nodded. "S'all righ'," he said, blood trickling from the corner of his mouth. "I couldn't torture anybody anymore anyhow."

Standing at the top of Merida Gap, Wizenbeak, Genzari, Count Braley, Captain Zeldones, and Jankura looked down at the village below.

"So. The Tarelians are making camp on the south side of Cobble Wash," said Genzari. "Think we should stir them up a little?"

"A night attack might be just the thing," said Count Braley, nodding in agreement. "We haven't so much as cut a sentry's throat the whole time we've been chasing around with them."

"Why not just fade away like we've been doing?" asked Wizenbeak.

"If we're going to wipe the sons of bitches out, we've got to take them off balance," Genzari replied. "Right now, they *know* we won't fight."

"And we have Sejenics with eight hundred men down there," said Count Braley. "Plus five hundred up here. Where should we hit 'em?"

"On the south end of their bivouac," said Genzari. "Just ride through Autmerida and roll 'em up. And then turn around and execute a fast advance to the rear."

"How will we coordinate the attack?" asked Zeldones.

"I'll fire one of my special rockets," said Wizenbeak, "a giant tamale dripping golden hot sauce will be the signal to begin. A second rocket, ten minutes later, will be the signal to withdraw, all right?"

"Make it fifteen minutes," said Genzari, fingering his closely clipped mustache. "Should we try for twenty?" He considered the matter for a moment and shook his head. "Fifteen. To start at midnight?"

The count glanced at the sun and nodded. "That gives us all the time we need," he agreed. "I'll get on the mirror to Sejenics and coordinate both groups. We go up into Merida Gap?"

"Where else?" asked Genzari.

The wizard looked pained. "What if they follow us?"

"That, Master Wizenbeak," said Jankura with regal politeness, "is the whole idea. If you'd stay awake at the planning sessions you'd know what all is going on."

A night attack is about three times more chaotic than normal warfare. Braley's men were in position, waiting for the rocket when Sejenics' men, advancing, failed to silence a sentry. In the still night air the plaintive cry "Corporal of the Guard! C—" sounded like the trumpet of doom.

"Move it!" snapped Braley. "Sound the attack!"

The bugler sounded the attack as Braley's men swarmed into the bivouac area, cutting tent ropes, killing half-awake Tarelians. Sejenics, hearing the attack had already started, launched his attack with the men that he had in place, about a third of his total force, rolling into the bivouac from the east as Braley hit them from the southeast. After about ten minutes they were beginning to encounter organized resistance when the last grains of sand in Wizenbeak's hourglass fell, and he lit the fuse on his rocket, signalling the start of the attack.

The rocket was beautiful and spectacular. And since all the attacking forces knew it was to begin the attack and end it, now that they were *already* attacking, it must logically signal the retreat. So Count Braley watched his men turn around without orders, and when he was unable to get them to resume the attack, he bowed to the inevitable and made the retreat as orderly as possible. Nick Sejenics was in a somewhat different case; leading his men personally, he was engaged in a series of swiftly shifting swordfights, and when the rocket went off, it was necessary to first disengage before withdrawing. The companies that had not reached the Tarelian's line, Instructor Retsji's group, stopped advancing toward the bivouac area and fell out on either side of the path they were following, waiting to rejoin Sejenics' group.

As Sejenics' force fought their way back along the predetermined line of retreat, they were hotly pursued by several companies of Tarelians, and as the sounds of battle carried through the night air, Instructor Retsji, the mercenary swordmaster from Peejisford Bridge, correctly interpreted them, and relieved Sejenics' force by ambushing their pursuers—a fortunate happenstance, which, had it been proposed for use would have been rejected as totally impractical for a night attack because of its excessive complexity. In the event, a larger force was surprised by a smaller one, and due to the darkness and prevailing confusion the larger force suffered moderate casualties and withdrew in panic.

Sejenics and Retsji formed up their troops and withdrew to the meadow where their horses had been held. There they mounted up and withdrew to Camp Merida at the edge of the altiplano, singing as they rode and making no effort to hide their trail.

"This is intolerable!" shouted Fadel the next morning. "I will not stand for it! They went up the road into Merida Gap, and we are, by God, going after them!!"

"You want to chase men on horseback with infantry?" asked Macedak sourly. "You want to march around the Semeryan until we come to the edge of the world? What will we do there?"

"One thing we learned from Wrascha," said Fadel, "was that he was held in Castle Wizenbeak, about sixty miles north of the gap. A castle, newly built and weakly held. They can run on horses all they want, but we can march up and strike their base such a blow that they'll never recover. I say we do it!"

"There's no water in the Semeryan, sir."

"Logistical details, General Macedak. Attend to them!"

The logistical details took the better part of a month, the first step being to secure the Merida Gap itself. Macedak had no intention of trying to move a long supply train up against a fortified mountain. Camp Merida was not a stronghold to be defended by a handful of men against an army, but it was a position of great natural strength. In the end, Macedak sent a column of twenty-five hundred men up to

Springhill, where they marched along the edge of the altiplano toward Merida Gap.

Lasco Genzari, apprised of their progress by his scouts, withdrew from Camp Merida the day before the Tarelians stormed it. Neither side suffered any casualties, and Witchfinder-General Dr. Fadel had his foothold on the altiplano.

# 25

# The March on Zenberg

CAMP Merida, built on the heights that dominated the Merida Gap, had, under Wizenbeak and Genzari been a collection of low adobe buildings, built for convenience and administration rather than defense. At most, Camp Merida might have housed several hundred men, and was not visible from the village of Autmerida. After Genzari withdrew, Dr. Fadel wished to celebrate this notable victory by raising King-Patriarch Kahun's battle standard to display to the world at large. Since Wizenbeak had felt it impolitic to flaunt his colors, no suitable flagpole was in place, and Kahun's flag could not be raised until a suitable flagpole was brought up.

Once the flagpole was set and the battle standard raised with suitable ceremony, Dr. Fadel, entranced with the ease of military engineering, proposed that Camp Merida be strengthened and made permanent. His lieutenant, General Macedak, demurred gently.

"Well, why in God's name *don't* we enlarge and fortify this very strategically located campsite?" asked Dr. Fadel, sitting on his great black horse. "As it is, there's hardly room for the headquarters personnel."

"Well, for one thing, there's no water," replied General Macedak, pulling his cloak tighter against the raw spring wind. "For another, you can waste a *lot* of time building, and we've *already* wasted a whole bloody month just getting up here." He looked over the camp's low adobe buildings, squinting against the bright morning sunlight. "I personally think it's disgraceful for an army to fortify itself against a force hardly a tenth its size. We ought to go out and smash them . . . or disperse them, if we can't catch them.''

"Are you still worried about catching them?" asked Fadel. "God will deliver them into our hands, I have no doubt."

"That may well be why His Majesty assigned me to direct your campaign," was the reply. "The Tarelians, with ten to one numerical superiority do, in fact, have God on their side, and they are truly outstanding fighters, but they are, after all, infantry. They walk. Genzari's men may fight on foot, but they're mounted. The cowardly witch-loving sons of bitches ride."

"You have no faith, general."

"I don't need faith, I need horses. We don't even have enough draft animals to haul our water wagons."

"Those enormous barrel wains? What do you need so many for?"

"Ah, Doctor Fadel. You have eleven thousand men, who are going into these waterless wastes to give battle to the enemy. Thirsty work, battles. And marching and countermarching in this wasteland is thirsty work, too." General Macedak leaned forward on his mount, and pushed his visored and turbaned helmet back on his head. "The village of Zenberg and Castle Wizenbeak is two days march north of here, supposedly. I allow three days, permitting a little lost time. The castle at last report, was a motte and bailey affair, with a board fence on top of the motte and a weak bailey. We should be able to take it by storm in an afternoon, right?"

"Ah, yes . . . yes, of course." Dr. Fadel recognized a rhetorical question when he heard one, but he could not imagine where Macedak was leading.

"I wouldn't bet on it," was the reply. "If we go out there and discover we *can't* take the place by storm, we have to turn around and march back home because we don't have the water to conduct a siege. So we take four days' worth of water to give us the time to besiege the place if we need to."

"What if we don't have to?"

"Hey, great! Wonderful! Look, Doctor Fadel, it really *is* cheaper to prepare for the worst case than to cut corners and scrimp to the point where any little bit of bad luck screws up your campaign. Would you rather spend too much and win, or lose because you spent too little?''

"Well, three days to get there, and four days to take the place isn't unreasonable,'' conceded the witchfinder. "But those barrel wains—what did you call them?''

"Water wagons.''

"Yes. Those water wagons. Each wagon provides water for the entire army for one day, right?''

"That isn't the way we use them,'' said General Macedak, "but, yes, that's just about right.'' Overhead a hawk soared, making lazy circles on a rising air current. *Why don't you swoop down and carry off my imbecile boss?* thought Macedak. *I'd report that you were a dragon and get on with the campaign.*

"We only need seven, general, six, really. Three to go out on a two-day march, four for a siege which may not be needed. You're building a dozen.''

"Yes.'' There was a rather long pause. "So?''

"We only need *seven*, for God's sake! Why the other five?''

"We do have to come back, after all,'' said Macedak mildly. "That's three of your five right there.''

"There is a well at Zenberg and another at Castle Wizenbeak,'' said the witchfinder-general. "We'll take them and refill our water wagons on the spot. You don't need those three. In fact, you don't need the last five!''

"In a war wells get poisoned, or polluted, or filled in, Doctor Fadel. If you are depending on the generosity of your enemy to ensure your survival, you won't last long . . . even with God's direct intervention. You, yourself were telling me last night what terrible people they are, after all.''

"So I was. So they are. So you need the three to come home. What about the other two?''

"In the desert a little extra water never hurt anybody,'' said Macedak. "Why do you begrudge them to me?''

"Because it's going to take days to get the draft animals to haul them,'' Fadel replied. "You're wasting time!''

Macedak's eyes went again to the soaring hawk. *That fool witchfinder would spend the whole damn summer building a fort we don't need against that utterly underwhelming rabble out there,* thought General Macedak resignedly. *But spend a day or* two in prudent preparation, and he goes mad with impatience. He shook his head.

"You might remember . . . I was given this honorable assignment because you asked the king for help to keep you from disgracing yourself, Doctor Fadel. If I succeed, that time will have been well spent, won't it?"

Three days later, the mules arrived for the last water wagons, and the next morning, Volsday, the Tarelians prepared to march on Castle Wizenbeak. It rained, not much, but enough to settle the dust, and a rainbow appeared, which was taken as either a good omen, or, as Dr. Fadel put it in his sermon to his troops, "a direct and heartening sign of God's interest and approbation." The sermon, which ran three hours, delayed the start of the march until after ten in the morning. Since Macedak had his extra water, he put up with it.

When they set out, Macedak called Dr. Fadel's attention to a small party of horsemen riding a few thousand yards ahead of them.

"Those are Genzari's scouts," he said. "What do you think we ought to do about them?"

The witchfinder squinted, but he was nearsighted, and saw nothing but a brownish blur where Macedak had pointed. "They don't look like so very many," he said doubtfully. "Should we chase them off?"

"No. They can't stop us, but we can't catch them, either. Besides, Doctor Fadel . . . most of our horses are under your own personal staff. If they pursued the enemy over the horizon and into an ambush, it would be a loss we could ill afford." A loss which might reflect adversely on my judgment back at court, he thought, never mind that they wouldn't be missed.

The Tarelians made camp at sundown, forty-seven miles south of Castle Wizenbeak.

On a little rise of ground to the north, Wizenbeak and Jankura, garbed as Queen Shaia, watched the Tarelian campfires, laid out in a neat rectangle of little points of light. With them were Lasco Genzari, Nick Sejenics, Count Braley, and Instructor Retsji, and others.

"Well, Master Genzari," said Jankura, "what think you of a night attack?"

"Not tonight, Your Majesty," said Genzari gravely. "General Macedak has posted a strong guard against exactly that possibility. I would leave them alone for tonight."

"I see." Jankura turned to the others. "Gentlemen?"

"I agree with General Genzari," said Braley. "The time to hit them is tomorrow night, when they will be about fifteen or sixteen miles from Castle Wizenbeak."

"I agree," said Sejenics. "Tomorrow will be decisive."

"I also," said Retsji, softly. "Let them stay awake for nothing tonight."

"Good," said Jankura. "Tomorrow night it will be, then." She reached into her pocket and produced a little seedcake which she fed to Mischka, who nibbled at it daintily.

Later, in the command tent, when she sat at a supper of flatbread and hard cheese with Wizenbeak, she asked how she was doing, seeking reassurance and approbation in the unfamiliar role which events had thrust upon her.

"So far, so good," said the wizard, taking a sip of herb tea. "Prince Dervian likes you. Princess Marjia thinks you're nicer than her real mother . . . which wasn't all that hard, evidently. Both of them seem willing to accept our strategic arrangement . . . more important, maybe, both of them seem to trust you." He watched the fragrant steam rising from his cup for a moment.

"Our interests coincide," said Jankura. "Of course, I couldn't play the part if they were opposed."

"Probably not," he conceded, "at least not as easily. Even so, you're beginning to have a certain plausibility—what did Genzari call it? 'street credibility.' Yes. The redoubtable Count Braley who *knew* the late Shaia, who was in conference with her the day she died, *he* accepts you as the rightful queen. If we win, nobody will doubt it." He took a second sip of the hot tea and put the mug on the table.

"Is that such a big if, master?"

The wizard misunderstood the question. "If we lose, we'll be dead, and you won't have to worry."

Jankura looked annoyed. "I accept that; I accept that if we lose, I'll die. *You* should accept the possibility that we might win. And if we win, master, life will become more than a little complicated.''

"What do you mean?''

"You ought to be making plans to deal with victory," she said. "Since you haven't, last night I summoned Genzari to my quarters." She looked composed and stern, and Wizenbeak felt suddenly uneasy, as if he were a schoolboy caught playing the truant or the fool. "He was there when you rescued me from the witchfinder; he knows that I am not what I pretend to be. He was bound to *you* by the mercenaries oath only, master. So I made him Prince Dervian's chief general, and mine, and he, in turn, accepted me as his liege and swore to serve us faithfully unto death. You know what he told me?''

The wizard took a sip of tea and raised an eyebrow.

"He said he was worried that he knew too much, that at some point we'd have to get rid of him. I told him our cause could not endure his loss.''

"No," said Wizenbeak, "we could go with Count Braley.''

"That's what Genzari said. And he suggested that I take oath from Sejenics as well.''

"Have you done so?'' he asked. Jankura nodded. "What about the other chap that was along that night?''

"Kulyk? He was killed in that night raid.''

"You might win at that," conceded the wizard, pushing his dark glasses up on his forehead and rubbing his eyes. "You, who have sworn to serve me, would be sitting on the throne as Shaia, Queen of Guhland . . . whom I have sworn to serve.'' He sighed. "I can see the relationship between us changing, oath or no oath.''

"I wouldn't be queen," Jankura said. "I'd be regent for my son, Prince Dervian.''

"A lovely boy, but not—'' the wizard checked himself. Sometimes it didn't pay to remember the truth too accurately, and if Jankura had internalized the role of Shaia, she'd play it better. "Absolutely," he said, contemplating his apprentice rising to the throne of Guhland. Genzari had been right to worry, he decided. "Riding a tiger is hard, but absolutely nothing compared to dismounting." He sighed. "Perhaps old Wizenbeak is the one that should try to dismount. You don't really need my poor services—"

"No, master! Kings and queens always have wise and trusted counsellors! You'd be my—what did Genzari call it? Gray Eminence. You'd give me wise advice to follow."

He smiled a little sadly. "You don't follow my advice now, you know."

"Only about troll-bats. You know about Gruchka, so you think you know about troll-bats. But when they socialize with each other, when they grow up in company with their families, if you know what I mean, they're different."

"You still don't follow my advice . . . and how do *you* know about the family life of troll-bats?"

"I just know. You aren't even asking the right questions."

"In some areas you have far surpassed me," conceded the wizard. "You are extremely good with animals, but—"

"There are great gaping holes in my knowledge," she agreed. "The oath was 'Till death or I release you.' If you want to release me and scuttle off, I won't stop you, but I could use your help. I'd like you to stay."

The relationship between us *has* changed, he thought with mild amazement. She wants me to stay and I feel obligated to do so. He took a sip of tea, heavily sugared from the bottom of the cup, and shrugged. Where would he be going, anyway? "So I'll stay," said Wizenbeak. "However, you should know that being a queen or a regent or whatever raises hell with one's judgment. So many people tell you what they think you want to hear that the truth is an aesthetic disaster."

"Yes, master," Jankura said. "I'll always know that you are giving me wise advice. And I'll do my best to make wise decisions."

Even if you don't agree with me, he thought. Well, maybe it would work out . . . she was right about the troll-bats.

Early the next morning the Tarelians broke camp and marched thirty-two miles before halting for the evening. Again, a heavy watch was posted, and the camp fires glowed in a precise rectangular grid.

Genzari looked at the black thread and the white thread in his hand, and nodded. "I can tell 'em apart, Your Majesty," he said softly. "Let's get started."

Jankura caressed Mischka and cooed to him for a moment, and then opened the canvas flap on the wagon behind her. Chirping and chittering, the male troll-bats came swarming out, climbing on her arms and nuzzling against her body. They were naturally nocturnal animals, but it was colder than they liked. She talked to Mischka, and looked out over the Tarelian camp as she gave the troll-bats their assignments. On the other side of the wagon, Master Dassenji and Wizenbeak opened the flap to let the females and young come out. There was a small iron camp stove fired up with charcoal to take the chill off, and a windlass with no rope or cable. Four volunteers stood by the spokes of the windlass, looking nervously at the troll-bats. Dassenji, who knew and raised them, was so unnerved by the prospect of working with troll-bats in a fully alert state that he had helped himself to the avricod brandy, and was consequently calm to the point of passing out.

After a few moments Mischka twittered.

"They're in position," Jankura said quietly. "Start feeding them."

Wizenbeak nodded to the volunteers who started walking around the unresisting windlass. "Go on, Gruchka," he said, "show us a little leadership."

Gruchka leaped off his shoulder and ran over to the shaft of the windlass, chattering and scolding. Two or three of the older females came over and joined him, as they each lay their soft, webbed hands on the freely rotating shaft. Then, one after another, the other troll-bats joined them, surrounding the shaft and hiding it with webbed hands. The volunteers were now beginning to work, pushing their way around, and Wizenbeak nudged Dassenji.

"Come on, old man," he said, "let's show these young weakies how it's done!"

"Yesh," Dassenji muttered, as the wizard led him over to the windlass. He took an arm, alongside the straining young man already pushing it, and Wizenbeak took his place on the arm opposite him as both pushed with all their might.

"We have it," Jankura said suddenly. "Start the attack, Mr. Genzari."

For answer there was a sudden drumming of hoofbeats as Genzari's first wave swept down on the Tarelian camp from the east, the gradually brightening sky at their backs to dazzle the night-adjusted eyes of the Tarelian sentries.

This was not a mounted infantry attack, such as the night attack that had been made outside Autmerida; this was the classical light cavalry attack with spear and sword, and as the Tarelians came pouring out of their tents, with arrows as well. Dark figures shadowed by brightening sky behind them loosed arrows at the men emerging into the first light of dawn, confused by the sudden onslaught and caught in the bright sunlight that did not yet illuminate their enemy. There were shouts and cries, and without prompting from their officers the Tarelians began to form up into hedgehogs, a defensive formation against cavalry, circular groups of men, with their spears held tangent to the circle. When fully formed, there would be archers inside the hedgehog, taking deadly aim from such cover as their comrades could afford.

Behind the cavalry came the second wave, Nick Sejenics leading the infantry—men who could not or would not fight on horseback—and as the Tarelians attempted to form up, they charged them, a wedge of spearmen on foot, and swords flashing in the morning light, shouting the battlecry "Dervian! Dervian!" They broke the first line, which had not properly formed, and hit the second line, driving it back as the cavalry swept around to turn its flank. The third line, however, was ready and standing firm, and it absorbed the retreating second line and was beginning to advance against Sejenics' men, when there was a cry from the center of the camp.

"The wagons! They've smashed the water wagons!"

The male troll-bats, following Jankura's orders had flown into the center of the Tarelian camp, where the water wagons, protected on all four sides, were parked for maximum security. As the attack began, the sentries were distracted and failed to see the tiny, shadowy figures pouncing on the huge barrel wains. The troll-bats spread webbed hands on the ends of the wooden barrels and released the force that was slowly being generated at the windlass in a sharp, powerful pulse. The barrels shattered, and the water poured out onto the ground as the troll-bats pounced on the next water wagon. A staff officer, one of Fadel's men, came charging out of his tent with a sword in each hand, striking at the elusive troll-bats, shouting for them to stop.

"Stand firm!" shouted Sejenics. Then from behind the Tarelian line came a scream, and terrified cry.

"Troll-bats! The Witch-Queen is using troll-bats!"

The Tarelian third line advanced a few paces, and then the head of one of Fadel's staff officers came arching over their ranks and landed between the lines, rolling—the visored and turbaned helm fixed firmly under the bearded chin; the neck not neatly severed, as a sword would have cut it, but twisted like a chicken's neck.

One of the junior officers, selected for ideological rectitude rather than bravery, started to run.

General Macedak himself grabbed a spear from one of his soldiers and threw it, catching the young officer between the shoulder blades. The man went down, but the cry, "Troll-bats!" was repeated, and another officer broke ranks.

"Charge!" yelled Sejenics, and hurled his infantry at the center of the Tarelian line, driving to engage General Macedak himself.

Suddenly, on the left of the line, Witchfinder-General Dr. Fadel appeared, trying to mount his horse. The horse, frightened by the noises of battle, was shying and pulling away from him, dragging Fadel by the reins wrapped around one wrist.

"Witchcraft!" he screamed, his hauberk pulled on over his pajamas. "Witchcraft! They smashed the barrel wains! All the water is spilled! Witchcraft and troll-bats! Run! Run! We've got to get away!" The sheer terror in Fadel's voice was the last straw. His officers, the ones he had appointed to ensure his control of the order, threw down their arms and started to run. Abruptly the Tarelian line began to disintegrate.

Macedak stood alone for a second, appalled at the rout he was witnessing.

"Tarelians!" he cried in a great voice. "TARELIANS! Stop running!"

A few of the men nearest him hesitated, and then Instructor

Retsji reached him, a few steps ahead of Sejenics, and brought his sword down in a single-handed cut at Macedak's head. There was a flash of sparks as the general's helmet deflected the blow, and Macedak cut at the inside of Retsji's extended leg, slicing through the hauberk and severing the femoral artery. Sejenics made a two-handed cut at the general's right side, cutting through the shoulder harness and into the cuirass, where his sword stuck. Macedak slashed at Sejenics, using wrist and forearm only, slicing the outer layer of his hauberk but not penetrating it, and then Retsji made a two-handed cut, severing the general's head, which looked almost serene as it hit the ground. The body stood for a second, supported by Sejenics' sword. Then the knees buckled, and as the general's body fell, Sejenics yanked his sword free. He turned to Instructor Retsji.

"Are you all right?"

Retsji looked at the blood pouring down his leg and shook his head. "I'm fine," he said, "I never made a better stroke, but the helmet turned the edge. To cut the enemy without fear of being cut . . ." He began to shiver, and clenched his teeth to stop them from chattering. "*You* saw it, Nick . . ."

"Yes. You were beautiful."

"To live as if ready to die at any moment-t-t." Retsji clenched his teeth and sank to one knee, thrusting his sword into the blood-soaked earth and leaning on it. "I taught that to my students, or tried to . . . c-c-c-cold, I'm cold . . . it wasn't this c-c-cold at Mewis Field." He sank to the earth, his sword remaining erect beside him, as one of Sejenics' lieutenants came up to him.

"We're formed up, sir, but the Tarelians are running in all directions. There's nothing for us to charge."

"Right. Bring up the horses and we'll keep 'em running." He looked at his friend lying beside his sword. "You heard? Ten to one, and we routed the bastards! We won!"

Retsji opened one eye. "Long live Shaia," he whispered.

"The Witch-Queen lives!" screamed Fadel. One of his staff officers, already mounted, seized the reins of his great black horse and held him while the witchfinder-general scrambled into his saddle.

Genzari, a hundred yards away with the cavalry, checked one

of his junior officers as the man drew his bow against the hapless witchfinder.

"What, general . . . do you pity him?"

"No." Genzari shook his head. "Let the son of a bitch spread all the panic he wants."

# 26

# Rebellion in the North

As King-Patriarch Kahun returned from early mass at Cymdulock Cathedral attended by a score of courtiers and bodyguards,
Archdeacon Gorabani approached him. A pair of muscular
bodyguards blocked his progress. Gorabani stepped to the right,
then left, without making progress as Kahun watched with the
faintest of smiles.

"Your Majesty! Father Kahun! I have news of some urgency!
Let me approach Your Majestic Holiness, for God's sake!"

"We are weary," said Kahun, who had gone to church directly from an entirely male revel, marked by loud singing,
gross eating, hard drinking, and athletic dancing. "Surely what
consumes you cannot be of such urgency that it will not wait
upon our rest?"

"We have news from the Semeryan," replied Archdeacon
Gorabani, "and if I thought it would wait on Your Holy Majesty's nap, I would have let you sleep." He reached into his pocket
and took out his diptych, extending it toward Kahun.

"What is this?" asked one of the young and handsome courtiers disdainfully, as he took the diptych from Gorabani's hand.

"Messages," replied the archdeacon. "Messages written on
silk ribbon and tied to the legs of carrier pigeons. The ribbons
then pressed onto the wax in my diptych as they were brought
to me for easy reference. They started arriving early this morning, our pigeons. Less than an hour ago, in fact, at the first light
of dawn. In my naivete I thought His Majestic Holiness would
be interested." He made an elaborate curtsey to the young

man. "In the event that His Holy Majesty deigns to peruse my humble offering, I would be most gratified, *extremely* gratified, I assure you, and were I to be honored with an invitation to enter the presence, indeed, even the intimation of such an invitation . . ."

Kahun snatched the diptych out of the courtier's hand and opened it. He read briefly and snapped it shut.

"Playing the fool doesn't become you, Gorabani," he growled. "Come with us to the privy council chamber."

"But Your Majestic Holiness had other plans . . ." protested the courtier who had held the diptych.

"Another time, perhaps. Go to bed." The dismissal was accompanied by a hand gesture of brusque impatience. The courtier's face fell, and he bowed and stepped backwards.

Kahun and Gorabani arrived in the privy council chamber to find the charladies at work. The women curtseyed and left, taking their mops and buckets with them, leaving behind a faint smell of soapy water from the half-cleaned flagstones.

Kahun opened the diptych and laid it on the polished wooden table before him. "Is this true?" he asked, and realizing himself how stupid the question was, he shook his head. "Forgive me. If it *is* true, what are we going to do about it?"

"Maybe it isn't true," said the archdeacon pleasantly, sitting back in his chair and crossing his arms. "If it isn't true, I won't have to tell you anything you don't want to hear, right?"

"Oh, shut up," growled the king-patriarch. "Probably the Tarelians are finished as an effective fighting unit. Not the first time, but before, the Tarelian Order was always able to field a new army. Eventually. Can they do it for us again?"

"I would say no, Father. The late Nasar-Namatu might have been able to pull it off, but not the witchfinder. Fadel put in a whole new hierarchy, one loyal to him, responsive to him, but not strongly connected to the institution, to the Tarelian Order itself." The archdeacon examined the rings on his gloved hands for a moment. "Right down to the junior officers. Fadel wanted his own people; he *got* his own people. After a disaster on the field—and this *is* a disaster, Father—Fadel and his people have got to be totally discredited. And the old hierarchy—the one he threw out—you can't unburn Nasar-Namatu any more than you can bring back his supporters after you've fired *them*."

"I suppose not," conceded Kahun. "Their loyalty would be doubtful, at best."

"Yes, Father. Suppose they returned the loyalty they received?"

Kahun ignored him and studied the terse messages mounted in the wax of the diptych. "Damnation! What's this garbage about a troll-bat attack?"

"I have no idea. You can't use troll-bats on a battlefield. They get upset and excited and out of control."

Kahun yawned and rubbed his eyes. "So I have been given to understand. Evidently the Witch-Queen has found a way."

"You mean the false Shaia, father?" asked Gorabani with a touch of impatience. "The Witch-Queen is undoubtedly dead."

Another yawn. "So you keep telling me. Dead or alive, this victory will do a lot to revive her."

In Autmerida Dr. Fadel was the first to bring news of the disaster, followed in the next few hours by the members of his personal staff who had the fortune to be mounted—a tiny handful out of the mighty army that had marched into the Semeryan a few days before. The witchfinder-general, his nerve badly shaken by the attack before Zenberg, ordered his staff to pack up and head south, and, unwilling to wait one hour longer, took a change of mounts and a bag of flatbread, and followed his own advice. He left behind him a badly demoralized crew of torturers and bullies (but not sadists; enjoying ones work was grounds for disqualification), headed by Witchfinder Tejiosi, who had demonstrated exemplary diligence under the approving eyes of his superior.

At dawn on the third morning after the defeat of the Tarelians, the wagons stood loaded in the yard before the headquarters of the Holy Inquisition. Stable hands were hitching up the draft animals as the drovers ate a hasty breakfast for the long day ahead, when Sejenics' mounted infantry swept into the village, clattering over the bridge with shouts of "Dervian! Long live Prince Dervian!"

Trapped, Witchfinder Tejiosi and his staff tried to defend the building, closing the doors and hoping that the mounted bow-men outside would be unable to mount a siege. Hangmen and witchfinders may be popular at times, but they are never loved. A stable hand whose mother and aunt had been burned at the stake opened one of the side doors leading into the kitchen. Tejiosi and two of Fadel's lieutenants fled to the top of the roof, where Nick Sejenics, disdaining the niceties of delegating au-thority, followed in hot pursuit. There was a brief clash of arms, and one officer, mortally wounded, took a slow step off the edge of the roof as his comrade sank to his knees and tried to close the cut across his belly with his two hands.

"I've done you no harm," protested the witchfinder, holding his empty hands out before him. "For the love of God, spare my life!" Sejenics took a step toward him, and the witchfinder took a step back.

"Fadel made me do it! I didn't want to burn those women!"

Sejenics took another step forward, and the witchfinder took a step back, standing at the very edge of the green copper roof beside the green copper gutters, filled with moldering leaves from last winter.

"I *didn't* burn anybody! The secular authorities burned them! For the love of God, don't kill me!"

"I won't kill you," said Sejenics, quite unexpectedly.

"Oh thank you! Thank you! God bless you!" babbled Tejiosi and as Nick Sejenics made a slow thrust at his eyes, he jumped backward automatically, screaming as he fell off the roof.

Sejenics wiped off his sword and sheathed it in one smooth motion. "I *didn't* kill you," he said softly. "The *fall* killed you." There was a sound of hoofbeats and neighing horses, and he looked up to see the arrival of Genzari's cavalry.

When Wizenbeak and Jankura rode down with Count Braley's column of mounted infantry late that afternoon, Genzari had already set up a recruiting station directly in front of the Syn-cretist Church.

"You don't waste any time, do you, Lasco?" said the wizard.

"We can't afford to," replied Genzari. "And anyway, the best time to recruit is after a notable victory when it looks like there won't be any fighting."

"Running off a few miserable witchfinders was a notable victory?" asked Jankura.

"No, Your Majesty, but it serves to confirm the destruction of the Tarelians . . . which was, indeed, a notable victory."

"I guess it was," said Wizenbeak. "How many men have signed on so far?"

Genzari picked up a scroll of parchment, bearing the signatures of the volunteers, next to their bloody thumbprints, in three neat columns. "Twenty-six," he said after counting.

"That's not very many, Lasco."

Genzari reached under the tarpaulin covering the table behind the recruiters and pulled out six more rolls. "Should be one hundred men on a roll, Doctor Wizenbeak," he said. "Total of six hundred twenty-six . . . which includes the local militia and most of old whatshisface's mercenaries."

"I see." The wizard nodded, pulling at his beard. "What next?"

"We'll head for Springhill," said Genzari. "We ought to be able to raise the north in a month. Six weeks at the outside."

"Did we encounter any serious opposition, General Genzari?" asked Jankura.

"No, Your Majesty. Not here, certainly."

"Then let's split our forces. You go west, toward Springhill, while Count Braley heads east toward Arhimjhar. Sweep the country clean of witchfinders and march off the recruits to Autmerida." She stroked Mischka and looked at the newly recruited soldiers standing around. "We'll assemble our army here, and train them up until you and Braley return. Two weeks, at the outside. Can you do it?"

"Ahh . . ." Genzari seemed momentarily at a loss for words.

"Your Majesty really ought to consult with wiser heads on the formulation of strategy," said Wizenbeak gently. "Splitting our small forces seems very risky."

"No, Doctor Wizenbeak! We encounter a strong force defending a strong point, we can ride around it, avoid it. At the moment, the initiative is entirely ours. Any potential adversary would be immobilized by doubt, uncertainty, and fear. Our risk is rather small, actually . . ."

Genzari fingered his neat mustache thoughtfully. "Two weeks, Your Majesty? I believe it can be done."

"Fear?" said the wizard. "Our numbers are insignificant. Why should we inspire fear?"

"We win as if by magic," said Genzari. "Shaia, in the company of a sinister necromancer, if you'll excuse the expression, has returned from the dead. How could we not inspire fear? Her Majesty is right. We must seek to take advantage of it."

"Also, our numbers are growing," said Jankura. "An army is forming around us, and if they—if Kahun doesn't fear us now, he must fear us a month from now."

"What about the training?" asked Wizenbeak. "Not to mention the logistics of feeding and housing all those people?"

"We can put Sejenics in charge of training," replied Genzari, watching as another volunteer nicked his thumb and signed on in blood. Retsji would have been better, he thought, but he's dead. "Logistics?" He grinned. "Your Majesty, Doctor Wizenbeak here would be outstanding for running the logistical end of our uprising!"

An informal buffet was held in the red drawing room, the comfortable lounge on the left side of Kahun's throne room. There was a wine punch, a fortified wine punch, and a lavish assortment of meat pasties and meat salads, with fish, fish roe, and cheese thrown in for good measure. A formal buffet would have had a dessert table and an orchestra.

King-Patriarch Kahun paced back and forth on the dark patterned carpet, dramatic as hell in the ornately magnificent white silk robes of the patriarch, stiff with bullion and dripping with pearls, that hung open over the austere black hexagons of his hauberk. Archdeacon Gorabani, in scarlet silk, sat on a gold brocaded couch beside Dr. Fadel who also wore the scarlet of an archdeacon, but with a lining of black silk as befitted the witchfinder-general. Unkind souls, among them Gorabani, said it was mourning for the Tarelian Order which he still headed. General Allojhi, wearing parade armor, stood elegantly by the punch bowl, while a dozen or so pillars of the realm stood or sat about the room. Archdeacons and deacons segregated themselves on one side, generals on the other, waiting for the king-patriarch to get down to business.

"What the *hell* are we going to do about the rebellion!?" demanded Kahun, at last.

Send up the army and crush the bastards, thought Fadel, hang the men and burn the women! But let somebody else suggest it . . . I don't want to draw attention to myself.

"Make terms with them," said Gorabani.

"What!" thundered Kahun. "You have the balls to suggest it! How dare you, sir!?"

"It might be cheaper dealing with Dervian the Pretender directly, rather than negotiating with the various dukes for their highly qualified support," replied Gorabani. "He is, after all, your half brother."

"I'll kill the wimp son of a bitch!" said the king fiercely. "Besides, the Witch-Queen won't deal!"

"Probably not," agreed Gorabani. One of us must be wrong about Shaia being dead, he thought, but right or wrong there's no use trying to persuade His Holy Majesty. Argue points you can win. "In that case, Father, you can send an army north, or you can wait for Dervian the Wimp to march on Cymdulock."

"Dervian the Pretender," corrected the king-patriarch. "As you pointed out, he *is* our brother. A little respect for the royal blood, Gorabani, would not be amiss."

Fadel tittered. "Yes, indeed, Your Majestic Holiness."

"Dervian the Pretender," agreed Archdeacon Gorabani. "You can let him come to you, or you can go after him. I would suggest that you go after him."

"That's very risky," said General Allojhi. "We can field an army of sixteen thousand infantry and three thousand or four thousand cavalry. No more. If we wait for Dervian to march south, we might muster two or three times that number."

"That's dumb," said Gorabani. "You're counting on the dukes to side with His Majestic Holiness, here. If, God forbid, they were to side with Dervian, changing sides as they went into battle—which is also not without precedent in Guhland's long and glorious history—our army of twenty thousand might be facing Dervian's army plus thirty thousand or forty thousand ducal turncoats."

"Well, can't we get the dukes to send some troops north with us?" asked the archdeacon.

"We can hire all we want to pay for," said Kahun. "How many lackwits have rallied to the Pretender up there?"

"Our spies report ten thousand infantry and about two thousand cavalry," replied General Allojhi. "It appears that many of them were our own units which went over en masse."

"Then they can go back the same way," said a general. "We outnumber them, we ought to go after them!"

"You know," said Archdeacon Darussis, "the reason they went over to the Witch-Queen in the first place was all that terrible witch burning we were doing up there. You burn a man's mother, he may suspect you don't have his best interests at heart. When you confiscate her property, he _knows_ you don't! You want him to come back to you, to you, Your Holy Majesty, you have to persuade him, you have to give him something—"

"The witch burning was very popular in the north!" snapped Fadel. "People came for miles to watch it!"

Darussis smiled at the witchfinder-general, and composed his hands in an attitude of prayer. "Which is, no doubt, why they rose in rebellion with such alacrity. We northerners _like_ disgusting things such as burning women and treason!"

"God damn you, Darussis!" shouted Fadel, his pale eyes bulging with fury as he stood up. "You lying bastard!"

"Shut up, Fadel," said Kahun. "I want to hear what Darussis has to suggest."

"Why, I was about to suggest that we march north with the army we have, but . . . in recognition of our errors which led them to rebel, poor souls, we should offer a general amnesty—"

"So they'll feel free to come back to us," Kahun nodded.

"Plus," continued Darussis, his plump face beaming with innocent joy, "a change in our policy which led them to rebel in the first place. An end to witch burning."

"You think that was what did it?" asked Gorabani, who was privately sure that it was, but who could no longer argue the point with Kahun.

"Oh, _yes_," said Darussis nodding his bald head. "Moreover, we should extend to them an apology for our past errors. We should admit our mistake—"

"IT WAS NOT A MISTAKE!" shouted the witchfinder.

"Theologically, it is possible to follow Mambrino to any length you want to go," agreed Darussis, "but when you follow him to the point where you provoke a secular revolution . . . you have made a secular mistake." He smiled. "*You*, Doctor Fadel, have made a mistake. His Holy Majesty, upon learning of it, took immediate steps to rectify the matter. He cannot restore those poor, unfortunate women to life, but he *can* administer justice to the wretch who slew them!"

"But I was not alone in this," protested Fadel. "The Mambrinistas of the Congregation of Clerisiarchs lifted me up, His Holy Majesty set me to be a scourge against the wicked . . . for God's sake, Darussis! I was only obeying orders!"

"I don't doubt it," agreed the chubby little archdeacon pleasantly, "but if His Holy Majesty *really* wants to end the Witch-Queen's rebellion, stopping the witch burning and hanging the witchfinder is an excellent way to begin."

"It would take a lot of the steam out of the rebellion," said Gorabani, twisting the signet ring on his red gloved forefinger.

"What about the danger of a troll-bat attack?" asked General Allojhi.

"No problem," said Darussis. "The little creatures are sybaritic gluttons. We have but to prepare kimjii, a well-known narcotic liqueur, wet sponges with it, put the sponges in barrels, put the barrels around the camp, and any troll-bats that come within range of the aroma . . . why, you'll find them stupefied inside the barrel."

"I see." Allojhi nodded. "We could take them, Father. We really could. Kimjii for the troll-bats, an amnesty for the rebels, and hang the witchfinder here for screwing up."

"Now, now," said Gorabani, "we're hanging the witchfinder to encourage the rebels to desert."

"That would be nice, too," agreed General Allojhi smoothly, "but if he hadn't lost the Tarelians, there wouldn't have been any rebellion. I say hang him; he richly deserves it!"

"I agree," said Darussis.

"Interesting," said the king-patriarch. "What do you think, Gorabani?"

"I agree, Father. I know you approve of burning witches,

but Fadel's enthusiastic and promiscuous incinerations have definitely weakened our position in the north. Once the false Shaia—"

"The Witch-Queen," corrected Kahun.

"The Witch-Queen is finally killed and the rebellion quashed, if you want to resume burning witches, I'm sure you could raise up another witchfinder."

Kahun nodded. "Yes," he said softly, "yes, we expect we could."

"Don't turn your back on me, Father," pleaded Dr. Fadel.

"We like you, Fadel," said Kahun sadly, "we really do. You loyally executed our policies in every respect. You have, indeed, become identified with them." His mouth smiled, but his eyes were sad. "But we have to change those policies, old friend. A political necessity may be unfortunate, it may be painful, but it is still a necessity." He turned. *"Guards!"*

Half a squad of guardsmen raced over and fell in before the king-patriarch. Kahun pointed to Dr. Fadel.

"Arrest us that traitor!" he said.

# 27

# Preparations for Battle

WIZENBEAK was sitting in his office with his slippered feet propped on his desk, looking down his nose at Gruchka rummaging around in his beard, when there was a discreet knock at the door.

"Hunh," he muttered, sitting up behind the massive wooden desk that had been a rack in Wrascha's dungeon. "What is it?"

An aide stuck her head through the door. "Master Dassenji is here to see you," she said.

"Oh yes." The wizard nodded. "Send him in, Gulda."

"Ah, Doctor Wizenbeak," said the old man, "so good to see you, again. What is it I can do for you?"

"I have to buy mother-of-glass," said the wizard. "I figure maybe a few thousand pounds. Can you help?"

"Ah, that's a lot, a few thousand pounds. I have maybe a hundred pounds of number one, and a hundred and fifty pounds of number two, both very good quality. Exceptional quality, doctor! Since you and the young lady took them out to break the Taralian water wagons, the subordinate males have been really, really happy."

"What do you mean by number one and number two?" asked Wizenbeak, who had been involved with handling troll-bats rather than quality control in his glass factory days.

"The color. We have a set of standards, ten colors running from water white for number one, down through white, cream, yellow, umber, red, murret, brown, dark brown, and black. I can make you a really, really good price."

"That's very kind," said the wizard, "but we *will* have to buy from other sources. We're making armor, basically—"

"Ah, then you wouldn't want my stuff," said the old glass merchant, nodding. "It's good quality, for windows or even cut crystal—very pure, very good. It would be a pity to use such good stuff for armor."

"I quite agree," Wizenbeak replied. "One of our problems is that we have what you might call a cash-flow problem—people don't want to extend us credit until after we win. So I have to pay cash for the merchandise, and money is very tight. How should I buy mother-of-glass?"

"For armor?" Dassenji pulled at his nose. "It should be very easy. Three things. Impurities. Total glass. And color . . . and you don't need color, you ask for number ten, or equal."

"What do you mean, 'or equal'?"

"Oh, if someone wants to move some murret or dark brown, and cuts his price a little . . . you know."

Wizenbeak took out his diptych and made a note with his stylus. "Hunh." He nodded. "How do you check?"

"Real easy, doctor . . . for total glass, you weigh out an ounce, to the nearest milliounce, and make a paste with water. You then put it to bake in a warm oven for about an hour. Overnight is better, but an hour is all right. You get a glass lump which you weigh. The worst mother-of-glass in the world should give you more than half glass, usually you get above sixty, sixty-five percent of that nominal ounce, and what you do, see, is pay on the basis of final glass."

"That's not too hard," agreed the wizard, writing it down. "And the impurities?"

"Dissolve an ounce of the stuff in water and filter it," said Dassenji. "You shouldn't get nothing, but if you get maybe a little trace, one or two percent, you can live with it. A lot means that you aren't getting the basis weight you're paying for . . . just worthless sand."

"That's it?"

"That's it for armor. Were you making fine crystal, you'd want to look at the color, and for dishes or pottery you'd look for the insolubles in alcohol. Stuff you don't need to know, a busy man such as you, doctor." Dassenji pulled his chair over to the desk and grinned. "Hey, you heard they hung the witch-finder?"

"Oh, yes," said Wizenbeak. "The usurper made a big deal about how he had been misled by his trusted courtier, and how the villain had secretly been doing the work of the Devil, and all that garbage."

"Smart," said the old glass merchant, tapping his forehead. "Kahun didn't do it, Fadel did it. And people believe it! My wife believes it, for God's sake!"

"I expect she'd rather be burned by accident than by the malice of the king. Enemies in high places are very scary, the higher the scarier." Gruchka crept out of his master's beard and walked across the table to Dassenji, rubbing his head against the man's arm.

"Ah, such a little gentleman, such a nice troll-bat," said the glass merchant, reaching into his pocket and producing a dried avricod, which Gruchka accepted without haste and examined carefully before starting to eat. "And the amnesty, what do you think of that?"

"Hunh." Wizenbeak sat back and pulled at his nose. "Kahun killed his parents and his brother to reach the throne, he killed his ally Nasar-Namatu to reach the patriarchy, and he killed his creature Fadel when there was trouble in the north. Would *you* trust an amnesty from that man?"

"No-o," agreed Dassenji, "but won't it encourage your men to desert?"

"That's what it's supposed to do," said the wizard, "but it's a hell of a lot easier to prevent a revolution from starting than to stop it once it gets started." He looked thoughtful as he twisted his mustache around his forefinger. "The soft line might make recruiting harder, though," he conceded.

"You don't need to worry, do you? I heard that you have plans to destroy Kahun by magic. Everyone says that you'll get him like you did the Tarelians!"

Wizenbeak laughed out loud. "Oh shit," he said at last, "I've been so busy working on the logistics end of the campaign that I haven't really had time to do anything sorcerous. Do *you* have any suggestions?"

"What would a poor maker of glass know about sorceries?"

"Why, you wanted to tell me about the dragon-human wars in the old days," said the wizard. "When I was in school I read Hadian, but that's about it."

"Hadian!? That humanophilic imbecile?! Don't believe what he tells you, none of it! Listen, doctor, do you want to know about dragons?"

Wizenbeak sat back and looked over his glasses for a moment. "Well, yes, as a matter of fact. Why don't I send for a pot of tea and some biscuits so you can tell me properly?"

"You're a busy man, doctor—"

"My staff is busy," said Wizenbeak, grinning. "You've heard of a wizard's staff, haven't you? All that I have to do is see that it doesn't screw up."

Mischka hung on to the left side of Jankura's face, one delicate webbed hand stretched taut over her ear, the other held flaccid and relaxed, resting on her chin, feet and tail braced against her neck and shoulder.

"Red team scores five, seven, seven, six, eight, and ten," she said. "Green team scores six, six, eight, seven, ten, and ten." There was a pause. "He says the blue team started off with a zero because the leadoff man shot a nine on the wrong target, and the captain is arguing about it."

Genzari put down his diptych. "The archery range is up at Camp Merida, Your Majesty," he said. "You can't even see it from on top of the roof. If the messenger brings in the same scores, I'll concede the wizard is talking to you." He sighed. "I believe it, you understand . . . but if we're going to use this on the battlefield, I want to *really* believe it, if you know what I mean."

"I know what you mean," she said. "You want to have faith in what your life depends on."

"Yes, Your Majesty," said her strategist. "The whole idea is bizarre. Putting the wizard up in a kite to spy on the enemy formations before we engage them is wonderful, if it works. But it certainly looks as if he could tell us—"

"The blue team's leadoff man shot over. We have a ten, five, four, eight, six, and nine."

"Yes, Your Majesty," said Genzari, making a note of the

scores. "The old saw is: 'Unhappy the man who puts his trust in princes,' and 'Wizards will say and unsay in the same breath.' God help me, I'm going to be getting my scouting information from a wizard talking to a prince through a couple of troll-bats." He shook his head.

"Princess, you mean."

"No, Your Majesty, you are the queen of Guhland, until you choose to become regent for Prince Dervian."

"But you said 'prince,' Lasco."

"I apologize, Your Majesty. No disrespect was intended. Is there any way that little monster could work for me?"

"I'm afraid not. Mischka is very much a one person troll-bat. Gruchka might . . . Master Wizenbeak's familiar."

Genzari rubbed his hand over his closely cropped hair. "Yes, but then he wouldn't be able to tell what he saw."

"I could ride the kite with Mischka."

"No, Your Majesty. The wizard, if we lost him we could go on and win. If we lost you, everything collapses. I'll talk to him through you. How did he come up with this cockamamie idea, anyway?"

"He was talking to Master Dassenji about the dragon-human wars, he said. That was one of the things the dragons used to do, so he thought we'd try it."

Genzari nodded. "Why wasn't it ever done before?"

Jankura smiled. Wizenbeak hadn't made it work; he didn't understand troll-bats that socialized with other troll-bats, only the neurotic darlings that socialized with humans. But *she* did . . . "I don't know. Maybe wizards skillful enough to use troll-bats wouldn't speak to each other. Or if they did, they kept it secret."

The kite was an enormous tetrahedron made up of smaller tetrahedra, with a lifting surface of green and white canvas, and a long, serpentine tail of green and white silk. The ground line was fastened to a harness, which was made of three pieces of cord, each the length of one full side, secured to the hook that held the ground line. Wizenbeak could control the angle the kite made with the wind by taking in one of the cords. When the wind was ten to fifteen knots, a dozen men had trouble holding the kite down, even with the wizard riding in it. Gruchka, of course, thought it was marvelous fun, and the most serious problem they had was his tendency to climb around with the wind whistling through his ears instead of tending to his responsibilities as a communications device. To give Wizenbeak some small measure of protection from any arrows that might come his way, some of the canvas around his saddle was impregnated with glass. When sent aloft, the base of the tetrahedron faced the wind, and the long silk tail attached to the apex waved gently to windward. The whole kite assembly could be dismantled and loaded on a wagon, with a second wagon required for the ground line and reel.

The Cymdulock Cathedral is of great antiquity, and within its foundations are catacombs, and within the catacombs are less savoury precincts. Archdeacon Gorabani, Captain of the Citadel, warden of Cymdulock, and most recent master of the moribund Tarelian Order, dismissed the guard who had accompanied him at the head of the final stairs. He went down to an iron-bolted door which opened at his demand, and hung his scarlet vestments on a wooden peg, setting hat and boots on the table, and tossing gloves and rings into his hat. He slipped on a grungy black robe, black slippers, and a tall, pointed black hat bearing some rather startling symbols. Gorabani looked at the map of Guhland hanging on the wall and then at the tiny slip of silk in his fingers.

"Where the hell is Sifoty?" he asked.

"In County Huit," said Darussis' apprentice, a young man with stringy, unwashed hair, as he walked over to the map and placed a little pin with a flag approximately where Sifoty would have been if the map had shown it. "North of Huitmire."

"The Witch-Queen's army has marched south to meet the king-patriarch," said Archdeacon Gorabani, studying the big map. "*They* are in Sifoty, biding our coming, while *we* are a few miles to the east, just off the Military Road to Springhill."

"Right." The apprentice took a second pin, with Shaia's colors, and carefully placed it in the hole made by Kahun's pin, and moved the pin with Kahun's colors a little closer to the highway.

"That's better." Gorabani nodded. "They've been coming

down thirty miles a day . . . I would have thought they'd try to avoid engaging a superior force, Darussis.''

"Shaia may be relying on her troll-bats," said the round-faced little man, looking up from a well-worn scroll that rested on a workbench cluttered with assorted mirrors, candles, and oil lamps under glass bell jars to maintain their purity of essence. "We have . . . not information, exactly, but a privileged guess that the troll-bats will play a decisive role in the coming battle.''

"We have a three-to-two superiority in the field, with a massive superiority in cavalry," remarked Gorabani, rubbing his nose with an unringed forefinger.

"You talk like a damn general. Young Max here has been running weather forecasts all afternoon . . . ask him what he found out, why don't you?''

"Well, Max?''

The apprentice walked over to the map. "Light winds from the north," he said, with an awkward gesture, "shifting to the northeast later in the day and becoming light to moderate. Maybe scattered showers in the late afternoon.''

"Sounds like a great day for a battle," said Gorabani. "What seems to be the problem?''

"The weather unambiguously favors the Witch-Queen," said Darussis mildly. "We don't know why." The weather, bad though it was predicted to be, had favored Kahun at Mewis Field.

Gorabani studied the map for a while. "The wind might be blowing the scent of kimjii away from the troll-bats," he suggested at last.

"You think it's a troll-bat thing?''

"No." The younger archdeacon-wizard shook his head. "Genzari commands for the Witch-Queen. I've seen the book on him. He's been unlucky, but he's as smart as they come. He wouldn't go into battle relying on a gimmicky surprise that wasn't a surprise anymore.''

"Shaia may have said, 'Go with the troll-bats,' " Darussis suggested, scrolling the manuscript. "After it worked with the Tarelians, why wouldn't he?''

"Because we know about them," said the other, composing his naked hands together in an attitude of prayer. "Half the soldiers in the damned army are wearing little sachets of ground kimjii root around their necks. It's no secret. Troll-bats won't do it for them, and they know it."

"Maybe they have something else," said Max, the apprentice, unhelpfully. "Maybe the Witch-Queen brought some evil enchantment back from hell."

"Then we should have seen it by now," replied Darussis, holding his diptych as he wrote out a phrase in an arcane language on the blackboard. "I, at least, should have seen it. We *know* that she's travelling with a large number of troll-bats."

"Maybe she's using them in her magic," the apprentice said.

"Maybe she is," his master agreed. "The weather forecast is troubling . . . for whatever reason."

"Oh?" said Gorabani, raising an eyebrow. He studied the blackboard intently for a moment, then used his finger to add an accent mark on one word.

"We aren't going to try to set Shaia's spirit free from her undead body again?" asked the apprentice uneasily. The spell called for blood drawn from a virgin, and he had been stabbed in thumbs, fingers, and earlobes until he was sick of the whole bootless business.

"Waste of time," said Darussis, shaking his head. "Our illustrious patriarch to the contrary notwithstanding, when the magic doesn't bite, don't argue with it. Can anything be done about the weather, Gorabani?"

"Maybe." Gorabani was scrolling through the book on the table. "The question is: Will what we *can* do make any difference?"

"You want to affect the weather tomorrow morning," said Darussis, standing up and wiping his pudgy hands on his unclean robe, "you'd better get started. Max, bring in a troll-bat for us."

"Weather magic is the devil," said Gorabani. "Even if we could get the wind to blow from the south, it might not do any good."

"Right," agreed Darussis, going into a storeroom at the back of the laboratory to rummage around in the dimly lit clutter. At last he emerged with a great wooden drum, carved with curious figures around the edge, the top covered with a well-cured human hide marked with yellowish stains. It was about two feet in diameter, but less than a handspan deep, and the other man set it on one end of his cluttered bench. "The oracle gave a bad forecast. The only question is: Do we try to change it?"

"*Can* we change it?" asked Gorabani, and answered his own question. "We won't know until we try, will we?"

Darussis opened drawers in his bench and looked through them, eventually producing a jar of evil-smelling salve and a small bottle containing a dram or so of milky liquid. He studied the liquid and read the stained label. "Right," he said. "And we do it right the first time, or we don't do it."

The younger man looked at the milky liquid. "There isn't time to make another batch," he agreed. "We have one shot at it."

Then Max backed through the massive door carrying a wire cage that held a small, sickly creature that covered its head with long, webbed fingers. Darussis took the salve and smeared it on the drumhead, copying his inscription from the blackboard on the slimy surface with his little finger. Gorabani took the troll-bat, who seemed drugged and passive, and poured the milky liquid into its hands. The archdeacon-wizard rubbed it into the whole webbing, and when he finished, he took the flabby, whimpering animal and spread-eagled it facedown on the drum. The whimpers became louder and curiously resonant, and as Darussis recited a mantra, Gorabani hung the drum on the wall, his hands tingling from contact with the milky liquid.

He stepped back, and Darussis invoked the name of the weather elemental. As the magic bit, the candles flickered and the temperature in the room dropped a full fifteen degrees, producing an aromatic mist. Gorabani shivered, and his hands shook. He clasped them together, but they went awkwardly, without feeling. The drum began to grumble in a muffled bass drone, like the north wind trying to escape the Trickster's bagpipes. Darussis took a silver tau nabla from his pocket and held it up to the grumbling drum.

"Vohar," he said firmly, "Elemental Master of the World's Weather, I bid you speak!" Gorabani started to fall, but Max caught him and gently eased him into a sitting position on the floor, his back against the workbench. Then the apprentice swiftly left the room, taking a ring of keys from beside the door.

"I am here, mortal . . ." rumbled the drum. "What would you have me do?" Gorabani's eyes rolled up into his head, and he slid limply against the wall.

"I would command the weather, at one certain place, called Sifoty Field, at one certain time, from darkest dawn tomorrow till high morning that same day."

"I know the time," said the bass voice. "Fix me the place on yonder map." Keeping his eyes fixed on the drum, Darussis walked unsteadily over to the map, his hand fumbling toward Sifoty, which he at last risked a glance at before thrusting home the point of his silver tau nabla.

"I know the place," said the voice from the drum. "What weather do you bid me bring?"

Darussis swallowed. "At that place, and at that time, oh Vohar, thou must make the wind blow from the south."

The drum laughed, the sound filling the cold, vaulted chamber. "Sou sorrr soo sourr soooo sorrrry," said the deep voice of Vohar. "At that time and at that place the wind blows from the north or not at all." And it laughed with deep, slow malice.

"Then," said Darussis, perspiring despite the cold air, "let there be no wind at all, at that time and at that place."

"I shall do so," rumbled Vohar, as Max, keys in hand, edged his way back into the room. "Seal thou then the bargain."

Darussis looked at Max, who held up the keys and nodded.

"Very well, Vohar, come thou with me . . ." said Darussis, and seizing the drum, he went out into the torchlit corridor, following his apprentice and trailed by a swirling fog. In less than fifty yards, two iron-bound doors swung idly open, unwatched by guards, and Darussis came to a certain cell marked with a chalk ideograph. He held the drumhead against the cell door.

"Here, Vohar," he muttered, "is thy fee." Inside the cell, a woman screamed and crunching noises were heard. Abruptly the presence left the drum, and the archdeacon-wizard handed it to his apprentice. They walked slowly back to the laboratory, locking the doors behind them. The mist in the passage was fading, the air in their chamber seemed almost warm.

"Scrape the troll-bat off and clean the drumhead up as best you can," the little old man muttered. "I'll tend to Gorabani."

# 28

# Sifoty Field

SIFOTY was a crossroads hamlet, clustered around the intersection of Sifotswash Road and the Mill Road. Sifots Wash was a meandering stream running generally south. It was narrow but deep and swift, and Sifotswash Road ran along the west bank, which was uphill from the other and less likely to flood. Genzari, who had grown up in that part of the world, had come to Sifoty Mill to make his stand against Kahun's army.

Sifoty Mill was a massive stone building, three stories tall, with a slate roof and a vertical waterwheel on the north side of the building. The mill road led through a shed, wide enough to hold two wagons side by side, and made a little loop for the wagons to turn around after unloading. The shed floor was massive, and built across the mill race, a wide and capacious bridge serving the convenience of the miller and his customers. The mill pond behind the mill was half a mile long, fed by the drainage from an old lake bed that had filled in to become a marshy meadow in summer and fall, and a bog in winter and spring. It was now late spring, but it had been a wet season, and the old lake bed was distinctly on the swampy side.

The mill race running into Sifots Wash flowed through a little meander for about sixty or seventy yards to a big old cherry tree that had been used to define the boundary. Thereafter, the mill race ran about six hundred yards through a ditch following the boundary line to run into Sifots Wash. The mill race was four feet wide and three feet deep at the cherry tree, six feet wide and five feet deep where it ran into the river, with sloping fieldstone banks layered in unmortared courses. Overgrown with brush, it was not visible from fifty yards away. It constituted a small terrain advantage, hardly an impedance to an uncontested advance, but Kahun's cavalry could not charge north, the mill race being a sufficient barrier to break their momentum.

Two hundred yards north ran a weathered ridge, generally parallel to the mill pond, mill race, and swamp, the high ground that dominated the plain below. Archers holding the ridge could wreak havoc with any slow advance against the mill below.

Jankura rode between General Genzari and Count Braley, and surveyed the battlefield Genzari had selected.

"What if Kahun rides north to come down behind us?" she asked, looking at the unimpressive stream that was to secure the left flank.

"East of Sifots Wash? We'll ride north to contest his crossing," said Braley. "South of here, there are fords; he can cross with no trouble. North . . . the road is on our side, we can wear him out marching and countermarching. No, he'll come from the south, on the west side of Sifots Wash, and we'll meet him at the mill."

"What if he goes around west, Lasco?"

"What, you mean around the swamp?" Genzari smiled. "Right now, Your Majesty, I'd guess that swamp is maybe fifteen miles long and five or six miles wide. He wants to take us on the right, he has a long way to go. No." He shook his head. "Kahun ought to attack at the meander, between the cherry tree and the mill. Our flanks are covered. We hold the high ground. And with Doctor Wizenbeak up in his kite keeping an eye on things, we can beat him."

"Even if he doesn't press the attack?"

"Oh." Genzari sighed inwardly. Her Majesty's position was far from hopeless, but she figured to lose. "No, Your Majesty. I should have said that we can hold him. He can, however, beat himself. One must give one's enemy every chance to snatch defeat from the jaws of victory."

"Will he? Snatch defeat, I mean," asked Jankura.

"Ask the wizard. I do my best, Your Majesty, but I can't tell the future."

She nodded and bit her lip. "And when will all this happen?"

"Tomorrow morning, Your Majesty," said Count Braley. "Kahun's army has made camp on the far side of that wood over there." He pointed, and they all looked to see if there was any late afternoon activity. Nothing. "Our scouts report he's thrown up a ditch and palisade around the camp. To prevent night attacks. I imagine the woods are alive with sentries. How far would you say they are from here, general?"

"Two, maybe two and a half miles. An easy hour's march across open country," Genzari replied, fingering his closely clipped mustache. "They'll break their fast at dawn, and move out an hour later."

"I see," said Jankura, holding Mischka to her. "And what is our order of battle?"

"We're putting up a shield pavilion between the mill and the cherry tree," he said. "That's the center, infantry with spears and pikes. Sejenics has the command. Archers on the ridge, under old Tomias. He's half blind, but he understands war, if you know what I mean. Count Braley, here—"

"What's a 'shield pavilion'?"

Genzari turned his horse around and pointed. "Over by the mill, see where they put the poles up?" Jankura nodded. "They've already started to rope the poles. When the battle is joined, the men will unfold their shields and hang them on the ropes so they overlap. It's static, but it protects against arrows, Your Majesty."

"Go on, general. Where is Count Braley?"

"Holding our left flank behind the mill race with infantry— spearmen and archers. Dragoons fighting on foot, mostly. Our cavalry is on the left, also, under Count Darji-Damuso. You liked his mustache when you met him. He's young, but he's energetic; he's brave to the point of being foolhardy, and if he's half as good as he thinks he is, he'd be the best in the business, which he may be. The cavalry's mission is to secure the river line, give Braley support as needed, and sally forth if the opportunity arises. The count was quite put out that we were giving the scouting detail to Wizenbeak, but with Kahun's cavalry superiority he couldn't have done much scouting, in any event."

"I see," said Jankura. "What about the mill shed?"

Good question, thought Genzari. It's the key to the battle,

actually, if we ever get the chance to use it, and she spotted it. Aloud all he said was: "It's a natural sally port, Your Majesty, so we haven't obstructed it. We'll hold it with pikemen and archers, under Captain Zeldones."

She nodded, studying the mill and the stone shed beside it, good country stonework, peaceful and prosaic in the afternoon sunlight. "And our right flank?"

"The mill pond. We have the mercenaries and the raw recruits holding it. Ragojis has the command. He isn't brilliant, he isn't even very smart, but he's steady enough."

"The right flank sounds weak. What if he needs help?"

"The right flank is really very strong, Your Majesty," said Count Braley. "The mill pond is a natural defense, so we don't need as many men to hold it. The cavalry can reinforce it at need, or we can pull the archers off the ridge."

Jankura nodded. "And where will *we* be, general?"

"There, Your Majesty," said Genzari, pointing to the ridge behind the mill. "We'll be up there for all the army to see, our banners flying in the wind, watching the battle unfold."

"Just watching? Aren't we going to *do* anything?"

"We'll tell our friends and supporters to go into battle," said General Genzari, "and sit there watching. They'll die for us; the least we can do is be their audience."

At Sifoty, the night before the battle was warm and humid with light southern breezes. There was no rain, but summer lightning flashed fitfully in the northern sky, and by morning a heavy dew had risen on the grass.

Kahun awakened with a cry.

"Are you all right, my lord?" asked the sentry, pushing open the tent flap, spear in hand.

"Your Majesty?" said General Allojhi, already dressed for the day's work, as he entered the tent.

"I had bad dreams," said Kahun, pale and distracted, his brow clammy with perspiration. "Shaia accused me of wickedness, and I could make no answer, not to my father, nor to my brother. My own heart spoke out in my breast and condemned me with the voice of Witchfinder Fadel!"

"These are nothing but unwholesome vapours from the night

air," Allojhi said firmly. "Put them out of your mind; they mean nothing."

"You may be right," said the king-patriarch, shivering. Then to his orderly, "Dress me for battle. Living or dark undead, real or imposter, today shall I put the quietus to the Witch-Queen once and for all!" He turned to Allojhi and smiled wanly, the corners of his mouth turning down, his dark eyes somber. "Kahun's himself again!"

By the second cock crow, Wizenbeak was dressed and eating sausage and eggs with flatbread in his tent, as all about him came the sounds of an army preparing for battle. The sky was brightening with the dawn when he went out on the north slope of the hill where his kite sat on the wagon, and supervised the crew chief as the crew put it together. The air was humid and oppressive and utterly still. The banners around the royal command post hung limp and silent.

"Looks like yer won't be going up today, wiz," said the crew chief.

"I had damn well better go up today," said Wizenbeak, pulling at his nose. He walked over the crest of the hill, and found Jankura and Genzari consulting with their officers.

"Begging your pardon, Your Majesty," he said, "we have a little problem getting the kite up with no wind."

"Hah!" said Darji-Damuso, "I *said* scouting should be left to the cavalry! It isn't too late to put patrols out, even now, general—"

"We can get up, young fella," said the wizard, "but I'm going to need help from Her Majesty here."

"What did you have in mind, Dr. Wizenbeak?" asked Jankura, pleased to be taking an active part in something.

"The troll-bats, Your Majesty. I figured if you put Dasher and Dancer and Comet and Cupid on the mounts of the kite, and the rest of the crew down in the mill—"

"The troll-bats could lift the kite," she said at once. "It might work. It just might. Could you control them?"

"Hunh. I don't know," said the wizard, pulling at his long white whiskers. "Probably Gruchka and I could manage." He looked out across the plain to the wood where Kahun's army was starting to form up. "For certain sure we don't have time to practice the maneuver."

"Excuse me, General Genzari," said Jankura, "I have to get Master Dassenji and the troll-bats."

Genzari looked bemused in the soft light of dawn and nodded. "Very well," he said, "but I'll need you back here when you have the good doctor aloft."

Jankura looked puzzled.

"Only you will be able to talk to him, Your Majesty," he explained, "and the whole army needs to know what he sees." He sighed and rubbed his mustache with his forefinger. The wizard sees something, Genzari thought, and he tells Gruchka, who tells Mischka, who tells Her Majesty, who tells me, who tells the army. Young Darji-Damuso may have been right.

"Of course, general," she said. "I'll leave Master Dassenji working the troll-bats in the mill as soon as we get them set up."

Half an hour later, the oaken shaft of the mill wheel was swarming with troll-bats, sucking up its power with webbed hands, and old Master Dassenji was doing his best to keep them from falling into the machinery. Jankura was back on the ridge with Genzari, and Wizenbeak, sitting in his green and white kite, was rising slowly into the still morning air, as the four troll-bats riding along with him converted the shaft power from the mill into lift for the kite. Below, Kahun's army had advanced to within five hundred yards from Genzari's lines, and were waiting for the signal to attack.

"So far so good," said the wizard, looking down from his lofty perch. "It looks like Kahun has put most of his weight in the center."

"Ask him where the cavalry is," said Genzari.

"The cavalry's back," said Wizenbeak, "massed behind their left flank. They have wains over there, too, a lot of wains, but I can't see what's in them. Let me have some more line, and I'll try to swing over a little."

"Oh hell," said Genzari, "Kahun's holding the cavalry in reserve." He turned to the crew chief. "The wizard wants more line, give him more line."

"That's all the line we got," said the crew chief, standing beside the winch. "Fifteen hundred feet, all played out."

At Wizenbeak's command, through Gruchka's mediation, the four troll-bats moved south, to an altitude of perhaps a thousand feet, well above arrow range, a thousand feet closer to Kahun's lines. The line remained taut, and the wagon holding the reel started to move off the crest of the hill. The crew chief put blocks under the wheels, and his men tried to hold the wagon in place. Wizenbeak urged the troll-bats to pull closer to where he wanted to go, and powered by the mill wheel, the wagon lurched over the blocks and started to drag the ground crew downhill. Many hands quickly came to their aid, and the reel and wagon was abruptly brought to a halt. The troll-bats, enjoying the feel of power flowing through their webbed fingers, increased their demand, and the mill wheel slowed in response. The line broke at the hook fastening it to the kite, and the kite, untethered in the calm morning air, sailed majestically over the battlefield, trailing its long silken tail behind it.

"That's better," said Wizenbeak. "The wains are full of barrels, tied in place with rope. Maybe two score."

"Right." Genzari nodded. A pontoon bridge to cross the mill pond, he thought. Our right flank isn't as secure as I thought it was. Damn!

On the other side of the battlefield, Kahun and General Allojhi sat on a carefully erected wooden platform, watching the kite sailing majestically over their lines, with such assorted courtiers, functionaires, and miscellaneous officers as the king-patriarch chose to keep around him.

"What the hell is *that*?" asked Kahun.

"A dragon!" said someone.

"There appears to be a man inside," said Archdeacon Rhimskaia, a lean, sour fellow but a competent wizard, "probably spying out our order of battle."

"A man riding a dragon? Very bad, very bad . . ." A whisper went rustling through the ranks of Kahun's army, making an almost visible ripple like a stone falling in a pond.

"The son of a bitch is coming lower," said Kahun, shifting his weight uneasily on his low stool. "Do we have to start the attack with a dragon flying overhead?"

General Allojhi would have preferred to do exactly that, but his training as a courtier led him to temporize. "It's coming lower, Your Majesty . . . it will soon be within bow shot."

"A hundred pieces of gold to the man that brings him down!" said the king-patriarch.

Kahun's army, well aware of the threat of troll-bats, had set out traps—barrels with sponges inside containing kimjii—and most of the individual soldiers wore sachets of ground kimjii root, a powerful psychoactive drug for troll-bats. The army *reeked* of kimjii, pleasant enough for humans, intoxicating for troll-bats. As Wizenbeak swung the kite around for a third pass, Dasher began chattering. Then Dancer and Comet. Cupid simply threw back his head and howled. The kite began to dive and swoop, more swiftly than it had done before.

"What the hell is going on?" asked Genzari from the top of the ridge.

"I don't know," replied Jankura. "We've lost touch with Gruchka. At least that's what it sounds like—"

"Arrows! They're shooting arrows!" came Wizenbeak's voice from Mischka's tiny webbed hand, "Climb! *Climb!* CLIMB!" Miles away, they watched the kite climb through a shower of arrows coming from all directions. Then Mischka folded his webbed hand as Gruchka ceased transmitting.

"That's crazy," said Genzari. "Those arrows will come down on their own people!"

Powered by the mill, driven by drug-crazed troll-bats, the kite turned and rolled, as arrows rattled off the glass-impregnated panels, and Wizenbeak held on for dear life. Cupid discovered that those panels were stiff enough to vibrate under his webbed little hand, and the next time that the kite swooped down, it screamed!

Comet joined in, and Dancer, producing a chord. It was still a scream, however, and when Dasher and Gruchka came in with overtones one and two octaves higher, as the kite came shrieking over the massed cavalry at a height of perhaps fifteen feet, the horses panicked and stampeded, charging totally out of control into Kahun's center, which was already shaken by the fall of their own arrows.

Genzari stood up. They'll never get that mess untangled, he decided, and he gave Sejenics the sign to advance in the center.

Nothing loathe, Sejenics moved out from under his battle pavilion with a line of pikes backed by spearmen and drove directly for Kahun's command platform. Genzari looked over and saw Count Braley watching him intently. Battles are so much fun when it happens to the other side, he thought, and signalled Count Braley to advance to cover Sejenics' flank. Behind Braley's men, young Darji-Damuso waited with his cavalry. Genzari sent a rider ordering him to assemble his forces behind the mill shed. We can't send in the cavalry until Wizenbeak gets that devil's kite out of the sky, he thought grimly. The son of a bitch doesn't care *whose* horses he spooks.

When his cavalry stampeded into his center, destroying the order of battle, King-Patriarch Kahun jumped up, swearing furiously, threatening death and eternal damnation to anybody that didn't get back where they belonged. Then the trumpets sounded, signalling Sejenics' advance, and as the northern pikes pushed into Kahun's chaotic and disorganized center, he ordered the right wing, which was still standing in place, to attack. What Kahun wanted was a spoiling attack on the flank of Sejenics' advancing center, which was extending past the cherry tree without support. What he got was the execution of the original plan, in which the right flank advanced against Count Braley, who was, by this time advancing himself.

Overhead, the green and white kite, bristling with arrows, sounded something like Bach's Toccata and Fugue in D Minor played very loudly on a dying stereo system. It would hit a horseman a glancing blow, knocking him from the saddle, and go careening twenty feet into the air, tumbling and twisting as the troll-bats on board sought out the source of all that intoxicating smell.

By the time Darji-Damuso's cavalry reached the shed by the mill, Kahun had panicked. He climbed off his command platform, and mounted his horse tied just behind it. As it happened, the horse carried a particularly potent charge of kimjii in the saddlebags, since an attack on His Majestic Holiness had been regarded as a very probable use for the Witch-Queen's evil creatures. As he whipped his horse around toward the south, the kite came after him, keening and wailing, with Wizenbeak hope-

lessly entangled inside it doing a little keening and wailing of
his own.

As the king-patriarch whipped his horse toward the woods,
he looked back and saw the kite gaining on him. Watching with
horrified fascination as it tumbled and howled, Kahun hit his
head on a stout oak branch, as his panicked horse entered the
woods running flat out. Neck broken, Kahun fell to the ground.

The kite crashed in the woods a second later, and Genzari
gave Count Darji-Damuso the signal to charge. By the time
Wizenbeak managed to extricate himself, the battle of Sifoty
Mill was over. Darji-Damuso's men found him kneeling by the
dead Kahun, weeping and rocking back and forth with Gruchka's body cradled in his good arm.

# 29

# Witch-Queen's Problem

WIZENBEAK lay propped up on his cot, left arm in a sling, head swathed in bandages. The tent had a rather overpowering medical smell, and flies buzzed around inside, despite the screening to keep them out.

"Good morning, doctor," said Genzari, wiping the perspiration from his face. "I hope you're feeling better."

"Hunh," grunted the wizard, opening one eye, "better than *what*?"

"Better than yesterday." The general pulled over a camp chair and sat down, feet apart, hands on knees. "I'm sorry about Gruchka," he said awkwardly.

"So am I. He was with me . . . it would have been twenty-one years a week next Grasday." There was a long silence. "Did you ever find the other troll-bats, Lasco?"

"Three of them. About a hundred yards into the woods. Kahun's mount had broken a leg, and they'd got into one of the saddlebags. They were all three dead. Master Dassenji said they were Dasher and Dancer and Comet."

"You didn't find Cupid?"

"Not a trace, doctor." There was a pause. "Look. Her Majesty wants to proclaim herself regent for Prince Dervian. I tried to talk her out of it, but she won't hear me. She listens to you. Can't you tell her not to do it?"

"I wonder where Cupid went?" mused Wizenbeak. "We lost a troll-bat and started tumbling . . ." He started to shake his head, and winced. "You know, Mischka is helping my bones

269

knit? Comes in with Jankura, and lays his little webby hands on the fractures, and they start healing. Master Dassenji told Jankura, and she just did it. If she'd asked me, I'd have told her it was a grandmother's yarn. I know a granny tale when I hear one. But she just did it. And my ribs don't hurt when I breathe . . . much.'' He lay looking at the tent wall for a while. "Today, she's going to work on my arm, or part of it. It's broken in three or four places." He scratched at the cast covering his arm, and grimaced. "Why should I tell her something she doesn't want to hear?"

"Why did we fight the battle?" asked Genzari, wiping his face again. "Kahun's dead, but that doesn't mean we have no more opposition. The dukes, the Syncretist Church, even the Orthodox Church are all looking to trip us up. If she just walks in without saying what her intentions are . . ." The general hesitated a moment. "I want her to be queen, I confess it."

"Poor Lasco," said the wizard. "You conduct a victorious campaign against incredible odds, and the history books are going to credit the magic. And Jankura doesn't want to be queen, when you made it possible." He brushed a fly away from his face. "She's a smart girl."

"Not this time. If she doesn't say *anything* about whether she wants to be queen or regent, the dukes and the Church are going to assume she wants to be queen. In her position, that's what they'd want, you understand?"

Wizenbeak brushed at the fly again. "So?"

"So they'll push her in the direction she wants to go. God, it's hot in here . . . are you comfortable?"

"Not really. Go on."

"The Church and the dukes will make a big deal about Prince Dervian being the rightful heir, and pound on the table demanding a regency. She can get what she wants, and concessions to boot." The general leaned forward, resting his elbows on his knees, folding his hands together. "If she goes in asking for a regency, the sons of bitches will ask whether or not this kid is really Prince Dervian."

"Hunh. He is, you know." Wizenbeak blew at the fly walking on his nose.

"Can you prove it? The thing is, our fallback position would be to crown Jankura Queen of Guhland . . . which she will not allow.''

"Hunh. Well, so what?''

"If we get stalled, Doctor Wizenbeak, as may very well happen, in six weeks our army has gone home, except for the mercenaries, and Dervian winds up with no throne. She won't see it!''

"He'll still be—what's his title, Duke of Cymdulock—won't he?''

"For a while. Without a king, the civil wars start up again. The enthusiasm for witch burning shows—'' A fly made a pass at Genzari, and he crushed it between thumb and forefinger ''—that.''

"Nice catch, Lasco,'' said Wizenbeak approvingly. "If all you want is a little flexibility on tactics, I'll see what I can do. After all, if Gruchka died to put—'' his eyes welled up with tears, and he controlled himself with an effort ''—to put Dervian on the throne, it ought to be done right. I'll talk to Jankura when she comes by.''

# 30

# Clerisiarch's Problem

THE Congregation of Clerisiarchs sat in sullen assembly on hardwood benches listening to the report of the battle of Sifoty Mill and King-Patriarch Kahun's death from Archdeacon Rhimskaia, who had been an eyewitness. The stained glass windows in the hall were flat and dark in the light from the chandeliers that had been lit hours before.

"At that point I was separated from him by less than a hundred yards, and the dragon came roaring after us, heading unfailingly for the king-patriarch. As it sank its claws into him, he drew his sword and struck repeatedly at it, wounding it mortally, but it lifted him from the saddle and crashed into the trees, dropping the king-patriarch on the ground from a mortal height. I struggled to his side, and upon reaching him, gave him the last rites, but he died without ever regaining consciousness. Then, since our army was in full flight, I got on my horse and rode south."

"What happened after the rout?" asked Archdeacon Rehbeinji, who had been raised by the patriarch to fill the late Archdeacon Fadel's place. "To the army, I mean."

"Quite a few of them regrouped at Huitmire," replied Rhimskaia. "General Allojhi among them. We have a force in the field, an army in being, but it is beaten and will not fight. The Witch-Queen will march unopposed into Cymdulock."

"Go to Allojhi and *make* him fight!" snarled Rehbeinji.

"I couldn't even make him stop running," was the sad reply. "You go, little witch burner."

"Well," said Rahbeinji venomously, "it looks like those vaunted wizardly skills of yours were useless when the crunch came."

"They were unable to douse the fire of rebellion your promiscuous witch burning kindled," agreed Rhimskaia sourly, pushing a strand of lank, black hair back from his forehead.

"Witchfinding was right!" shouted the gap-toothed little man furiously. "It was right, and it was *popular*! The people wanted it!" The Mambrinistas on the right side of the chamber began applauding and shouting. "Hear! Hear!"

Gorabani pounded on the table with his gavel. "A little order! A little order, please! Archdeacon Rhimskaia has the floor. The question of the propriety of witch burning is not at issue."

"Not now, maybe," was the grim reply, "but do you think the Witch-Queen will let it slide by so easily?"

"One thing at a time, please," said Gorabani, rapping for order. "Does the congregation accept that King-Patriarch Kahun died at Sifoty Mill?" There was a general murmur of assent. "If the patriarch is dead, as appears to be the case, we have two choices. We can abolish the office . . . which will require a majority of two thirds of all the congregation. Or we can elect a new patriarch, which will require only a two thirds majority of those present and voting. Archdeacon Rehbeinji?"

"Move we abolish the patriarchate!" There were numerous seconds.

Many hours later, after much heated and passionate discussion, the motion was voted down for the third time. Gorabani took a sip of water.

"Archdeacon Darussis?"

"I would remind this congregation that there is a precedent for a ruling monarch to appoint the patriarch. I would remind this congregation that the Witch-Queen is marching unopposed on Cymdulock. And I would urge my Mambrinista brethren to forget about abolishing the patriarchate, as they now wish to do, and elect a patriarch." There was a general murmur of "Hear, hear," and hissing from the right side of the hall.

"Whatever the hell for?" asked someone in the rear of the room.

"Because Shaia will if you won't," said Darussis. "I nominate Archdeacon Rhimskaia for patriarch!'' There was a scattering of seconds, and Rhimskaia stood up.

"I must respectfully decline," he said. "I agree with Darussis that the congregation must act, and I agree, without false modesty, that I am the best man for the job, but I cannot be elected, and time is too precious to waste trying." He yawned, covering his mouth with a white gloved hand. "I should like to nominate Archdeacon Gorabani."

"Too smooth!" somebody shouted. "The son of a bitch is slicker than a silk stocking full of shit!"

"You would prefer the rough-hewn integrity of Doctor Wizenbeak?" yelled Darussis. "The man is a lay preacher, and don't forget it!"

"Better Wizenbeak than Gorabani!" said Rehbeinji, his black eyes flashing.

"As patriarch I could afford to forget that you were Fadel's dog," said Archdeacon Gorabani. "However, if you really prefer Doctor Wizenbeak to me, Binji, he being eligible and all, I will second his nomination if you choose to make it."

Rehbeinji glared, but held his peace.

"You are wise to fear him," said Gorabani. "In all humility, then, I accept the nomination in order to defend the Church and this congregation to the best of my poor ability."

"I nominate Doctor Rehbeinji!" said someone, and there was a second on the right.

"I accept with all humility," the little man declared, without waiting to be asked, "and move the nominations be closed!" That motion was also seconded on the right, and passed on a voice vote.

The tally of the first ballot was twenty-one for Rehbeinji, eighteen for Gorabani, at which point, Gorabani adjourned the meeting until nine that morning.

As the clerisiarchs were leaving, Archdeacon Darussis fell in step with Gorabani.

"Nice try, old friend," he said softly, "but tomorrow they'll ask you to step aside."

"Let them ask," said Gorabani. "They might swing Prosji and Osnos away from us, but they need three more votes after that, and they won't get them."

"Rehbeinji has the clear majority," said the little archdeacon. "For the good of the Church you'll have to step down, to make it unanimous."

"Will *you* go over to Rehbeinji without my leave?"

Darussis shook his head. "That's not the point. You can't deadlock the election until the Witch-Queen takes matters into her own hands, and God knows, you can't win it."

"Hey, I *can* deadlock the election. And I will. And I *can* win the election and I am going to do so!"

"Oh?" The little man raised an eyebrow.

"I'll see Wizenbeak as patriarch before I'll let Binji have it!" said Gorabani. "And maybe Binji feels the same way, but when the crunch comes, the Mambrinistas will buckle!"

# 31

# The Return of the Witch-Queen

LATE in the afternoon Jankura entered Wizenbeak's tent with a bowl of chicken soup, followed by Princess Marjia, Mischka, and a troll-bat even younger than Mischka.

"How do you do, master?" she said, sitting on the bed beside him, fluffing his pillow, chasing away the juvenile troll-bat, and petting Mischka, all without spilling the soup.

"Hunh, and double hunh," he grunted. "You didn't bring that little monster for *me*, did you? I'll pick my own damn troll-bat!"

"Oh, no," said Jankura, tucking a white linen napkin over his beard and feeding him a spoonful of hot soup. "Branka is with Princess Marjia. She's very good with him, aren't you, Marji?"

Wizenbeak sprayed soup halfway across the tent. Jankura patted his back solicitously, but the hairs on the back of his neck remained standing. You simply do *not* give a troll-bat to a child! You do not let children play with dangerous animals. And if Jankura didn't know it, how did Dassenji permit it . . . no, Dassenji would have given the second troll-bat to Jankura. Something was seriously wrong here.

"He's a real doll baby," said the little girl with saccharine sweetness. "Branka is my darling, aren't you, baby?"

Listening with his full attention to what she said, the wizard tried to remember what a real child would sound like. Was the princess speaking with a little more mature inflection than she ought or was that his imagination? Was all that gooey sweetness real?

Wizenbeak ate his soup and watched Marjia playing with an animal that could tear her to pieces. She has a nice touch, he conceded, relaxing a bit. In fact, she could be a natural . . . maybe better than Jankura, who was the best I ever saw . . . except that her style looks practiced. Which is impossible. "How long have you had Branka, princess?" he asked.

"I got him two days ago," she said. "Mr. Dassenji gave him to me." She smiled prettily, showing dimples in her cheeks.

Dassenji *did* give it to her!? The old fool should know better, thought the wizard as something akin to panic began to tug at the corners of his mind. A responsible grown-up wouldn't give a kid, a practical infant, a troll-bat. I wouldn't; Dassenji wouldn't either . . . so how did she get it? In his mind he rehearsed the mantra for serenity. Princess Marjia must have gone in as if she owned the place, picked herself out a troll-bat, and Dassenji was afraid to say no . . . that made sense. Would pretty little Marjia be able to inspire fear? *He* was lying in bed terrified. How much would it take to intimidate Dassenji? He finished the last of the soup, and Jankura put the bowl on the bedside table.

"Would you like some flatbread?" Jankura asked him.

"No. I'm not up to chewing anything." Even the chicken soup was sitting heavy on his stomach. He sat propped up on the pillows while she set Mischka gently on his broken arm. The troll-bat spread its webbed hands over the fracture near the elbow and concentrated on knitting the bones. Princess Marjia watched them intently for a while.

"You have more than one break in your bones," she said. "Could I help with Branka?"

Hell and damnation, thought Wizenbeak. Healing with troll-bats is more training than talent. How in God's name could little Marjia have got trained at her age . . . the question, once asked, resonated in his mind. She couldn't. Marjia could not, possibly, have the training needed. But she had made the offer, and Jankura, who ought to know better, was standing by as if it was perfectly all right. He repeated the mantra for serenity to produce a specious sense of calmness, and turned her statement over and over in his mind. The prosody, the dance of the speech rhythms, sounded like someone he had known.

"No, thank you," said the wizard. "I have something I want to talk over with Jankura, here, and I know Mischka, but your little Branka . . . well, frankly he scares me."

"Lots of people are afraid of troll-bats," the little girl said cheerfully. "Master Dassenji told me so."

Of course the prosody is familiar, he thought, she's her mother's daughter. She'd pick up Shaia's speech mannerisms from sheer proximity to her mother . . . only she never had much to do with her mother, if the gossip was true. The hair began to rise again. Shaia couldn't be bothered with children, so she gave them to nurses to raise.

"What was it you wanted to talk to me about?" asked Jankura.

"A matter of policy, actually. Not making policy, implementing it. You understand?" Jankura nodded, and Wizenbeak looked at the princess. "How about you, Marjia?" he asked kindly.

"I understand, Master Wizenbeak."

She just might, thought the wizard. She knows troll-bats and words like "implementing" and she's nine, maybe ten years old. No. She has Shaia's speech patterns and some of the vocabulary as well . . . his mouth was dry after eating a bowl of chicken soup . . . and some of the talents? At the very end, when Shaia knew the mob was about to storm the palace, she'd made an attempt to get her children to safety. That's reasonable. Facing death and the ruin of her policies, would she try one last conjuration? All unbidden a title floated to the surface of his mind: Mowpater's Forty-Second Spell.

"Fine," he said. "The policy is: we put Prince Dervian on the throne and make Jankura here his regent, right?" Mowpater had tried to slip the fist of death by transferring his spirit to the body of another in the hour of dying. It was said that he had used the forty-second spell himself . . . and it was not known that he had failed. Wizenbeak shivered. The spell was known to him by reputation only, an untested procedure to be used in case of extreme emergencies only.

"My son will be king of Guhland," said Jankura calmly, "but until he is of age, I will, of course be regent."

Now I've told her and told her that Dervian isn't her son, thought Wizenbeak, but I can't shake her loose from it . . . and she's rational enough on everything else. So it has to be a geas on her. From Shaia, working through Marjia on behalf of Dervian. New hands executing an old policy.

"Absolutely," he said. "I agree one hundred percent." He turned to Marjia. "That's wizard talk for 'all the way.' "

Princess Marjia nodded gravely.

"The problem is finding the best way to do it," said Wizenbeak. Am I imagining things, he mused, or am I addressing Shaia herself? If I play to the child am I being subtle or just an old idiot? Well, we'll just have to see how it goes. "There is opposition in Cymdulock, you know."

Princess Marjia nodded again. Jankura simply smiled. "They will present no problem," she said.

"What we want to do is let the opposition use their own strength to help us," the wizard continued. Shaia, if her spirit was in fact residing in the body of her daughter, must be out of the web of gossip and intelligence that she had been used to. Could she be persuaded of the rightness of his course? "If Your Majesty pretends she'd like to be queen, they . . . the dukes, and the Church and whoever . . . will say 'No, no! Prince Dervian must be king! Shaia can only be regent until he grows up.' "

Jankura simply smiled. If she heard him, she gave no sign. "Whereas if you begin by saying: 'Prince Dervian must be king,' the opposition could say two things. First: 'Yes, but Duke Falenda . . . or someone, anyone but you . . . must be regent.' "

Jankura sat relaxed and calm, guiding Mischka's hands over his cast, tolerant, loving, paying him no heed. I wonder if she even hears me? thought Wizenbeak. And if Marjia hears me, does Shaia understand, and if she understands, does she agree with me, and if she agrees with me does she see me as a clear and present danger to her because I may know who she is? "So," he continued, "Your Majesty doesn't even have to pretend, if you don't want to. You just don't say anything at all about Prince Dervian or being queen or regent. They—and we know who *they* are, don't we Princess Marjia? They will say to themselves, 'Shaia wants to be queen! No, no! Prince Dervian must be king! Shaia can only be regent until he grows up.' ''

Marjia nodded, looking completely engrossed. Jankura simply smiled and let a gentle warmth flow into his broken bones.

"Now then," said Wizenbeak, "the second thing that might happen if Your Majesty begins negotiations by saying 'Prince Dervian must be king! I will be regent until he grows up!' is that the Church and the dukes and all will say, 'How do we know that Prince Dervian is who you say he is?' ''

Jankura simply smiled. Marjia looked very concerned. "But Dervian is my brother. I'd *tell* them who he is!"

A child's response, thought the wizard. She knows I know, I think, but she is pretending so I can go on pretending that I don't know who she is, really . . . this gets very complicated. If I wasn't afraid of getting killed, I wouldn't play her silly game, he concluded to himself.

"Hunh, hunh, hunh! Excuse me, princess . . . I wasn't laughing at you. I was just thinking of *them* saying, 'Oh, yes, princess. We're so sorry. We didn't know.' ''

"They wouldn't believe me?" she asked.

"They might not. And if they didn't, we'd be in trouble because Jankura here couldn't just say, 'All right for you, I'm going to be queen!' Because she isn't really your mother, is she?"

Marjia shook her head.

"We know that, but they don't. Not until she doesn't *try* to be queen. Then they'll know," said Wizenbeak softly. "What should we do about it?" No point in worrying about it anymore: we're committed, he thought.

"I don't know," said Marjia. "What *should* we do about it?"

"We shall march into Cymdulock and make Prince Dervian king," said Jankura pleasantly. "And I shall be regent until he comes of age."

"Well," said Wizenbeak, gently lifting Mischka off his arm and setting him in Jankura's lap. "Your Majesty seems to have made up her mind. My advice, if you were to ask it, would be to wait for General Genzari and old Doctor Wizenbeak to make Prince Dervian king . . . don't try to do it by yourself, especially not as a first bargaining position." He shook her hand. "Thanks for coming by, Jankura. It's always nice to see you."

"Take care of yourself, master," she replied. "I'll need your advice to run the show down there, I really will. Is your arm better?"

He wiggled the fingers extending from the cast. "A little bit, I think. A few more treatments, it'll be good as new."

The next morning Genzari came into the tent.

"Her Majesty says that she'll let the two of us negotiate to make Dervian king! How did you get through to her?"

"By indirection," said Wizenbeak. But a chill ran up his spine. So the Witch-Queen *is* in the body of her daughter, he thought. And maybe the way I did it, we can pretend it isn't so. But I know, and she knows I know. Now what?

That night in the small hours of the morning, he heard his tent canvas rustle, and he opened his eyes. In the darkness visual clues were hard to come by . . . but a small black figure entering his tent was obscurely outlined in the doorway against the slightly less black night sky. He listened and heard a troll-bat breathing. There was the faint, clean odor of a perfumed soap. What does she want? he wondered, and as a cold knot of fear congealed in the pit of his stomach, he reminded himself that she could probably get it. Cooperate with the inevitable, he thought, a resolution which brought him scant comfort.

"Good evening, Your Majesty," he said evenly. "May I light a candle for you?"

"Don't bother, Doctor Wizenbeak. We find the darkness most comfortable," said the voice of Princess Marjia. "And no more 'Your Majesty.' The form of address is 'Your Highness,' or 'princess.' You understand?"

"Yes, Your Highness." The response was automatic. If he had had any lingering doubts that he was in the presence of Shaia, they were gone. The wizard hesitated, as a fly instinctively stops struggling when the spider comes out on his web. "Please feel free to make use of whatever small comfort my tent affords." The troll-bat squeaked and landed on the foot of his bed, closely followed by Marjia.

"We have some business to transact, the two of us," she said calmly. "As a gesture of our goodwill, Branka and I will also seek to knit your broken bones. Take my word for it, Branka is good. The question is: do you trust *me*?" She moved up on the bed, and he reached out to her with his good hand to encounter a small, bare shoulder. As he withdrew his hand, she grasped it and pressed it against the ruffled muslin of her nightdress. Branka chattered softly. Wizenbeak sighed to himself. Whether he trusted her or not, she and Branka could kill him without any difficulty. On the other hand, a gesture of trust might, just possibly, be reciprocated. His fate was in other hands than his own. Oddly, the knowledge relaxed him.

"I trust you," he said, hoping for the best. "Go ahead and see what can be done with the fractures." The troll-bat spread its webbed fingers on the cast, and Marjia sat holding his cast hand as she guided Branka's ministrations with the other.

"How is that?" she asked after a few moments.

Wizenbeak considered. "Pretty good," he said at last. Her touch was . . . well, different than Jankura's, but the healing flow was emphatically there. "Branka is doing very well for you."

"Thank you." A pause. "I'm going crazy, you know."

He thought about that for a while. If Queen Shaia was in fact inside the body of her nine-year-old daughter, she'd be incredibly isolated—and if she was keeping it a secret, as he suspected she was, the problem would be even worse. So if he knew, he'd be a confidant, somebody to talk to. "Are you lonely, Shaia?"

"Stick to 'Your Highness,' if you don't mind," she told him. " 'Marjia' if you must."

"*Are* you lonely?"

"Well, yes . . . but I was always an isolani," she said. "That isn't the problem."

Wizenbeak lay back in the dark as the troll-bat ministered to his arm and wondered what the problem was. "I give up," he said at last. "Having so recently deduced your continued carnate existence, I feel totally incapable of deriving your damn problem. What is it?"

Marjia shifted her grip, slipping his incapacitated hand under one arm and resting both her hands on top of the troll-bat's webbed fingers. The sensation in his arm changed, becoming focussed around the ache of the break. "For one thing, my perspective has changed. Putting my son on the throne is one thing. I would have cheerfully ruled as Guhland's regent on his behalf. Manipulating Jankura, even if it were possible in the long run, is something else entirely."

"I don't understand, Your Highness." This isn't the main issue, he thought; she's going crazy, and she doesn't want to talk about it. Well, keep the conversation going and see what turns up. "Power is power, regardless of which levers you have to pull."

"It's the difference between fencing and coaching a fencer, Doctor Wizenbeak. As Princess Marjia, nine going on ten, I can not possibly do my own fencing. And if I try to run Jankura, I'll spoil everything."

"She's resisting your takeover?"

"Let's say that I'm working with some terribly refractory material here," said Princess Marjia softly. "Your apprentice is committed to putting my son . . . who is also my dumb brother . . . on the throne. We put a geas on her, yes, but it was one she accepted more or less willingly. The thing is, I have control but no flexibility at all." Branka chittered, and the wizard could feel her grip easing through the cast.

"What do you need flexibility for?"

"Think about it, doctor. Situations change, sometimes pretty rapidly. Also, I know the territory, the secret histories of the laws and people she'll be working with, that she'll need to rule; but if I try to do very much hands-on control Jankura *will* resist." A sigh in the darkness. "She has a lot of talent, your apprentice."

"Yes," agreed the wizard. "She does. You think if she resists she'd break your geas?"

"She might." Her grip and Branka's shifted on the cast, and the ache slowly returned to where they had been working. "It's something I'm afraid of, anyway."

Ah, thought the wizard, I have something she wants. This is maybe a side issue, but it gives me a hand on things. "Well, Your Highness," he said, "Jankura is oathbound to me, as my apprentice. I, in turn, was oathbound to Prince Gatsack, who bound me to act as his preferred agent on your behalf. Since he's dead, I am now oathbound to *you*. You could advise me of what was required, and I could pass the word on to Jankura.''

"The thought had occurred to me," she conceded.

"Would you like me to reaffirm my oath in somewhat more positive terms, Your Highness?''

Again she sighed. "No, Doctor Wizenbeak. In the circumstances any oath you offered would have to be considered as given under duress.''

Truer words were never spoke, thought the wizard. "A good point, Your Highness. Shall we then proceed to proceed upon the good trust and mutual faith we have so assiduously piled up between us in the past?''

He had expected a giggle, but all she said was, "Yes.''

"Right," said the wizard. "Now, I have all sorts of access to Jankura in the normal course of business. What I need is some sort of regular access to you. I could be your tutor, perhaps.''

"That would be nice," said Princess Marjia. "Jankura was saying that I'd have to have a tutor, soon. If you volunteered for the job, she'd give it to you, I imagine.''

She doesn't sound very enthused, he thought. Is this just the prospect of a kid going back to school, or is it something else? We've taken care of at least *some* of the business, so maybe it's time. Or maybe it isn't. Oh hell. Take a shot at it.

"How did you happen to choose your daughter?''

"What? Oh, you mean why did I choose to send my spirit into *her* body? By the time I had decided to try Mowpater's Forty-Second Spell, the choice was her or one of my mute maid-servants. You need a cooperative donor, among other things.''

She sounds depressed, thought Wizenbeak, but that wasn't it. We might as well stop playing guessing games and ask straight out. "You said you were going crazy just now. Would you like to tell me about it?''

She took her hands off the cast and put them on her face and began to weep. Branka looked up and walked over to his mistress, trying ineffectually to console her. After a while she regained control of herself.

"There, now," said the wizard, patting her on the head with his good hand. "Tell grampa all about it.''

"You mean what's driving me crazy?'' Shaia's voice, except

for the hiccups, was reasonably controlled. She reached up and took his gnarled hand in her soft ones. "Marjia . . . this body I'm in . . . is on the edge of puberty, and she's highly sexed."

The wizard was suddenly aware that his good hand was held firmly against firm young female flesh. "Your Majesty," he said a bit huskily, "I remain bound to you by the oaths I took to Prince Gatsack. I am your most loyal servant."

"I'm glad to hear that, Doctor Wizenbeak. You may be the only one by now." There was a long pause, as if she were somehow distancing herself from her body. "The problem I have as Marjia is vague, inchoate longings . . . which, unfortunately, as Shaia I know all too well how to satisfy." Another pause. "As I said, I'm going crazy."

"Puberty, Your Majesty? You're only nine years old . . . the onset of puberty is maybe thirteen or fourteen."

"Except in the North," she said, "where an excessively lean diet delays menarche to seventeen or eighteen. I, on the other hand, have always been well fed. Maybe excessively so."

"What are you saying?"

"That puberty begins at age thirteen or one hundred pounds, whichever comes first. Producing vague and inchoate longings." Branka chattered, and she felt the troll-bat climb off her lap to go sit at the end of the cot.

"Inchoate longings," Wizenbeak agreed cautiously, as she held his hand. "What would you like me to do about it, Your Majesty?"

Again his question provoked a burst of tears. "I'm in love with Zeldones," she wailed at last, "and that long drink of water doesn't even know I'm alive!"

A love potion would seem to be contraindicated, decided the wizard, removing his hand from her grasp to scratch an itch. "A child's heart and a woman's mind was never a happy mixture," he said. "Maybe the telling will help."

There was a long pause. "I always flattered myself that my control of my emotions was a sign of moral superiority," said Shaia, sounding more or less under control. "I looked down on women who chose to be ruled by their bodies." She hesitated. "At nine my daughter has stronger sexual feelings than I did at three times her age. So much for moral superiority.'' Marjia put his hand down and sat silently on the edge of the bed.

"But you love Zeldones?"

"Since just after Shaia came into this body. We were trying to reach the citadel in a sedan chair, and when we couldn't, the mercenary escort plundered us. One of the mercenaries was going to rape me, and Zeldones faced him down. And just like that, my whole body said 'I love him!' "

"He leaves something to be desired as a royal consort," said the wizard, dubiously.

"Don't I know it! But that . . . that incredible surge of emotion never happened to me before. I never knew that bodies were capable of such rapture. The trip north with him was the happiest time of my life! I was hungry and cold and wet and miserable and utterly happy, all at the same time! Can you understand?''

"It sounds like Your Highness enjoyed an extended wallow in pure emotion," he said, shaking his head. "If you were applying to be my apprentice, that would disqualify you. For all your talents. Emotion destroys concentration, which is fatal for any serious work." He sighed. "I understand, but I don't know what to do about it."

"I don't know what to do about it either," she said. "He's tall and brave and not subtle at all." A hiccup. "If I tried to conduct an intrigue with him, he'd get himself killed as sure as anything!" There was a long pause.

"You were right, doctor," she said in a different voice. "Talking about it helped. That was something I knew and wouldn't admit, and when it just popped out, well, it's true. Poor Zeldones."

"Poor Marjia," said the wizard.

"Poor Marjia," agreed the little princess, wiping her nose. "Well, if you're going to be my tutor, maybe you'd better take over Branka for me. Several people have made remarks about my having a most unsuitable pet."

"He's your troll-bat," Wizenbeak observed. "Will he stay with me?"

"The little monster, he'd better! I'd hoped to use him to control Jankura better, but if I can use you instead, why that's the way to go."

"I should think so," he agreed. "Coaching from the side-lines, as it were, you should be very useful."

"I hope so. And we can both train up Branka to be a fine broth of a troll-bat."

That may not be too good an idea, thought Wizenbeak; the troll-bat with two masters may end up obeying neither. On the other hand, it would certainly be better than letting the princess flaunt him before all the world. Also, it would make Jankura happier, once she's able to think about it. Besides, I can't very well refuse. "I'll do it, Your Highness," he said. "Come here Branka, darling . . ." Marjia giggled, and Branka walked very slowly up the wizard's leg, stopping just out of reach of his extended fingers. The little girl stood up.

"Stay here, Branka," she said. "I'll come see you in the morning."

"By all means, Your Majesty," said the wizard.

"Maybe between the two of you . . ." she began and started for the tent flap. The troll-bat whined. She paused, "Stay, Branka!" Then she was gone.

Some situations have no solutions, only outcomes. The troll-bat stayed with Wizenbeak, and Princess Marjia came over to play with her most unsuitable pet under the guise of being tutored. She was not, however, interested in the repetitious hard work that was needed to fix the skills of wizardry in mind and hand.

Even when she was interested, she was unable to keep her mind fixed on practicing for more than a very few minutes. She continued to talk to Wizenbeak as an equal when they were alone, but he noticed, or thought he noticed a slight regression over time, as Shaia's unfixed memories shifted like the stuff of dreams in the brain of her daughter. Not all her memories were unfixed, however, and now and again he was startled by the sharpness of her insights.

As the days passed, Wizenbeak became quite fond of the young princess and entirely sympathetic to the restless and unhappy spirit of Queen Shaia. He even learned to tolerate Branka, who was spiritually a Siamese cat where Gruchka had been a water spaniel.

# 32

# Electing the Patriarch

EARLY one fine summer morning, Count Darji-Damuso's cavalry rode up to the gates of Cymdulock and seized them in the name of Prince Dervian, the rightful ruler of Guhland. By noon, Count Braley's dragoons had arrived, and all the gates into the city had been secured. By evening, Count Braley had taken the Citadel without any sort of fight, being admitted through a small side entrance by sympathizers on the inside, and Cymdulock settled down to wait for the arrival of the Witch-Queen.

"For the love of God, Gorabani," rasped Archdeacon Rehbeinji, "give up your egotistical, your megalomaniacal pursuit of the patriarchy and concede! You haven't the votes! You will *never* have the votes! The Witch-Queen's army is at the gates, and we must elect a patriarch before she, herself, arrives." The gap-toothed little man pulled a handkerchief from his sleeve and wiped his forehead.

"That will be three days, if she comes with her main army," said Gorabani pleasantly, turning the gavel over in his hands. "I don't see that we have to hurry our deliberations at all."

"There is a report," said Darussis, "a rumor, at least, that she came, dressed in men's clothes, with Count Braley. She could be here at any moment."

That set off a demonstration on the right side of the aisle, as the Mambrinistas shouted and screamed and hurled abuse at Gorabani. Finally he pounded for order, and the noise slowly subsided.

"You have asked me to resign," he said calmly, "so that the

noble, the honorable, the ideologically rectitudinous Doctor Rehbeinji may be elected patriarch, the better to defy the Witch-Queen. I have refused, and I shall continue to refuse. Nevertheless, until now I have not bothered to explain myself to the distinguished faction on the right of the aisle. Partly because it is a waste of time arguing with fools. Partly because the time was not then ripe.'' He sat back in his tall, thronelike chair and smiled grimly.

''The time is now ripe, and I am not arguing with anybody, I am simply telling you what is going to happen, and explaining why.

''To begin with, it cannot be in the interest of the Church and this congregation to adopt an adversary stance with the secular authorities. Doctor Rehbeinji has, unfortunately, played a large role in the events that led to the death of the Witch-Queen, and her return to the living is perhaps less remarkable than her return to power. Whether or not she, for reasons of policy or whatever, is willing to live in peace, Binji has made amply clear his intention to once *again* bring her down. In light of what Binji's policies have cost us in the past, I submit that we cannot afford to continue them in the future.

''It is my considered opinion that the Syncretist Church would be better off electing *no* patriarch than to elect Doctor Rehbeinji to that office, even if that were to permit the Witch-Queen to appoint her own patriarch.'' He gaveled the protests into silence. ''I make a distinction here, which the Mambrinistas do not, between the Syncretist Church and the Congregation of Clerisiarchs. I don't doubt that if the Witch-Queen appoints the patriarch, the congregation will suffer. Some of us may even suffer martyrdom. But the Church will survive!''

''Blasphemy!'' said a voice on the right. ''The Church is eternal!''

''The witchfinder intended to use the Holy Inquisition to destroy not only witches, but also the Orthodox Church,'' said Gorabani, holding the gavel in his white gloved hands. ''Our claim to be eternal descends through them. If *they* can be destroyed—as Doctor Fadel and Doctor Rehbeinji clearly believed—so can *we*!'' Again, he gaveled the congregation into silence.

''In my judgment, electing Rehbeinji patriarch is a threat to the life of the Church, and I will not permit it! If I die as a result, so be it!'' The uproar that followed was markedly different than previously. Among the Mambrinistas, groups of two and three were putting their heads together and talking, even as some of them still stood shouting at the chairman.

Finally Archdeacon Gorabani pounded the gavel for silence.

''Enough,'' he said. ''Let us have done with this tumult! I will, if elected to the office of patriarch, do my best to preserve and protect the Church. And I shall at the same time strive to maintain the authority of this congregation.'' Insofar as it doesn't conflict with the authority of the patriarch, he thought blandly. ''Either you can elect me to deal with the Witch-Queen, or the Witch-Queen will appoint Doctor Wizenbeak to deal with *you*! Binji, here, isn't in the running anymore!''

''But I have more votes than you do!'' yelled Rehbeinji.

''How sad. We will now take a secret ballot. The last ballot. I've told you what your choices are. If I can't beat Wizenbeak—'' He laughed. ''The son of a bitch might make a decent patriarch!''

''Request permission to caucus,'' said one of the Mambrinistas.

Gorabani turned a small hourglass over, setting the sand running.

''Permission granted,'' he said. ''You have fifteen minutes.''

Several groups went out, and after the sand ran out, Gorabani sent the sergeant at arms to fetch them. They straggled back into the room looking very subdued.

''A question, please,'' said Archdeacon Obuskaia, a big, bear of a man who was deeply involved with the internal politics of the Mambrinistas. ''If you are elected patriarch, will you defend the individual members of the congregation as well as the institution as a whole?''

''Yes, of course,'' replied Gorabani without hesitation.

''I'm glad to hear it,'' said Obuskaia. ''Does that include Archdeacon Rehbeinji?''

''Yes. I will not permit the Witch-Queen to have Archdeacon Rehbeinji.''

The big archdeacon studied him for a moment and shook his massive head.

When the vote was tallied, Archdeacon Gorabani had been elected patriarch by a single vote.

# 33

# Conditional Surrender

Upon arriving at Cymdulock with the main army, the court of the Witch-Queen took up residence at the Czajka Palace, the city home of the late Prince Gatsack, which had been renamed Our Lady of Mewis Field Convent, but not yet redecorated, some dispute having arisen over the disposition of the furniture. Wizenbeak, Jankura, General Genzari, and Count Braley were in the sitting room adjacent to Jankura's bedroom, considering the negotiations with Patriarch Gorabani the next day. The agenda theoretically concerned only the coronation of Prince Dervian, at a time and place to be decided, but there were a number of intractable problems being considered.

Princess Marjia came into the sitting room through her "mother's" bedroom, barefoot, in her nightgown, with a large plushy bear under her arm. She walked over to the wizard and took his hand.

"Tell me a bedtime story, Pop-pop," she said, sweetly.

"Go to bed, Marjia," said Jankura. "He hasn't got time to play with you. We are concerned with matters of consequence, here."

"Hunh," grunted Wizenbeak. "For all the progress we're making, I might as well tell the princess a bedtime story."

"Go ahead," said Count Braley, rubbing his eyes with thumb and forefinger. "I could use a break. Shall I send for another pot of tea?"

Genzari stifled a yawn. "Sure. And a tray of fried meat pastries. It's going to be a long night, from the look of it."

The little girl led the wizard off, clutching his arm in one hand and the teddy bear in the other. When they reached her bedroom, she climbed under the pink comforter and sat up against the lace trimmed pillow, as Wizenbeak settled himself on the end of the bed. "Once upon a time—" he began.

"Shut up, you old fool!" she snapped. "I was listening at the door, and the lot of you haven't a clue as to what to do next."

"The problems are very hard, princess."

"Bullshit! The problems are very hard, but they aren't our problems. You have your diptych? You'd better take notes."

Wizenbeak pulled his diptych out and opened it, taking his stylus in hand. "Go ahead," he said mildly.

"Fine. When you go in to see the patriarch, you get his attention. Archdeacon Rehbeinji must die!" Wizenbeak dutifully wrote it down.

"May one ask why?"

"He organized the Holy Inquisition," Marjia said. "Fadel lacked the brains and the fire in the gut—Rehbeinji provided them. Fadel was . . . well, politic. Kahun liked his smell, maybe. Archdeacon Rehbeinji, however, is our irreconcilable and deadly enemy."

"Rehbeinji dies," agreed Wizenbeak. "Who else?"

"Archdeacons Obuskaia, Relyji, . . ." she rattled off a dozen names, "are the leading Mambrinistas. They should die, but if you can't get them now, we can get them later. What you do is make up a list with those names on parchment, and give the list to Patriarch Gorabani. Not one of them is a friend of his, but he'll try to defend them. I think. He should try to defend them, anyway. If he doesn't, good. If he does, you can let them all go but Rehbeinji."

"And then can we ask about the coronation?"

"Yes." The little girl snuggled under her comforter. "Jankura had it straight about the coronation. And Genzari is right about dealing with the dukes—"

"Lasco had no idea how to deal with the dukes," protested Wizenbeak.

"You weren't listening. He said we had to wait for them to make a move, and then react to them. They can't possibly all act together, but we can't sort them out in advance."

"Very well," he said, writing it down. "Go on."

"We'll have to deal with them eventually," said the little girl, holding the teddy bear to her, "but the longer we can put it off, the better for us . . . and maybe the better for Guhland. After the coronation, we'll have our hands full settling with the Church. We don't need to take on the dukes at the same time." She yawned. "This body—God, Wizenbeak, I've got to go through adolescence again, and there's nobody but you I dare talk to. I'll never make it."

"I'd be happy to teach you magic," said the wizard, "if you'll forgive my presumption."

Marjia yawned again. "I don't know," she said. "When I *used* to be nine, if you know what I mean, I'd have jumped at the chance. But now . . . even killing Rehbeinji, I lack the passion that whips the blood. It's the thing to do, but it's an academic exercise, cool, so cool . . ." She snuggled down into the comforter. "The whole thing is like a story my mother told me. I can remember it, but I'm not involved . . . and I'm beginning to forget." She smiled, showing her dimples. "Kiss me good night, you old fart."

The next morning, Patriarch Gorabani, lean and handsome, and Archdeacon Darussis, short and pudgy, arrived at the Royal Palace with a considerable retinue. They were escorted to the privy council chamber, still dominated by a wall-sized *Apotheosis of King-Patriarch Kahun* showing His Late Majestic Holiness ascending into heaven to give a grateful God some much needed assistance. Wizenbeak and General Genzari rose as they came in.

"Be seated, gentlemen," said Gorabani after the introductions, and took the tall seat at the head of the table which Kahun had used. There was a moment of awkward silence, and then Wizenbeak took out a small scroll of parchment and pushed it across the table.

"We want them dead," said Genzari.

Darussis took the parchment and unrolled it. "This is a deadly blow to the Congregation of Clerisiarchs," he said, handing the list to Gorabani who read it with studied disinterest. "I'm afraid we can't oblige you, doctor."

"Pity," said Genzari. "We *will* take Archdeacon Rehbeinji . . . and if we take him by force, we might as well take the others."

"We won't be any worse off," explained Wizenbeak. "That gap-toothed son of a bitch is guilty of high treason, after all."

"I see," said Gorabani. The list, he thought, agreed with his own private estimate of who had voted against him as far as it went. I'd be better off without them, maybe, but I can't let them go, more's the pity. "You can't have them. Seize them, and we shall pronounce anathema upon you!"

"In for a penny, in for a pound," said Genzari. "When you started to throw your weight around with the Tarelians, your religious sanctions lost their moral cutting edge." He fingered his closely trimmed mustache. "Some of our senior officers are survivors of Mewis Field . . . living proof of the efficacy of your curses. How are you doing rebuilding the Tarelians, by the way?"

"Very well," lied the patriarch. "By next spring they should be up to full strength."

"We could, perhaps, lift the excommunication from Prince Gatsack's army," suggested Darussis. "It would be a seemly thing to do, at this point."

"Make a note of it," said Gorabani. He smiled and folded his white gloved hands. "We are not interested in cooperating with the Wi—I mean, with the secular authorities."

"Then turn over Rehbeinji," said Wizenbeak. "The others, we'll deal with them later."

"No," replied Gorabani. "I gave my word that I would defend Archdeacon Rehbeinji."

"Then we'll grab off the lot," said Genzari politely. "Next spring maybe the Tarelians can grab them back for you."

"Then there will be no coronation," Darussis said.

"Shaia wishes a coronation," replied Wizenbeak, "but in the event that the Church is obdurate, she is prepared to rule as Queen Revenant . . . as the already crowned queen returned." He pulled at his beard and twisted a strand of white whiskers around one finger. "I had suggested an Orthodox coronation, but she said no, she meant to rule the whole of Guhland, not just the north."

"Queen Revenant?" Gorabani shook his head. "What about Prince Dervian, the rightful heir to the throne?"

The wizard grinned. "Oh, I imagine that Shaia would put him on the throne as soon as possible . . . say when he was forty or fifty."

"We would frankly prefer that Shaia not rule," said the patriarch at last. "A regency might, perhaps, be acceptable."

"That would require a coronation," said Genzari, "which is out of the question since we are going to be hanging witchfinders in high places."

"Hell," said Gorabani, at last, "I promised I'd protect Archdeacon Rehbeinji. Give me a couple of days to demote him to deacon, and you can have him . . . but not the others."

"Agreed," said Genzari. "And the coronation?"

"We'll crown Prince Dervian as king, with the Witch-Queen—" He shrugged. " 'Scusi. With the queen-mother as regent. Dervian to assume the throne on his eighteenth birthday."

"Precedent holds for twenty-one," said Genzari politely.

"Nineteen," murmured Darussis. "We could go nineteen, I think."

"Her Majesty is devoted to precedent," said Wizenbeak. "There are a couple of little details we might consider first, however."

"Oh?"

"The property seized from the witches you burned," said the wizard. "It goes back to their heirs. If no heirs are found, it goes to the royal treasury."

"Agreed," said the patriarch.

"And we need a direct line to the Congregation of Clerisiarchs," said Wizenbeak. "This may surprise you, but I am a lay preacher, and her Majesty has asked me to accept the hat of an archdeacon—" He had intended to say 'contingent upon it being offered,' but both clerisiarchs started laughing.

"Excuse me," said the wizard with a touch of frost, "I have seen archdeacons considerably less prepossessing than myself."

"It wasn't that," said Gorabani. "I promise to explain it some time." How can I tell him the congregation almost preferred him over me as patriarch? "You have your hat, I swear it."

"Hunh," said Wizenbeak, "well, in that case, I suppose we could set the regency to terminate at Dervian's nineteenth birthday."

"*You* an archdeacon?" said Darussis. "Eighteen?"

"Coronation a week Volsday?"

"Make a note of it, Darussis," said the patriarch.

"Eighteen," said Wizenbeak.

# 34

# The Coronation

A WEEK after the following Volsday, Prince Dervian, age thirteen years and ten months, was crowned King of Guhland, and Jankura, accepted as Queen-Mother, was crowned regent.

They lived in interesting times ever after.

# Enjoy
# the Wonder
# and
# Wizardry
# of
# Elizabeth
# H. Boyer